Music for Common Worship 1

Music for Sunday Services

edited by John Harper

MUSIC FOR COMMON WORSHIP
GENERAL EDITOR: JOHN HARPER

Published by	RSCM Press
	The Royal School of Church Music
	Cleveland Lodge
	Westhumble
	Dorking
	Surrey RH5 6BW
	Telephone: 01306 872800 Fax: 01306 887260
	E-mail: cl@rscm.com Web: www.rscm.com

ISBN	0 85402 100 0
Published	2000
	10 9 8 7 6 5 4 3

This is the first in the series of volumes, *Music for Common Worship*, compiled and published by The Royal School of Church Music.

The other volumes now available are:

Music for Common Worship II: Music for the President
Music for Common Worship III: A Basic Guide

Type set by	Alistair Warwick in Gill Sans
Music set by	Alistair Warwick in Score
Cover design by	Smith and Gilmour Ltd
Printed by	Halstan & Co Ltd

Contents

Music for Common Worship I: Music for Sunday Services includes musical settings of liturgical texts for use at the Holy Communion, at A Service of the Word, and at Morning, Evening and Night Prayer, the principal Sunday services of the Church of England. It includes both modern and traditional forms of the texts (with an emphasis on modern texts), together with metrical versions of some key sung texts.

The book is in four parts:

Anthology of Music for the Holy Communion

Dialogues with the President and the Eucharistic Prayers

Anthology of Music for A Service of the Word (including Morning, Evening and Night Prayer)

Anthology of Psalms and Canticles (including a seasonal group of psalm songs)

Each of the four parts of the book has its own introduction, in addition to the general introduction provided here.

Music for all to share

The books contain music for all those attending and sharing in worship. All of it can be sung by everyone present. To be so all-embracing means that there are limits to the extent of the vocal ranges and of technical difficulty. Most of the music is provided in just one version. That does not preclude adaptation. Most of the music can be sung in unison without accompaniment. Much of the music does not have a separate accompaniment.

There is a wide range of sources and styles for the music, but this is no random collection. All the music has integrity, liturgical purposefulness, and belongs under the broad umbrella of worshipping idioms that is characteristic of the English Anglican tradition. Just as diversity is apparent in the English language and in the Church of England, so is that diversity apparent in this music which draws on a wide range of sources.

Resonances in the resources

The breadth of the collection indicates five principal sources of influence, which can be heard in the music itself, 'resonances' from five cultural sources. There are

- resonances with the distant Christian past in the use and adaptation of plainsong, and in the use of medieval modes even in some of the new music;
- resonances with the Anglican tradition in the use and adaptation of harmonised chant, of hymnody, and of four-part vocal writing;
- resonances with other cultures and other Christian musical traditions, including our immediate neighbours in the British Isles and Western Europe, but also with Africa, Northern, Central and Southern America, Eastern Europe and Russia;
- resonances with contemporary musical traits evident in Christian worship, especially those that draw on folksong, on lyrical modern styles, and on the specific repertories of the community at Taizé and of the Wild Goose Resource Group;
- above all, there is resonance with the liturgy of *Common Worship*, its theology and its spirituality – this is music intended to help us to encounter God in worship, to offer God our prayer and praise, and to be open to the transforming power of the Holy Spirit made apparent to us through the incarnation of Jesus Christ.

Using the book

As with *Common Worship*, *Music for Common Worship* requires every worshipping community to consider its pattern of worship, to plan its local practice and to prepare for its implementation. Searching for a particular idiom or piece in the collection is no substitute for getting to know the whole collection, understanding its nature, judging what is best suited for local resources and local use of *Common Worship*, and deciding how it is to be integrated in the celebration and conduct of that worship.

As well as extensive preparation before decisions are made, there needs to be some testing – either by a designated group, or (with care) by all who worship. If you are searching the book to 'fill a slot' in your service you may be approaching the problem from the wrong angle. You may find it useful to consult the companion to these musical resources, *Music for Common Worship III: A Basic Guide*.

Local use: copyright and reproduction

Worshipping communities will want to be selective in their use of the musical resources, and may wish to include extracts in their local booklets. In most instances the copyright arrangements allow reproduction of selected items for local use, so long as proper acknowledgement is made. Exceptions are identified by red print in the copyright acknowledgement at the end of each piece, and in the list of copyright holders at the end of the volume. Churches which hold CCL and/or Calamus licences may be entitled to reproduce some of the restricted items under the terms of the specific licence. See the specific advice on copyright and reproduction on page 410.

Local use: matching your own resources

Whatever your resources, all the materials included in the book are intended for use by everyone, although this may require the local choices and decisions about the way it is sung. The scores are deliberately kept clean of detailed instructions to allow for this. Where one church has a choir another may use a cantor; where some use organs others may use keyboard or other instruments; in small churches there may be no one specially designated to lead the singing or play an instrument. Some may wish all present to sing a particular item, while others may wish to designate it to a particular group. Broad suggestions are included in the introductions to each section, but more detailed decisions need to be made at a local level.

The great diversity of musical resource within the Church, in both extent and nature, is reflected both in the content of the book and the presentation of the music. Some of the music consists of single lines, some is in two or three parts, some in four parts, some has a separate accompaniment. All the music can be sung by everyone present, and much can be sung as a single line without accompaniment even where these are included. Where there are additional voice parts, these may become more familiar over time to all those present. There is considerable innate ability even among those who claim not to be musical or to be unable to read music. Instruments can be a helpful support, but the organ is not the only means of accompaniment (and not always the most enabling). Adaptation or arrangement to meet local needs may be necessary, but beware making it complicated: there is strength and directness in simplicity, and even some of the greatest symphonies include remarkably few notes when reduced to their basic elements. Many of the settings offer opportunities for dialogue. You will need to decide how best to achieve this. It may be with cantor and people, choir and people, two equal groups, or other combinations and permutations.

Other resources

We have already mentioned the introduction and guide to these resources found in *Music for Common Worship III*. The first of two related volumes, *Music for Common Worship II*, includes music for the president at Holy Communion. This contains music to be sung in dialogue at the greeting, the collect, the gospel, the peace, and the dismissal. There is also an extensive collection of music for the eight Eucharistic Prayers. Further music for the Eucharistic Prayers can also be found in *Common Worship: The President's Edition* published by Church House Publishing. The contents of these two volumes are introduced both in the guide (*Music for Common Worship III*) and in the opening of *Music for Common Worship II*.

The making and shaping of the book

The underlying thinking which has informed this volume was undertaken at consultations organised and funded by the RSCM in York (July 1999), Salisbury (January 2000), and Mirfield (March 2000), with additional financial support from the Church of England, Hymns Ancient and Modern, and McCrimmon Publishing Company Ltd. At the consultations composers, liturgists, musicians and pastors worked at some of the fundamental issues of music in worship, and established criteria for the selection of music.

Those who took part in one or more of these consultations were: Fr Peter Allan CR, Gordon Appleton, Malcolm Archer, Professor Peter Aston, Mark Bick, Bishop Andrew Burnham, Canon Jeremy Davies, Revd Mark Earey, Rosemary Field, Robert Fielding, Revd Ian Forrester, Fr George Guiver CR, Professor John Harper, Timothy Hone, Simon Lole, Adrian Lucas, Venerable John Marsh, Revd Peter Moger, David Ogden, Canon Jane Sinclair, Christopher Tambling, Dr Jonathan Wainwright, John Wardle, Venerable Norman Warren, Geoff Weaver, Revd Wendy Wilby, and Alan Wilson. In addition, the preparation of music for the Eucharistic Prayers was guided by a working group set up by the Church of England's Liturgical Commission and Liturgical Publishing Group, chaired by Bishop David Stancliffe.

In the process of compiling this volume we have sung through thousands of settings of liturgical texts, some found in published collections, but many more in manuscript or local editions intended to meet local needs. The range of music is testament to the willingness and enthusiasm of musicians – professional and amateur – to serve their local church, by writing music tailored to very specific resources and stylistic expectations. I am grateful to the RSCM Music Team for their help in reviewing submissions, and to Geoff Weaver in particular who has worked through the materials making preliminary recommendations to facilitate the work of larger groups. The setting of music and text has been undertaken by Alistair Warwick who has continually exercised his musical and liturgical sensibilities as well as his computer skills.

At the end of the day this is a transitional collection, transitional in the sense that many of the materials existed before *Common Worship* or were written before it was introduced, and transitional in that it is a first step in musical formation for the new liturgies. We shall look forward to gathering feedback, suggestions and new materials as we take this work forward.

John Harper

¶ Notes on musical instructions, signs and symbols

Instructions in the musical scores are kept to a minimum.

Dialogues are indicated by the use of normal and **bold** type. This may indicate dialogue between minister and **people**, cantor and **people**, choir and **people**, minister and **choir**, or cantor and **choir**, according to the context in the service as well as local practice and resource.

Where the music includes **refrains** (and in some instances bold text is also used), these may be sung by all, while the other material is sung by cantor or choir. However, there will be instances where it is appropriate for everyone to sing the whole piece, or for other divisions to be employed (e.g. antiphonal singing).

In **chanted music**, where there is no regular pulse or metre, the notation consists of stemless noteheads. As a general rule, white noteheads o are used for recitation, black noteheads ● for single syllables, double black noteheads ●● for lengthening.

In addition to the familiar single and double barlines, three other forms are used, especially in the chanted music:

    indicates a break or caesura,

    indicates a breath or short break,

    indicates pointing which is marked in the related text.

In **pointed texts** there two methods are employed.

1. Single-mark pointing. In the plainsong tones and in some of the pointed texts in the Anthology of Music for A Service of the Word, there is a single mark ' in each half of a verse which indicates the point at which to change from the reciting note to the next notes of the chant. The note after the mark ' is not necessarily stressed. In this pointing you should then change the note (or chord) on each successive syllable. There may be more than one syllable to sing on the last note (or chord) of the chant.

2. Bar-mark pointing. In the Anglican, 'Cantor' and simple chants, the pointing corresponds to that used in The Parish Psalter. Each mark ' corresponds with the equivalent sign in the music of the chant. In many instances the syllable after the mark ' is stressed. Where there are two chords and two syllables between two marks, each syllable is sung to a different chord. Where there are three or four syllables between two marks, the chord normally changes on the last syllable, except where a dot · is included between two syllables. Where there is a dot · , the chord is changed on the syllable which follows.

Very occasionally, a vowel has two dots placed over it. This indicates that two notes (or chords) of the chant should be sung to that syllable.

For further guidance on singing chanted texts, see the introduction to Part Four, Anthology of Psalms and Canticles on pages 290 to 293.

Tempo markings are indicative: the size of the group singing, the acoustic and the occasion may affect your own choices.

Dynamic markings are used sparingly, and often not included. Again, this allows for local choice.

Accompaniments and/or chord symbols are included in some items. The accompaniments are not hard, nor are they designated for a specific instrument. Some may need to be adapted or arranged for more idiomatic use on a specific instrument (especially in the lyrical modern music).

Unaccompanied singing. Where accompaniments are not included, it is generally intended that the music should be sung without accompaniment. If instrumental support is needed, it should normally be limited to the notes printed in the score, perhaps doubling at the octave above and/or below. Improvised harmonies are not intended. See the section in the Introduction above on 'Local use: matching the collection to your own resources'.

¶ *Part One*

Anthology of Music for the Holy Communion

The anthology of music for Holy Communion is divided into eight sections: Kyrie, Gloria in excelsis, Gospel Acclamation, Creed, Response to the Intercessions, Sanctus and Benedictus, the Lord's Prayer, Agnus Dei.

Chants for the Greeting, Collect, Gospel, Peace, and Dismissal, and music for the Eucharistic Prayers are included both in the second part of the book and in *Music for Common Worship II: Music for the President.* (The Eucharistic Prayers appear in full in the second volume; the first volume includes Dialogue, Sanctus and Benedictus, Acclamations and Conclusion.)

Psalms to be sung after the first reading can be found in the fourth part of the book.

Some of the texts of A Service of the Word may also be appropriate: settings of these can be found in the third part of the book.

Kyrie

Each Kyrie setting may be treated in several ways. It may be sung through as a whole, or it may be interpolated by spoken or sung petitions. Optional tones for reciting the petitions are provided. If the petitions are spoken, a chord (or single note) may be sustained either by the singers or by a sustaining instrument. The Kyrie itself may be sung throughout by a single group (or by all), or in alternation between cantor and people, choir and people, cantor and choir, or by two equal groups (even two cantors). These alternations can be sung *kKcCkK* or *kkKKccCCkkKK* in most instances (where 'k' indicates cantor or choir, and 'K' indicates people). A more extended treatment may be appropriate in the penitential seasons when there is no Gloria in excelsis. Most of the settings can be sung by unison voices alone. Instruments can be used even where no separate accompaniment is marked, or each may be sung without accompaniment. Settings 1 and 2 can be sung as a melody or in a harmonised form, or the two versions may be combined (most suitably in the pattern *kkKKccCCkkKK*, where 'k' is melody only, and 'K' is harmonised).

Gloria in excelsis

There are distinct stylistic differences in these nine settings. The modern text is used in the first six settings. The lively and swinging setting by David Ogden (2) may be sung straight through; alternatively the opening strain can be used as a refrain at each double bar. Alan Wilson (3) offers a simple and direct setting with few technical problems, while John Barnard's *Elek Mathe* Gloria (5) includes optional parts for choir. The popular Peruvian Gloria has been adapted for use with the liturgical text. This can be sung by choir and people (4a) or by cantor and people (4b). There is plenty of scope for additional instruments (including percussion) where these are available, but the setting is very strong when sung unaccompanied. The two remaining settings in this group offer more reflective treatments (emphasising the petitionary section in the middle of the text). The first (1) is set in the manner of a Russian chant. It is best sung unaccompanied and in harmony (by everyone), but can also be sung as a unison line with or without accompaniment. The second (6) is based on the melody of a plainsong Kyrie. In all of these settings it is possible to divide the singing between different groups or for them to be sung throughout.

The other three settings of the Gloria text include two of the traditional text, and one metrical text to be sung to a hymn melody. The first of the traditional text settings (7) is simple and requires limited keyboard skills for the accompaniment. The second (8) comes from Martin Shaw's well-known Anglican Folk Mass written in the early years of 'Parish Communion'. Christopher Idle's metrical text (9) reminds us that Gloria in excelsis is a hymn, and this can be sung to any suitable melody with the trochaic metre 6565D, perhaps chosen on a seasonal basis.

Gospel Acclamation

There are two groups of Acclamations – the first with 'Alleluia', the second for Lent and Passiontide. Each has a simple tone for the singing of the verse. The seasonal verses are provided with simple pointing for these tones; it is also possible to extract a key verse from the Gospel of the day and to sing it to that tone. Each Acclamation can be sung in a number of ways – straight through by everyone, or by two groups (as in the Kyrie). At its simplest the singing may be done as *aA|verse|A* or *aA|verse|aA* (where lower case represents choir or cantor, and capital indicates music sung by all). But in the case of the Alleluia adapted from the medieval Worcester Acclamations (1) this might be sung line by line, alternating cantor or choir with people. If the Acclamation is sung during a Gospel procession it may need to be extended by several repetitions. It may also be sung again after the Gospel, though most likely without the verse. As before the music can be sung in unison without accompaniment, or there may be opportunities for vocal and/or instrumental embellishment.

Creed

The long text of the Creed can be a challenge for those who wish to sing it. Six accessible settings are offered here. First a setting of the modern text using a form of a Russian Chant, best sung unaccompanied in harmony (though other treatments are possible), and then a new chant setting. Christopher Walker's refrain (3) is best combined with a spoken recitation of the modern text (by a single speaker, or shared between several speakers). The chords may be sung or played quietly below the speech (though care needs to be taken over balance if there is no amplification of the speech). The traditional text (4) is provided with John Marbeck's melody, first published in 1550. By way of alternative, an authorised metrical text (5) may be sung to any hymn tune with the trochaic metre 8787 or 8787D. There is a large choice, and it should be possible to have a rota of seasonal alternatives. A further setting of an authorised Affirmation of Faith is included in the Anthology of Music for A Service of the Word.

Response to the Intercessions

Most of the prayer responses set the usual text ('Lord in your mercy, hear our prayer'), but other texts are included. The response may be treated in various ways. It may be divided into two: 'Lord in your mercy' and 'hear our prayer', or sung as a single phrase. If sung as a single phrase it may be sung first by choir or cantor, and then repeated by all. The alternative texts are longer. It may be useful for a choir or cantor to sing them over first, but thereafter to have no repetition. Such choices may depend on the pace of the service as a whole, and on the mood and extent of the period of intercession. The refrain of the settings of Psalm 141, included in the Anthology for A Service of the Word, is also suitable.

Sanctus and Benedictus

There are eight settings of the modern text and three settings of the traditional text (9-11). The traditional texts include the long-established settings by Marbeck and Shaw, as well as a more recent setting by Martin How. The modern texts include three based on metrical melodies (2, 6, 7). Some are very direct in style (John Bell, 1, Peter Ollis, 5), others are more lyrical (Christopher Tambling, 4, Alan Wilson, 8), and there is the haunting Jewish melody (3).

Another substantial collection of Sanctus and Benedictus settings can be found in the next part of this volume, where they are presented within whole settings of the Eucharistic Prayers. It is possible to use these additional settings of Sanctus and Benedictus on their own, or to substitute an appropriate setting from this anthology into a setting of the Eucharistic Prayer. Settings of the Dialogue, the Acclamations, the Conclusion are also included.

The Lord's Prayer

There are five settings of the modern text, and two settings of the traditional text. If the Lord's Prayer is to be sung then it should be sung by all, whether in unison or in harmony. Congregations can be encouraged to sing in harmony with confidence, and the setting adapted from Rimsky- Korsakov (1) can be learnt readily and sung unaccompanied. The plainsong (2) and harmonised settings (3-4) offer simpler alternatives, while that adapted from Zabolotski is more of a 'piece' (4). Marbeck's melody provides a well-known version of the traditional text (6), while the last setting (7) can be sung as a unison melody or in harmony.

Agnus Dei

There are fourteen settings of Agnus Dei. The five settings of the 'Lamb of God' form of the text in modern language are complemented by five settings of 'Jesus, Lamb of God'. In their traditional language versions there are two settings of each text. We are reminded that Agnus Dei is a litany sung during the breaking of the Bread. The very short plainsong and harmonised settings (2, 3, 9, 11) might be repeated more often if the action takes longer. As with other texts with repetitions the Agnus Dei may be sung in a number of ways, either sung by all throughout or divided between cantor and people, choir and people, or two equal groups. There is scope in most of the settings to make these decisions. One of the settings uses the hymn tune *Caswall* (10). Among the settings of the traditional texts that by Grayston Ives (14) is particularly lyrical; the accompaniment would lend itself to performance with string quartet.

Kyrie 1a

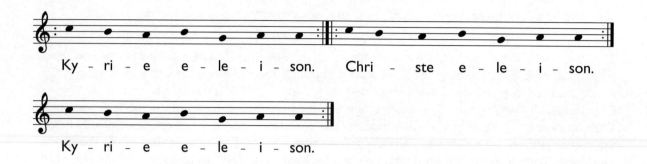

Ky – ri – e e – le – i – son. Chri – ste e – le – i – son.

Ky – ri – e e – le – i – son.

Traditional chant

Kyrie 1b

♩ = 66

Ky – ri – e e – le – i – son. Ky – ri – e e – le – i – son.

Ky – ri – e e – lei – son.

Chri – ste e – le – i – son. Chris – te e – le – i – son.

Chri – ste e – lei – son.

Ky – ri – e e – le – i – son. Ky – ri – e e – le – i – son.

Optional

Ky – ri – e e – lei – son.

Traditional chant, arranged by John Harper
© 2000 The Royal School of Church Music

Kyrie 1c

Traditional chant, arranged by John Harper
© 2000 The Royal School of Church Music

Optional tones for sung petitions

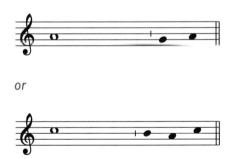

or

Kyrie 2a

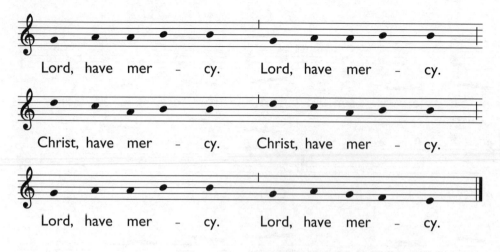

Lord, have mer - cy. Lord, have mer - cy.

Christ, have mer - cy. Christ, have mer - cy.

Lord, have mer - cy. Lord, have mer - cy.

Traditional chant

Kyrie 2b

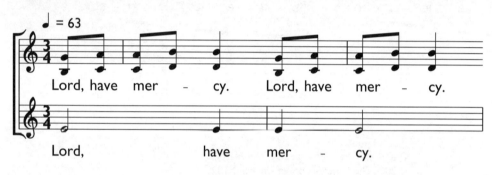

Lord, have mer - cy. Lord, have mer - cy.

Lord, have mer - cy.

Christ, have mer - cy. Christ, have mer - cy.

Christ, have mer - cy.

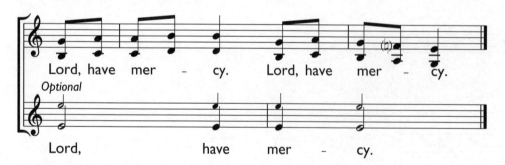

Lord, have mer - cy. Lord, have mer - cy.

Optional

Lord, have mer - cy.

Traditional chant, arranged by John Harper
© 2000 The Royal School of Church Music

Optional tones for sung petitions

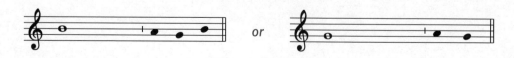

or

Kyrie 3

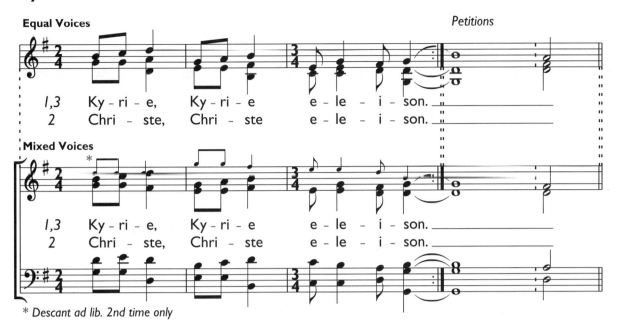

* Descant ad lib. 2nd time only

Music: Jacques Berthier
© Ateliers et Presses de Taizé, 71250 Taizé-Community, France

Optional tones for sung petitions

Kyrie 4

Russian

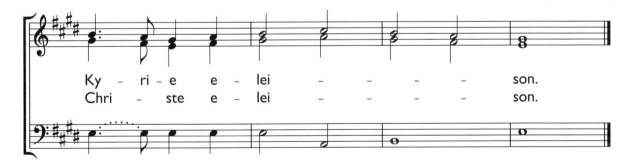

Russian Orthodox chant

Optional tone for sung petitions

Slowly and expressively

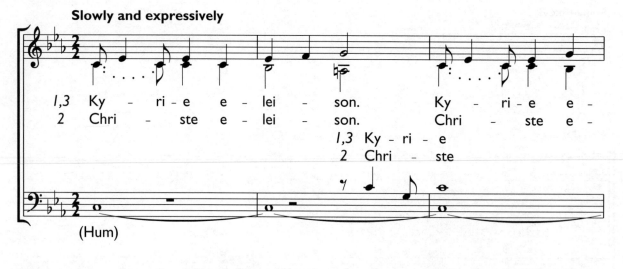

(Hum)

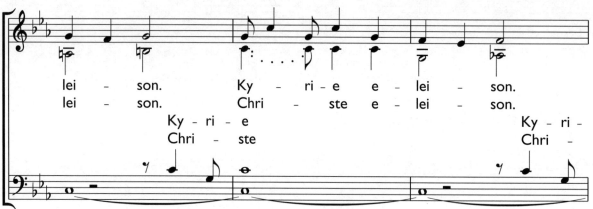

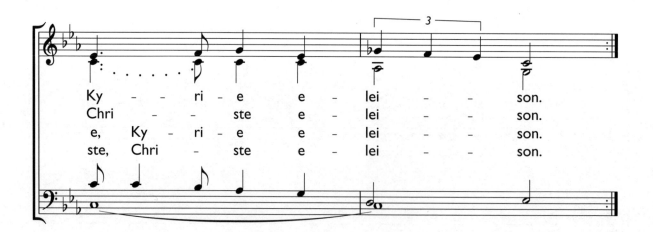

Music: Dinah Reindorf, arranged by John Bell
from *Many and Great* (Wild Goose Publications 1990),
melody © 1987 Dinah Reindorf,
arrangement © 1990 WGRG, Iona Community, 840 Govan Road, Glasgow G51 3UU, Scotland

Optional tone for sung petitions

Kyrie 6

Lord, have mer-cy. **Lord, have mer-cy.** Christ, have mer-cy. **Christ, have mer-cy.**

Lord, have mer - cy. **Lord, have mer - cy.** ___

Music: Norman Warren
© Norman Warren

Optional tone for sung petitions

Kyrie 7

1,3 Lord, have mer - cy,   Lord, have mer - cy,   Lord,   have mer - cy.
2   Christ, have mer - cy,   Christ, have mer - cy,   Christ,   have mer - cy.

Music: Peter Ollis
© Peter Ollis

Optional tone for sung petitions

Kyrie 8

Glastonbury

Music: Robin Walker

© Robin Walker / Music from Glastonbury

Optional tone for sung petitions

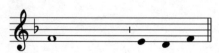

Kyrie 9

Lord, __ have mer – cy. **Lord, __ have mer – cy.**

Christ, __ have mer – cy. **Christ, __ have mer – cy.**

Lord, __ have mer – cy. **Lord, __ have mer – cy.**

Music: Ian Forrester
© Ian Forrester

This Kyrie may be sung with or without the optional petitions.

If the petitions are used they may be said or sung.

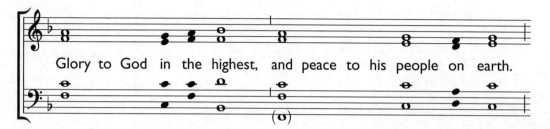

Glory to God in the highest, and peace to his people on earth.

(o)

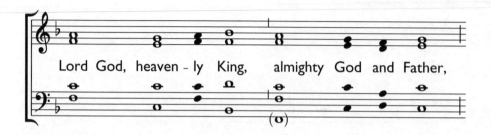

Lord God, heaven – ly King,   almighty God and Father,

(o)

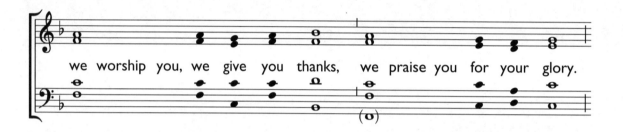

we worship you, we give you thanks,   we praise you for your glory.

(o)

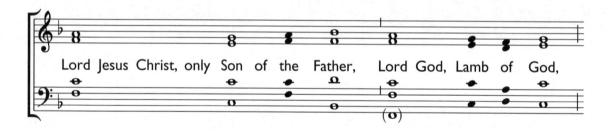

Lord Jesus Christ, only Son of the Father,   Lord God, Lamb of God,

(o)

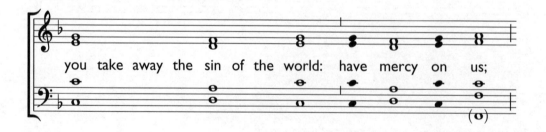

you take away the sin of the world: have mercy on us;

(o)

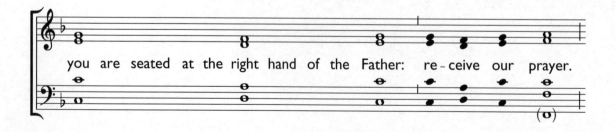

you are seated at the right hand of the Father: re – ceive our prayer.

(o)

For you a-lone are the Holy One, you a-lone are the Lord,

you a-lone are the Most High, Je-sus Christ, with the Ho-ly Spirit,

in the glory of God the Father. A-men.

This setting may be sung with refrains as indicated, or sung straight through.

2 Lord Je-sus Christ, on-ly Son of the Fa-ther, Lord God, Lamb of God, _____ you take a-way the sin of the world: have mer-cy on us, have mer-cy on us; you are sea-ted at the

Refrain ad lib.

right hand of the Fa-ther: re-ceive, re-ceive our prayer. _____

Gloria 3

This setting may be sung in unison or with the optional second voice part.

take a-way the sin of the world: have mer - cy on us; you are

you take _ a-way _ the sin of the world: have mer-cy on us; you are

seat – ed at the right hand of the Fa-ther: re-ceive our prayer.

seat – ed at the right hand of the Fa-ther: re-ceive our prayer.

For you a-lone are the Ho-ly One, you a-lone are the_ Lord,

For you a-lone are the Ho-ly One, you a-lone are the_ Lord,

Words: ELLC © 1988 ELLC
Music: Alan Wilson © Alan Wilson

Gloria 4a

Peruvian

Rhythmic, quiet

Glo-ry to God, glo-ry to God, glo-ry in the high - est, and

Glo-ry to God, glo-ry in the high - est,

Glo-ry to God, glo-ry to God, glo-ry to God, glo-ry to God, and

peace to his peo-ple, peace to his peo-ple, peo - ple on earth.

and peace to his peo-ple, peo - ple on earth.

peace to his peo-ple, peace to his peo-ple, peace to his peo-ple, peace to his peo-ple,

Lord God, hea - ven - ly King, al - migh - ty God and Fa - ther, we

Glo-ry to God, glo-ry to God, glo-ry to God, glo - ry, we

Lord God, hea - ven - ly King, al - migh - ty God and Fa - ther, we

wor-ship you, we give_ you thanks, we praise you for your glo - ry.

wor-ship you, we give_ you thanks, we praise you for your glo - ry.

wor-ship you, give you thanks, praise you for your glo - ry.

Words: ELLC © 1988 ELLC
Music: Traditional Peruvian, arranged by John Harper
© 2000 The Royal School of Church Music

Gloria 4b

Rhythmic, quiet

Glo-ry to God, glo-ry to God, glo-ry in the high - est, and

peace to his peo-ple, peace to his peo-ple, peo - ple on earth.

Lord God, hea - ven-ly King, al - migh - ty God and Fa - ther, we

wor-ship you, we give_ you thanks, we praise you for your glo - ry.

Glo-ry to God, and peace to his peo-ple, glo-ry to God, his peo-ple on earth.

Lord Je - sus Christ, on-ly Son of the Fa - ther, Lord God, Lamb of God, you

take a-way the sin of the world: have mer - cy on us; you are

seat-ed at the right hand of the Fa - ther: re - ceive, re - ceive our prayer;

Glo-ry to God, and peace to his peo-ple, glo-ry to God, his peo-ple on earth.

For you a-lone are the Ho - ly One, you a-lone are the Lord, you a-

lone are the Most High, Je - sus Christ, with the Ho - ly Spi - rit,

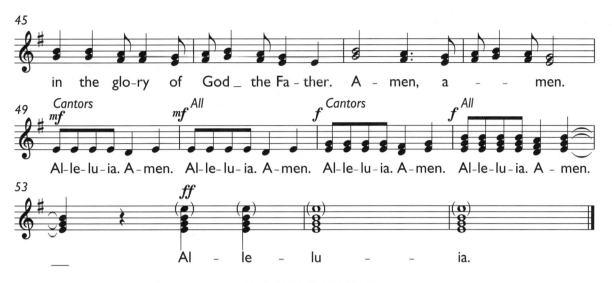

in the glo-ry of God _ the Fa-ther. A - men, a - - men.

Al-le-lu-ia. A-men. Al-le-lu-ia. A-men. Al-le-lu-ia. A-men. Al-le-lu-ia. A - men.

Al - le - lu - - ia.

Words: ELLC © 1988 ELLC
Music: Traditional Peruvian, arranged by John Harper
© 2000 The Royal School of Church Music

Gloria 5

'Elek Mathe'

Glo - ry to

God in the high - - est, and peace to his

Gloria in excelsis   **33**

peo – ple on earth, Lord _____ God, _____

hea – venly King, _____ al – migh – ty God _____ and

Fa – – ther, we wor – ship

Words: ELLC © 1988 ELLC
Music: John Barnard
© John Barnard / Jubilate Hymns

Gloria 6

Glo - ry to God in the high - est, and peace to his peo - ple on earth.

Lord God, hea - ven - ly King, al - migh - ty God and Fa - ther,

we wor-ship you, we give you thanks, we praise you for your glo - ry.

Lord Je - sus Christ, on - ly Son of the Fa - ther, Lord God, Lamb of God,

you take a - way the sin of the world: have mer - cy on us;

you are seat-ed at the right hand of the Fa - ther: re - ceive our prayer.

For you a - lone are the Ho - ly One, you a - lone are the Lord,

you a - lone are the Most High, Je - sus Christ, with the Ho - ly Spi - rit,

in the glo - ry of God the Fa - ther. A - men.

Words: ELLC © 1988 ELLC
Music: Traditional chant, adapted by John Harper
© 2000 The Royal School of Church Music

Anglican Folk Mass : traditional text

In the time of ordinary slow reading

Glo-ry be to God on high. And in earth peace, good will towards men.

We praise thee, we bless thee, we wor-ship thee, we glo-ri-fy thee,

we give thanks to thee for thy great glo-ry, O Lord God, hea-ven-ly King,

God the Fa-ther Al-migh-ty. O Lord, the on-ly-be-got-ten Son, Je-sus Christ:

Gloria 8

This setting may be sung in unison or in two parts.

1. Glory in the highest to the God of heaven;
   Peace to all your people through the earth be given.
   Mighty God and Father, thanks and praise we bring,
   Singing Alleluia to our heavenly king.

2. Jesus Christ is risen, God the Father's Son;
   With the Holy Spirit, you are Lord alone.
   Lamb once killed for sinners, all our guilt to bear,
   Show us now your mercy, now receive our prayer.

3. Christ the world's true Saviour, high and holy one,
   Seated now and reigning from your Father's throne:
   Lord and God, we praise you! Highest heaven adores:
   In the Father's glory, all the praise be yours!

Words: Christopher Idle
© Christopher Idle / Jubilate Hymns
Music: 'Evelyns', W H Monk

This text may be sung to any 6565D hymn tune.

Gospel Acclamation 1

Music: from *Christus Vincit* (Worcester Antiphoner), adapted by John Harper
© 2000 The Royal School of Church Music

Gospel Acclamation 2

Verse

Music: Traditional chant

Texts for the Acclamation verses may be found on pages 58 – 61.

Gospel Acclamation 3

Al – le – lu – ia, al – le – lu – ia. Al – le – lu – ia, al – le –
lu – ia. Al – le – lu – ia, al – le – lu – ia, al – le – lu – ia.

Verse

Music: from Honduras, arranged by John Bell
from *Come All You People* (Wild Goose Publications 1995),
arrangement © 1995 WGRG, Iona Community, 840 Govan Road, Glasgow G51 3UU, Scotland

Gospel Acclamation 4

Al – le – lu – ia, al – le – lu – ia, al – le – lu – ia.

Verse

Music: from a Magnificat by G P da Palestrina, adapted by W H Monk

Gospel Acclamation 5

Verse

Music: Abraham Maraire
© Abraham Maraire, United Methodist Church Service, Mutambara, CPS Box 61, Cashel, Zimbabwe

The harmony in this Acclamation follows African rather than European conventions, and the final D in the bass is intended.

Taizé

Music: Jacques Berthier
© Ateliers et Presses de Taizé, 71250 Taizé-Community, France

Gospel Acclamation 7

Music: David Ogden
© 1992 David Ogden

Verse

Gospel Acclamation 8

Celtic Alleluia

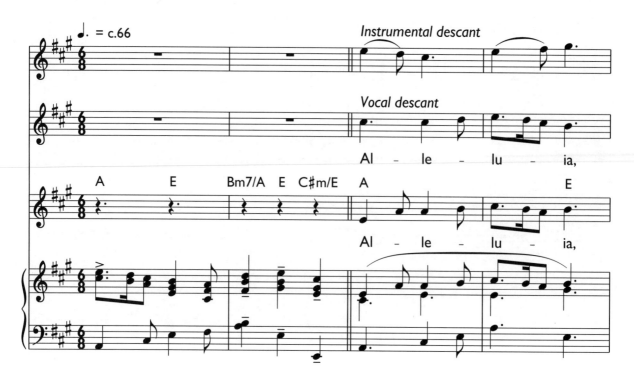

Music: Fintan O'Carroll and Christopher Walker
© 1985 Fintan O'Carroll and Christopher Walker.
Published by OCP Publications, 5536 NE Hassalo, Portland, OR 97213, USA.
All rights reserved. Used by permission.

Verse

Gospel Acclamation 9

Verse

Music: Peter Moger
© 1999 Peter Moger

Gospel Acclamation 10

Verse

After the verse

Music: Peter Jones
© 1994 Peter Jones. Published by OCP Publications, 5536 NE Hassalo, Portland, OR 97213, USA.

Gospel Acclamation 11a

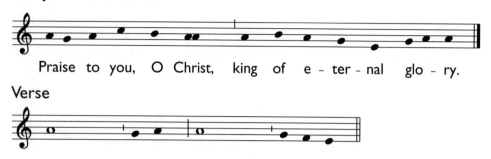

Praise to you, O Christ, king of e – ter – nal glo – ry.

Verse

Music: John Harper
© 2000 The Royal School of Church Music

Gospel Acclamation 11b

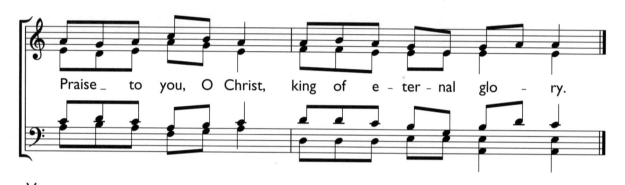

Praise _ to you, O Christ, king of e – ter – nal glo – ry.

Verse

Music: John Harper
© 2000 The Royal School of Church Music

Gospel Acclamation 12

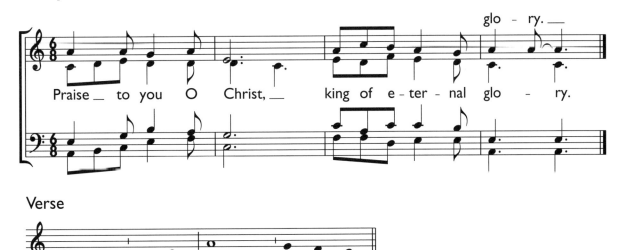

Praise __ to you O Christ, __ king of e - ter - nal glo - ry. glo - ry. __

Verse

Gospel Acclamation 13

♩ = 88

Praise to you, O Christ, king of e - ter - nal glo - ry.

Verse

Verses for Gospel Acclamations in Ordinary Time

1

Speak, Lord, for your servant is ' listening.
You have the words of e'ternal life.
1 Samuel 3.9; John 6.68

2

I am the light of the world, says ' the Lord.
Whoever follows me will never walk in darkness
but will have the ' light of life.
cf John 8.12

3

My sheep hear my voice, says ' the Lord.
I know them, and they ' follow me.
cf John 10.27

4

I am the way, the truth, and the life, says ' the Lord.
No one comes to the Father ex'cept through me.
cf John 14.6

5

We do not live by bread ' alone,
but by every word that comes from the ' mouth of God.
cf Matthew 4.4

6

Welcome with meekness the implant'ed word
that has the power to ' save your souls.
James 1.21

7

The word of the Lord endures for ' ever.
The word of the Lord is the good news an'nounced to you.
cf 1 Peter 1.25

Verses for Gospel Acclamations during Specific Seasons

From the First Sunday of Advent until Christmas Eve
Prepare the way of the Lord, make his ' paths straight,
and all flesh shall see the salva'tion of God.
cf Isaiah 40.3-5

From Christmas Day until the Eve of the Epiphany
The Word became flesh and dwelt a'mong us,
and we have ' seen his glory.
John 1.14

From the Epiphany until the Eve of the Presentation
Christ was revealed in flesh, proclaimed among the ' nations
and believed in through'out the world.
cf 1 Timothy 3.16

The Presentation of Christ in the Temple
This child is the light to enlighten the ' nations,
and the glory of your ' people Israel.
cf Luke 2.32

From Ash Wednesday until the Saturday after the Fourth Sunday in Lent
The Lord is a great God, O that today you would listen to ' his voice.
Harden ' not your hearts.
Psalm 95.7-8

The Annunciation of Our Lord
The Word became flesh and lived a'mong us,
and we have ' seen his glory.
John 1.14
If the Annunciation falls in Eastertide, use the text provided for Christmas

From the Fifth Sunday of Lent until the Wednesday of Holy Week
Christ humbled himself and became obedient unto death,
even death on ' a cross.
Therefore God has highly exalted him
and given him the name that is above ' every name.
Philippians 2.8-9

Maundy Thursday
I give you a new commandment, says ' the Lord:
Love one another as ' I have loved you.
cf John 13.34

From Easter Day until the Eve of the Ascension
I am the first and the last, says the Lord,
and ' the living one;
I was dead, and behold I am alive for ' evermore.
cf Revelation 1.17-18

Ascension Day
Go and make disciples of all nations, says ' the Lord.
Remember, I am with you always, to the end ' of the age.
cf Matthew 28.20

From the Day after Ascension Day until the Day of Pentecost

Come, Holy Spirit, fill the hearts of your faith ' ful people
and kindle in them the fire ' of your love.

Trinity Sunday

Glory to the Father, and to the Son, and to the Ho ' ly Spirit,
one God who was, and who is, and who is to come, – ' the Almighty.
cf Revelation 1.8

All Saints' Day

You are a chosen race, a royal ' priesthood,
a holy nation, God's own people,
called out of darkness into his mar ' vellous light.
1 Peter 2.9

From the day after All Saints' Day until the day before the First Sunday of Advent

Blessed is the king who comes in the name of ' the Lord.

Peace in heaven and glory in the ' highest heaven.
Luke 19.38

On Saints' Days

I have called you friends, says ' the Lord,
for all that I have heard from my Father
I have made ' known to you.
cf John 15.15

Verses for Gospel Acclamations at Pastoral Services

The Marriage Service

God made them male and ' female
and the two shall be'cöme one
cf Mark 10.8

God ' is love;
let us love one another
as God ' has loved us.
cf 1 John 4.8-1

The Funeral Service

God so loved ' the world
that he gave his ' only Son.
cf John 3.16

Blessed are those who die in ' the Lord
for they rest ' from their labour.
cf Revelation 14.13

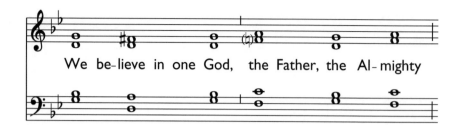

We be-lieve in one God, the Father, the Al-mighty

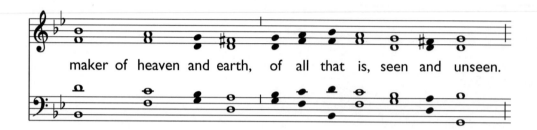

maker of heaven and earth, of all that is, seen and unseen.

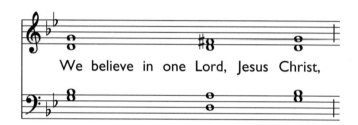

We believe in one Lord, Jesus Christ,

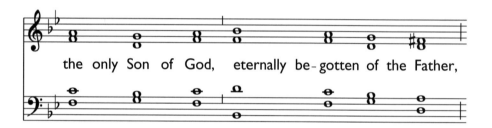

the only Son of God, eternally be-gotten of the Father,

God from God, Light from Light, true God from true God,

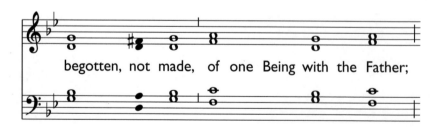

begotten, not made, of one Being with the Father;

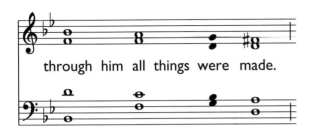

through him all things were made.

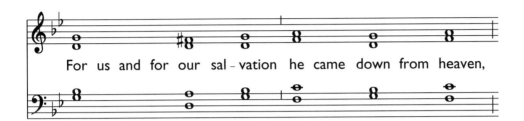

For us and for our sal-vation he came down from heaven,

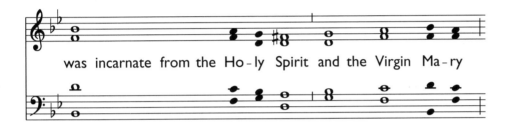

was incarnate from the Ho-ly Spirit and the Virgin Ma-ry

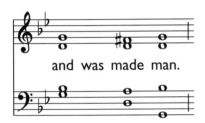

and was made man.

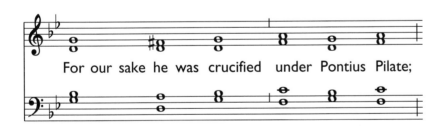

For our sake he was crucified under Pontius Pilate;

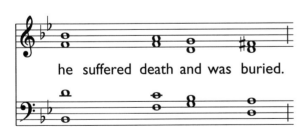

he suffered death and was buried.

On the third day he rose a-gain in accordance with the scriptures;

he as-cended into heaven and is seated at the right hand of the Father.

He will come a-gain in glory to judge the living and the dead,

and his kingdom will have no end.

We believe in the Holy Spirit, the Lord, the giver of life,

who proceeds from the Father and the Son.

who with the Father and the Son is worshipped and glorified.

who has spoken through the pro-phets.

We believe in one holy catholic and apostolic Church.

We ac-knowledge one baptism for the forgiveness of sins.

We look for the resurrection of the dead,

and the life of the world to come. A - men.

Words: ELLC © 1988 ELLC
Music: Russian chant, adapted by John Harper
© 2000 The Royal School of Church Music

Nicene Creed 2

We be-lieve in one God, the Fa-ther, the Al-migh-ty,

ma-ker of hea-ven and earth, of all that is, seen and un - seen.

We be-lieve in one Lord, Je - sus Christ,

the on - ly Son of God, e - ter-nal - ly be-got-ten of the Fa-ther,

God from God, Light from Light, true God from true God,

be - got - ten, not made, of one Be - ing with the Fa - ther,

through him all things were made.

For us and for our sal - va - tion he came down from hea - ven,

was in - car-nate from the Ho - ly Spi - rit and the Vir - gin Ma - ry

and was made man.

For our sake he was cru - ci - fied un-der Pon-tius Pi - late;

he suf-fered death and was bur - ied.

On the third day he rose a-gain in ac-cord-ance with the scrip-tures;

he as-cen-ded in-to hea-ven and is sea-ted at the right hand of the Fa-ther.

He will come a-gain in glo-ry to judge the liv-ing and the dead,

and his king-dom will have no end.

We be-lieve in the Ho-ly Spi-rit, the Lord, the giv-er of life,

who pro-ceeds from the Fa-ther and the Son.

who with the Fa-ther and the Son is wor-shipped and glo-ri-fied.

who has spo-ken through the pro-phets.

We be-lieve in one ho-ly ca-tho-lic and a-pos-to-lic Church.

We ac-know-ledge one bap-tism for the for-give-ness of sins.

We look for the res-ur-rec-tion of the dead,

and the life of the world to come. A - men.

Words: ELLC © 1988 ELLC
Music: John Harper
© 2000 The Royal School of Church Music

Nicene Creed 3

Words: ELLC © 1988 ELLC
Music: Christopher Walker, SATB arrangement by John Harper
© Christopher Walker. Published by OCP Publications, 5536 NE Hassalo, Portland, OR 97213, USA.
All rights reserved. Used by permission.

The refrain is sung at the beginning of the Creed, and at the points marked in the text. While the text is recited, the ostinato on the right-hand page is played and/or sung as an accompaniment.

Ostinato

Voices and/or instruments

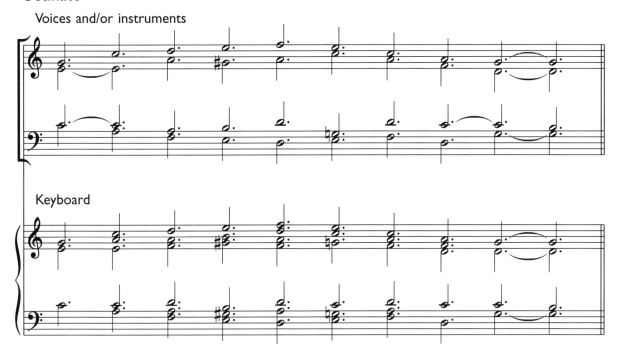

Keyboard

Refrain

We believe in one God,
the Father, the Almighty,
maker of heaven and earth,
of all that is,
seen and unseen.   *Refrain*

We believe in one Lord, Jesus Christ,
the only Son of God,
eternally begotten of the Father,
God from God, Light from Light,
true God from true God,
begotten, not made,
of one Being with the Father;
through him all things were made.
For us and for our salvation he came down from heaven,
was incarnate from the Holy Spirit and the Virgin Mary
and was made man.   *Refrain*

For our sake he was crucified under Pontius Pilate;
he suffered death and was buried.
On the third day he rose again
in accordance with the Scriptures;
he ascended into heaven
and is seated at the right hand of the Father.
He will come again in glory to judge the living and the dead,
and his kingdom will have no end.   *Refrain*

We believe in the Holy Spirit,
the Lord, the giver of life,
who proceeds from the Father and the Son,
who with the Father and the Son is worshipped and glorified,
who has spoken through the prophets.   *Refrain*

We believe in one holy catholic and apostolic Church.
We acknowledge one baptism for the forgiveness of sins.
We look for the resurrection of the dead,
and the life of the world to come. Amen.   *Refrain*

Marbeck : traditional text

I be-lieve in one God the Fa - ther al - migh - ty,

ma - ker of heaven and earth,

and of all things vi - si - ble and in - vi - si - ble:

And in one Lord Je - sus Christ, the on - ly be-got-ten Son of God,

be - got - ten of his Fa - ther be - fore all worlds,

God of God, Light of light, ve - ry God of ve - ry God,

be - got-ten, not made, be - ing of one sub-stance with the Fa - ther,

by whom all things were made;

who for us men and for our sal - va - tion came down from heaven,

and was in - car - nate by the Ho - ly Ghost of the Vir - gin Ma - ry,

and was made man,

and was cru - ci - fied al - so for us, un - der Pon - tius Pi - late.

he suf - fered and was bur - ied,

and the third day he rose a-gain ac-cord-ing to the Scrip-tures,

and as-cen-ded in-to heaven, and sit-teth on the right hand of the Fa-ther.

And he shall come a-gain with glo-ry to judge both the quick and the dead:

whose king-dom shall have no end.

And I be-lieve in the Ho-ly Ghost, the Lord, the giv-er of life,

who pro-ceed-eth from the Fa-ther and the Son,

who with the Fa-ther and the Son to-geth-er is wor-shipped and glo-ri-fied,

who spake by the pro-phets.

And I be-lieve one ho-ly ca-tho-lic and a-pos-to-lic Church.

I ack-now-ledge one bap-tism for the re-mis-sion of sins.

And I look for the re-sur-rec-tion of the dead,

and the life of the world to come. A - men.

The rhythm reflects Marbeck's original notation, but should be interpreted with freedom.

Words: The text of The Book of Common Prayer is the property of the Crown in perpetuity;
the material is reproduced by permission of the Crown's Patentee, Cambridge University Press.
Music: John Marbeck, edited Alistair Warwick
Music © 2000 The Royal School of Church Music

Nicene Creed 5

I We be-lieve in God the Fa-ther, God al-migh-ty, by whose plan
earth and hea-ven sprang to be-ing, All cre-a-ted things be-gan.

2 We be-lieve in Christ the Sa-viour, Son of God in hu-man frame,
Vir-gin-born, the child of Ma-ry Up-on whom the Spi-rit came.

Alternatively, F♮ (soprano) and C (alto)

1   We believe in God the Father,
     God almighty, by whose plan
     Earth and heaven sprang to being,
     All created things began.

2   We believe in Christ the Saviour,
     Son of God in human frame,
     Virgin-born, the child of Mary
     Upon whom the Spirit came.

3   Christ, who on the cross forsaken,
     Like a lamb to slaughter led,
     Suffered under Pontius Pilate,
     He descended to the dead.

4   We believe in Jesus risen,
     Heaven's king to rule and reign,
     To the Father's side ascended
     Till as judge he comes again.

5   We believe in God the Spirit;
     In one Church, below, above:
     Saints of God in one communion,
     One in holiness and love.

6   So by faith, our sins forgiven,
     Christ our Saviour, Lord and friend,
     We shall rise with him in glory
     To the life that knows no end.

Words: Timothy Dudley-Smith
© Timothy Dudley-Smith
Music: 'Lux Eoi', Arthur Sullivan

This metrical text may be sung to any 8787 or 8787D tune

Prayer Response 1a

Lord, in your mer – cy hear __ our prayer.

Prayer Response 1b

Lord, in your mer – cy hear our __ prayer.

Music: John Harper
© 2000 The Royal School of Church Music

Prayer Response 2a

Lord, in your mer – cy hear our prayer.

Prayer Response 2b

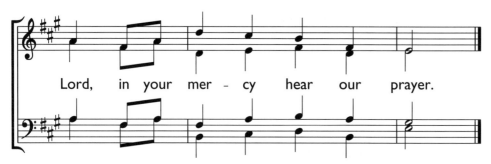

Lord, in your mer – cy hear our prayer.

Music: John Harper
© 2000 The Royal School of Church Music

Prayer Response 3

[petition] Lord, in your mer – cy hear our __ prayer.

sustain or hum play or hum hear our __ prayer.

Music: Alan Wilson
© 2000 Alan Wilson

Prayer Response 4a

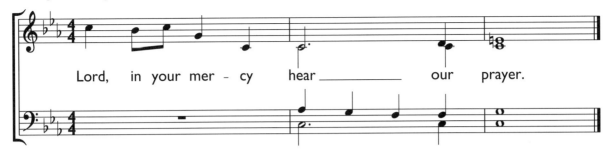

Lord, in your mer – cy hear _____ our prayer.

Prayer Response 4b

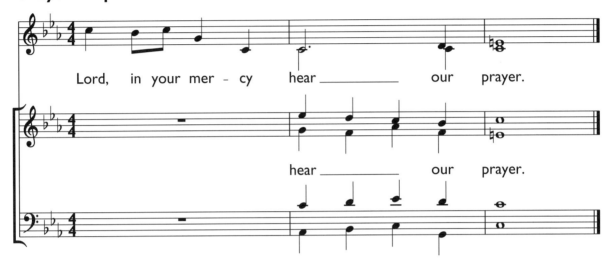

Lord, in your mer – cy hear _____ our prayer.

hear _____ our prayer.

Music: John Bell, from *There Is One Among Us* (Wild Goose Publications 1998)
© 1995, 1998 WGRG, Iona Community, 840 Govan Road, Glasgow G51 3UU, Scotland

Prayer Response 5

Through our lives and _ by our prayers, _ your _ King-dom come.

Words & music: John Bell, from *Come All You People* (Wild Goose Publications 1995)
© 1995 WGRG, Iona Community, 840 Govan Road, Glasgow G51 3UU, Scotland

Prayer Response 6

Lis – ten, Lord, lis – ten, Lord, not to our words but to our _ prayer.

Words & music: John Bell, from *Come All You People* (Wild Goose Publications 1995)
© 1995 WGRG, Iona Community, 840 Govan Road, Glasgow G51 3UU, Scotland

Prayer Response 7

Gently ♩ = 95

Lord___ Je - sus Christ, lov - er of all. Trail wide the hem of your gar - ment. Bring heal - ing, bring peace.

poco rall.

In the last response play the same accompaniment until the coda on the right.

Last response

Lord Jesus Christ, lover of all. Trail wide the hem of your

garment. Bring healing, bring peace. Bring healing, bring peace.

organ continues:

Words: John Bell, from *Heaven shall not wait* (Wild Goose Publications 1987)
© 1995, 1998 WGRG, Iona Community, 840 Govan Road, Glasgow G51 3UU, Scotland
Music: Paul Stubbings   © 1999 Paul Stubbings

The refrain from Psalm 141 may also be used as a prayer response. *See pages 230 to 233 and 277.*

Sanctus 1

St Bride

Words: ELLC © 1988 ELLC Music: John Bell, adapted by John Harper
© 1995 WGRG, Iona Community, 840 Govan Road, Glasgow G51 3UU, Scotland

Sanctus 2

American traditional

Ho - ly, ho - ly, ho - ly Lord, __ God of power and might, _____ heaven and earth __ are full of your glo - ry. Ho - san - na in ____ the high - - est.

Bless - ed __ is he who comes __ in the name of the Lord. _____ Ho - san - na in ____ the high - - est. __ Ho - san - na in _____ the high - - est.

Words: ELLC © 1988 ELLC
Music: 'Land of Rest', American traditional melody, adapted by Marcia Pruner, harmony by John Campbell
© 1980 Church Pension Fund / Church Publishing Incorporated

Sanctus 3

Jewish melody

Ho - ly, __ ho - ly, __ ho - ly __ Lord, God of __ power, of __

power and __ might. Heaven and earth are full, _____

full of your glo - - - ry. _____ Ho - san - na, ho -

san - - na, ho - san - na in the high - est.

Bless - ed is he who __ comes, ____ who comes in the name of the

Lord. _____ Ho - san - na, ho - san - na, ho -

san - na in the high - est.

Acclamation (for use with Prayers A, B, C, E, G)

Christ has __ died: Christ has __ died: Christ is ___ ris - en:

Christ is ___ ris - en: Christ will come ___ a - gain.

Christ will come ___ a - gain. Christ __ has died,

Christ __ is ris - en, Christ __ will come a - gain.

Amen (for use with Prayers B, C, E and F)

A - men. A - men. A - men. A - men.

Words: ELLC © 1988 ELLC
Music: Jewish melody, adapted by David Ogden
© in this version 2000 David Ogden

Sanctus 4

name of ____ the Lord. ____ Ho - san - na in the high - est, ho - san - na in the high - est.

Words: ELLC © 1988 ELLC
Music: Christopher Tambling
© Christopher Tambling

Sanctus 5

comes in the name of the Lord. _____ Ho - san - na _____ in the

high - est. _____

Words: ELLC © 1988 ELLC
Music: Peter Ollis © 1999 Peter Ollis

Sanctus 6

comes ___ in the name of the Lord. ___ Ho -

san - na in the high - - est. ___ Ho -

san - na, ___ ho-san-na, ___ ho-san-na in the high-est.

Words: ELLC © 1988 ELLC
Music: Original unknown, arranged by Norman Warren
arrangement © Norman Warren

Sanctus 7   Glenfinlas

1 Ho - ly, holy, ho - ly Lord, God of power and _ might, ___
2 Bless - ed is he who comes in the name of the Lord. ___

heaven and earth are full of your glo - ry. Ho-san-na in the high - est.
Ho - san - na in the _ high-est, ho-san-na in the high - est.

Words: ELLC © 1988 ELLC
Music: 'Glenfinlas', K G Finlay, adapted by Gordon Appleton © Broomhill Church of Scotland

Sanctus 8

Words: ELLC © 1988 ELLC
Music: Alan Wilson © Alan Wilson

Ho - ly, ho - ly, ho - ly, Lord God of hosts,

hea - ven and earth are full of thy glo - ry.

Optional in Order Two

Glo - ry be to thee, O Lord most high. [A - men.]

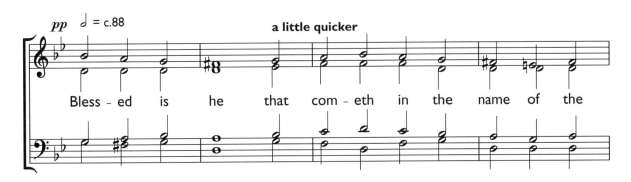

Bless - ed is he that com - eth in the name of the

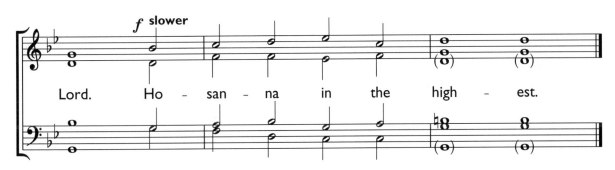

Lord. Ho - san - na in the high - est.

Sanctus 10

Ho - ly, ho - ly, ho - ly, Lord __ God of __ hosts, heav'n and earth are full of thy glo - ry.

Glo - ry be to thee, O Lord most high.

Sanctus 11

Marbeck : traditional text

Ho – ly, ho – ly, ho – ly Lord God of hosts,

heaven and earth are full of thy glo – ry.

Glo – ry be to thee, O Lord most high.

Bless – ed is he that com – eth in the name of the Lord.

Ho – san – na in the high – est.

The rhythm reflects Marbeck's original notation, but should be interpreted with freedom.

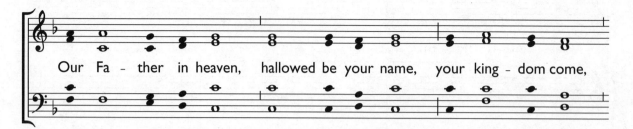

Our Fa - ther in heaven, hallowed be your name, your king - dom come,

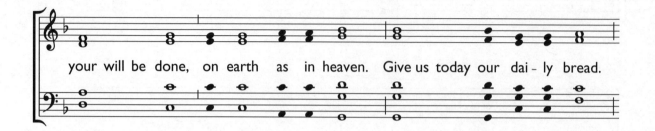

your will be done, on earth as in heaven. Give us today our dai - ly bread.

For - give us our sins as we for - give those who sin a - gainst us.

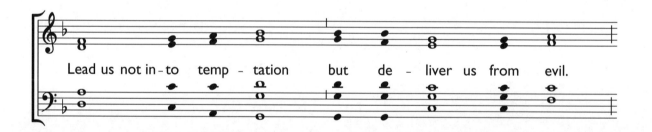

Lead us not in - to temp - tation but de - liver us from evil.

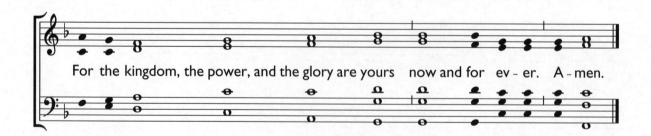

For the kingdom, the power, and the glory are yours now and for ev - er. A - men.

The Lord's Prayer 2

Our Fa-ther, in hea-ven,

hal-lowed be your name;

your king-dom come,

your will be done,

on earth as in hea-ven.

Give us to-day our dai-ly bread.

For-give us our sins

as we for-give those who sin a-gainst us.

Lead us not in-to temp-ta-tion

but de-liv-er us from e-vil.

For the king-dom, the power, and the glo-ry are yours

now and for ev-er.

A - men.

Words: ELLC © 1988 ELLC
Music: Traditional chant adapted by John Harper
© 2000 The Royal School of Church Music

The Lord's Prayer 3

As our Sa - viour taught us, so we pray

Our Father in heaven, hallowed be your name,

your kingdom come, your will be done, on earth as in heaven.

Give us today our dai - ly bread.

Forgive us our sins as we forgive those who sin a - gainst us.

Lead us not into temp - ta - tion but deliver us from e - vil.

For the kingdom, the power, and the glo - ry are yours

now and for ev - er. A - men.

Words: ELLC © 1988 ELLC
Music: John Harper
© 2000 The Royal School of Church Music

This appears in traditional form of the text on page 274.

The Lord's Prayer 4

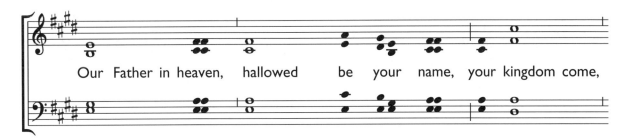

Our Father in heaven, hallowed be your name, your kingdom come,

your will be done, on earth as in heaven. Give us to-day our dai-ly bread.

For-give us our sins as we for-give those who sin a-gainst us.

Lead us not into temp-ta-tion but de-liv-er us from e-vil. For the kingdom,

the power, and the glo-ry are yours now and for ev-er. A - men.

Words: ELLC © 1988 ELLC
Music: Alan Wilson
© Joseph Weinberger Ltd. Reproduced by permission.

The Lord's Prayer 5

e - vil. For the king - dom, the pow - er and the glo - ry are

yours __ now and for ev - er. A - men.

Words: ELLC © 1988 ELLC
Music: N Zabolotski, arranged by John Bell, adapted by John Harper
Copyright control. This version © 2000 The Royal School of Church Music

The Lord's Prayer 6

Marbeck : traditional text

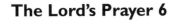

Our Fa - ther which art in hea - ven, hal - lowed be thy name; thy king - dom come;

thy will be done; on earth as it is in heaven. Give us this day our dai - ly bread.

And for - give us our tres - pass - es, as we for - give those who tres - pass a - gainst us.

And lead us not in - to temp - ta - tion; but de - liv - er us from e - vil.

For thine is the king - dom, the power and the glo - ry, for ev - er and ev - er. A - men.

Words: The text of The Book of Common Prayer is the property of the Crown in perpetuity;
the material is reproduced by permission of the Crown's Patentee, Cambridge University Press.
Music: John Marbeck

The Lord's Prayer 7

traditional text

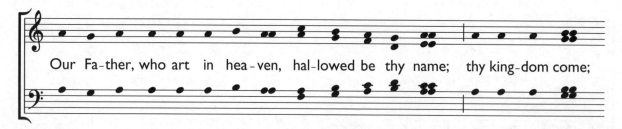

Our Fa-ther, who art in hea-ven, hal-lowed be thy name; thy king-dom come;

thy will be done; on earth as it is in hea-ven. Give us this day our

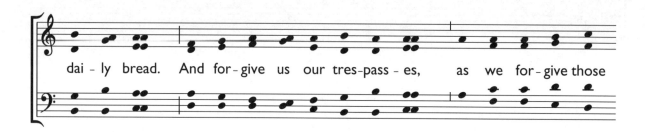

dai-ly bread. And for-give us our tres-pass-es, as we for-give those

who tres-pass a-gainst us. And lead us not in-to temp-ta-tion; but de-

liv-er us from e-vil. For thine is the king-dom, the power and

the glo-ry, for ev-er and ev-er. A-men.

Agnus Dei 1

Words: ELLC © 1988 ELLC   Music: Jacques Berthier, adapted and with second descant by John Harper
© 1991 Jacques Berthier. All rights reserved.
Reproduced by permission of Studio SM, 34 Rue Michel-Ange, F 75016 Paris, France.

Agnus Dei 2

Lamb of God, you take a-way the sin of the world,

1,2 | 3

have mer-cy on us. grant us peace.

Words: ELLC © 1988 ELLC
Music: Traditional chant adapted by John Harper
© 2000 The Royal School of Church Music

Agnus Dei 3

Lamb of God, you take a-way the sin of the world,

1,2 | 3

have mer-cy on us. grant us peace.

Words: ELLC © 1988 ELLC
Music: John Harper
© 2000 The Royal School of Church Music

Agnus Dei 4

Lamb of God, you take a-way the sin of the

Agnus Dei

Agnus Dei 5

Words: ELLC © 1988 ELLC
Music: Raymond Warren © Raymond Warren

Agnus Dei 6

'Elek Mathe'

Je - sus, Lamb of __ God, have mer - cy on us. Je - sus, bear-er of our sins, have mer - cy on us. Je - sus, re-deem-er of the world, __ grant us peace.

Words: ELLC © 1988 ELLC Music: John Barnard
© John Barnard / Jubilate Hymns

Agnus Dei 105

'For All Seasons'

Words: ELLC © 1988 ELLC
Music: John Harper
© 1992, 1999, 2000 The Royal School of Church Music

Agnus Dei 8

Words: ELLC © 1988 ELLC
Music: Alan Wilson
© Alan Wilson

Agnus Dei 9

Je – sus, Lamb of God,

have mer – cy on us.

Je – sus, bear – er of our sins,

have mer – cy on us.

Je – sus, re-deem-er of the world,

grant us peace.

Agnus Dei 10

Caswall

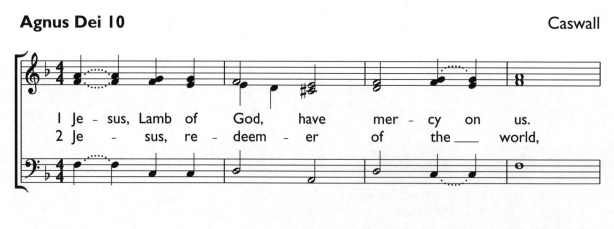

1 Je – sus, Lamb of God, have mer – cy on us.
2 Je – sus, re – deem – er of the ___ world,

Je – sus, bear – er of our sins, have mer – cy on us.
grant ___ us ___ peace, _____ grant ___ us ___ peace.

Agnus Dei 11

traditional text

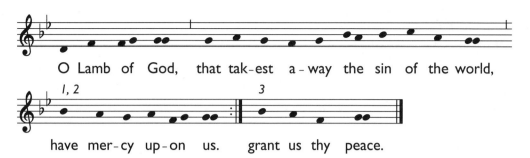

O Lamb of God, that tak-est a-way the sin of the world,

1, 2   *3*

have mer-cy up-on us.   grant us thy peace.

Music: adapted from traditional chant
© 2000 The Royal School of Church Music

Agnus Dei 12

Anglican Folk Mass : traditional text

O Lamb of God, that tak-est a-way the sins of the world, have mer-cy up-on us.

O Lamb of God, that tak-est a-way the sins of the world, grant us thy peace.

Music: Martin Shaw
© 1918, 1946 J Curwen & Sons Limited. All rights reserved.
International copyright secured. Reproduced by permission.

Agnus Dei 13

Broadly, but not too slow

molto legato

O Lamb of God, that

molto legato

O Lamb of God, that

Broadly, but not too slow

Solo

Sw. *p* legato

Ped.

ta – kest a – way the sins of the world,_ have mer – cy up –

ta – kest a – way the sins of the world,_ have mer – cy up –

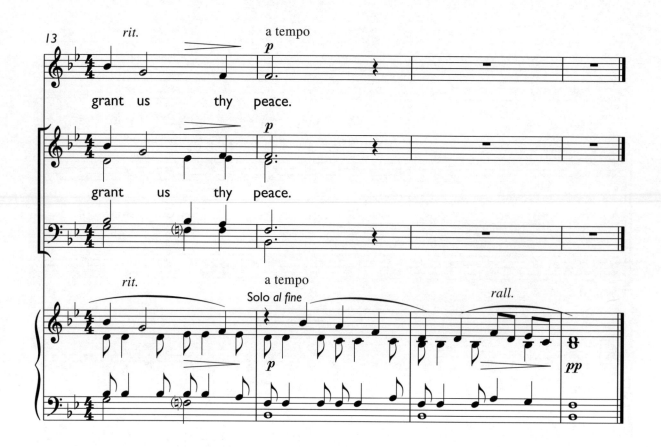

grant us thy peace.

grant us thy peace.

Music: Grayston Ives
© 1987 The Royal School of Church Music

Agnus Dei 14

Music: William Harris © 1939, 2000 The Royal School of Church Music

¶ *Part Two*

*Dialogues with the President
and the Eucharistic Prayers*

¶ Dialogues with the President and the Eucharistic Prayers

The contents of Part Two are complemented by *Music for Common Worship II: Music for the President* which includes complete texts of the Eucharistic Prayers, and by the President's Edition of *Common Worship* which includes the traditional chant, and three of the special settings. Part Two includes chants to be sung in dialogue with the president for the Greeting, Easter Greeting, Collect. before and after the Gospel, the Peace, the Dismissal and the Easter Dismissal.

The Dialogue, Sanctus and Benedictus, Acclamations and Conclusion from each of the settings of the Eucharistic Prayers are also provided here, together with the complete text of Eucharistic Prayer H. These are presented in four groups: simple traditional chant, 'authentic' traditional chant, new chant, and special settings.

A more extensive introduction is provided in *Music for Common Worship II: Music for the President.*

Dialogues with the President in Holy Communion

There are key moments within Holy Communion where a brief dialogue is exchanged between president and those assembled: the Greeting, the Gospel, the Peace, and the Dismissal. These may be heightened and made more particular by singing. The two proper prayers at the end of the Gathering (Collect) and at the end of the Liturgy of the Sacrament (Post-Communion) may also be emphasised by singing. While singing may not be appropriate at every celebration or all the moments for which music is now provided, it may be helpful to sing these dialogues on specific days or during particular seasons as a means of drawing attention to their significance.

The chants provided in *Music for Common Worship II* are offered in two forms for the Greeting, the Easter Greeting, the Peace, the Dismissal and the Easter Dismissal. The first is based on the traditional form of the Sarum chant adapted to the English text. The second is simpler, but still derived from the same tone.

At the Gospel distinction is made between the tone for ordinary Sundays (where the tone falls a semitone) and major feast days (where it falls a minor third.)

The Eucharistic Prayers

The 'wholeness' of the Eucharistic Prayer

In The Book of Common Prayer it is apparent that what we now identify as the Eucharistic Prayer is there presented as three separate items: the Dialogue, Preface and Sanctus; the Prayer of Consecration; and (after the communion) the Prayer of Oblation. The twentieth-century reform of the liturgy has brought these three elements together within one prayer (as was the case before the Reformation back to the early centuries of the Church). There is, however, still a tendency to segment the Eucharistic Prayer by posture and/or by musical treatment. In some churches all stand for the Dialogue, Preface and Sanctus, but then kneel for the remainder of the prayer.
Where the Dialogue, Preface and Sanctus are sung, the remainder of the prayer is often said.

How do we bring out the wholeness of the Eucharistic Prayer?
In part it is a question of understanding that wholeness, whatever the posture(s) or musical treatment. But that understanding may be enhanced by the use of posture and/or music.

Challenge to the president: how shall I sing? what shall I sing?

Not all priests are confident singers, and there is no way in which the presidency at Holy Communion should be impaired by an obligation to sing. There are, in fact, very few people indeed who are incompetent as singers; mostly they lack experience, basic training and self-confidence. The rediscovery of a culture of singing is a challenge for the future.

For those who can 'hold a note' there are settings with varying vocal demands and varying musical idioms. In due course there will be a demonstration recording which will help those learning the prayers. At this stage encouragement and guidance from a musician in the church should get you on your way. And in singing even the plainsong tones you may find it helpful for the reciting tone to be sustained very quietly on the organ or by another sustaining instrument (but only the reciting note, not a chord except in those settings where it is specified).

For those who are diffident about singing a whole Eucharistic Prayer the question remains, how should the unity of the prayer be articulated, and in what ways might music contribute to both its unity and its solemnity? Parts of the prayer may be sung, and parts spoken. Music, even the melody of the chant, might be played while the president speaks the prayer. Where there is a chordal sequence under the chant, that might accompany spoken recitation.

If only the people's parts of the prayer are sung, this raises questions of getting them started and of sustaining the continuity of the prayer: instrumental introductions to short refrains may be cumbersome and disrupt the flow.

Much may be gained by exploring the Eucharistic Prayer settings informally outside worship, or by using them initially on an occasional basis, even at special celebrations with a worship committee and/or the choral and/or music groups of the church.

Which setting of the Eucharistic Prayers shall we use in Order One?

There are four groups of settings of the Eucharistic Prayers.

1 Simple traditional chant. *Music for Common Worship II* makes provision for the singing of seven Eucharistic Prayers complete (Prayers A-G), and for all seasonal, common and proper prefaces with a very simple chant derived from the Latin (and interchangeable with it).

2 Authentic traditional chant ('Sarum' chant). The music in the President's Edition of *Common Worship* makes use of the traditional chant adapted from the medieval Latin liturgy for the Dialogue and all the Prefaces (ordinary, seasonal, common and proper), responses, acclamations and doxologies of Eucharistic Prayers A, B, C, and E. It omits Sanctus and Benedictus. Eucharistic Prayer B is set in full.

3 New chants. *Music for Common Worship II* also makes full provision for the singing of Prayers A-G to a new, largely pentatonic chant. There is a separate simple chant to sing Prayer H in dialogue.

4 Special settings. *Music for Common Worship II* includes special settings of five of the eight Eucharistic Prayers: A, B, D (2 settings), F (2 settings), and G (2 settings). Three of these settings (for Prayers D, F, and G) also appear in the President's Edition.

In a number of instances it is possible to interchange parts of the settings within group 4 and with those in groups 1, 2, and 3. They can also be used with other settings of Sanctus and Benedictus found in *Music for Common Worship I*.

What provision is there for Eucharistic Prayers in traditional language?

There is provision for singing the Eucharistic Prayers in traditional language (both Order One and Order Two) in groups 1-3 listed above, but there are no special settings – though some could be adapted.

The traditional and new chants in detail

Simple traditional chant. This provides very simple forms of the chant for Prayers A-G. Where congregations and priests already know the traditional melodies of the opening Dialogue they may find it easier to continue to use them: the simple forms are entirely interchangeable with the traditional melodies. For the less familiar parts of the Eucharistic Prayer, the simple chants may offer an accessible means of singing in a plainsong idiom.

Authentic traditional chant ('Sarum' chant). The opening Dialogue is based on a form of the Latin melody used in England before the Reformation. The Sanctus and Benedictus are also derived from a Latin model. The Acclamations are derived from those used in the modern Roman Catholic Latin Mass. Other responses and refrains are composed within the modal framework of the chant.

New chants: *Eucharistic Prayers A-G.* This is an entirely new chant, and has been adapted for use with Prayers A-G. It offers an alternative for those who want to move away from the traditional idioms, but want a single melody which can be sung to all these prayers.

Any of the elements of this setting can be interchanged with Prayer D (first setting), and Prayer F (second setting).

Eucharistic Prayer H. This straightforward setting of the prayer has only a small number of melodic phrases and can easily be picked up by a congregation. Singing this prayer makes it far easier for everyone to recite together, and enhances its dialogue structure.

The music of the special settings

Eucharistic Prayer A. This is a strong and accessible setting which congregations should find easy to grasp. An accompaniment is provided for those parts sung by all, but it is not obligatory.
The chants for the president, included in *Music for Common Worship II: Music for the President*, have indications for simple chords to be sustained optionally under the singing of the prayer. They may also be played under a spoken recitation, to emphasise the unity of the prayer and to keep everyone mindful of the pitch of the parts sung by all.

Eucharistic Prayer B. This setting is derived in part from the tone used in the French Roman Catholic Church, and some of the elements are therefore interchangeable with the traditional and simple settings. This prayer is best sung unaccompanied.

Eucharistic Prayer D: *first setting*. The text of this prayer was originally written with young people in mind, and this lively setting will offer them a challenge. The accompaniment provides a raw outline from which keyboard players or instrumental groups might improvise (but remember to balance those singing the text). The elements of the accompaniment can be applied to the whole prayer printed in *Music for Common Worship II: Music for the President*. If the president's part of the prayer is spoken there is still scope for improvising under the text. It is important to keep the flow of the prayer when the refrains are sung: a long gap while they are started will break things up too much. Whether the president is singing or not, a cantor or choral group can best start each refrain to set the pace.

Eucharistic Prayer D: *second setting*. This is set in a more reflective style. It offers a very different reading of the prayer, and the melodies all derive from the Sanctus, itself based on an old Latin plainsong setting.

Eucharistic Prayer F: *first setting*. This prayer can be supported by a constant drone throughout (either fixed or changing). This background pitch is a sonority against which the prayer is sung. It should be treated as a constant presence rather than drawing attention to itself, though a shift to upper or lower registers may be appropriate at some points in the prayer. The prayer can also be sung unaccompanied.

Eucharistic Prayer F: *second setting*. The negro spiritual 'Go down Moses' is the musical source for this prayer. Although its use is likely to be occasional, it is very powerful and appealing, and may be especially appealing to young people. The rhythm looks complex because it tries to represent free improvised singing. It is best sung with spirit and confidence, and without too much concern about the exact notated rhythm. The prayer can be sung very effectively without accompaniment. However, there is an outline for accompaniment as a basis for improvisation by keyboard players and instrumental groups. Elements of the spiritual melody can be improvised throughout the prayer (under spoken or sung recitation) as an accompaniment

Eucharistic Prayer G: first setting (with two options for the people's parts). This lyrical tone has already proved popular, and the very simple settings of the people's parts work well in very large gatherings. There are alternative settings of Sanctus and Benedictus, Acclamations and Doxology in a rhythmic and more 'composed' lyrical style. These can be sung as written (either accompanied or unaccompanied) or easily adapted for four-part singing.

The chords suggested as accompaniment to the president's text in *Music for Common Worship II: Music for the President* may be used to support sung or spoken recitation. Use of different registers of the keyboard for different parts of the prayer may enhance the effect, so long as the approach is simple and unfussy: often only three notes (with different spacings) will be sufficient. The chords may also be sung by a vocal group, so long as they can sing sustained chords in tune for long periods.

Eucharistic Prayer G: second setting. This is set in a plainsong idiom. The sustained chords (best played on the organ) provide a slow moving harmonic colouring throughout. As in other cases, the chords may be used even when the prayer is spoken.

The Greeting

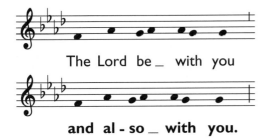

The Lord be _ with you

and al - so _ with you.

or

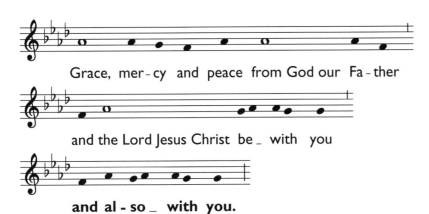

Grace, mer - cy and peace from God our Fa - ther

and the Lord Jesus Christ be _ with you

and al - so _ with you.

The Greeting

simple tone

The Lord be with you

and also with you.

or

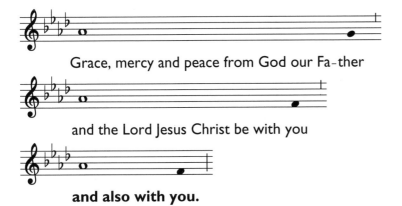

Grace, mercy and peace from God our Fa - ther

and the Lord Jesus Christ be with you

and also with you.

The Easter Greeting

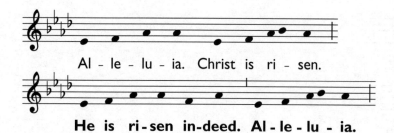

Al – le – lu – ia. Christ is ri – sen.

He is ri – sen in-deed. Al - le - lu - ia.

The Easter Greeting

simple tone

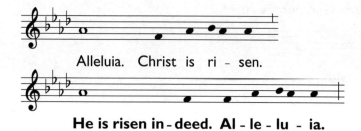

Alleluia. Christ is ri – sen.

He is risen in - deed. Al - le - lu - ia.

The Collect

Prayer   end - ing   A - men.

Before and after the Gospel

Hear the gospel of the Lord Jesus Christ according to *N.*   *or*   Mat-thew.

Glory to you, O Lord.

This is the gospel of the Lord.   **Praise to you, O Christ.**

Before and after the Gospel

on major feast days

Hear the gospel of the Lord Jesus Christ according to *N.*   *or*   Mat-thew.

Glory to you, O Lord.

This is the gospel of the Lord.   **Praise to you, O Christ.**

The Peace

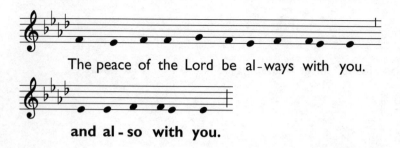

The peace of the Lord be al-ways with you.

and al-so with you.

The Peace

simple tone

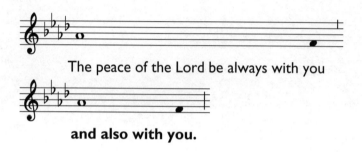

The peace of the Lord be always with you

and also with you.

The Dismissal

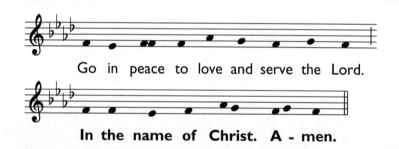

Go in peace to love and serve the Lord.

In the name of Christ. A - men.

or

Go in the peace of Christ.

Thanks be to God.

The Dismissal

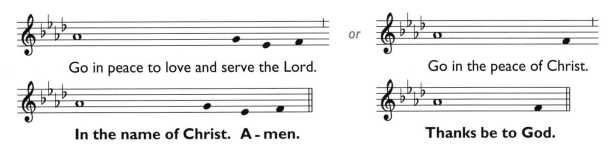

or

Go in peace to love and serve the Lord.

Go in the peace of Christ.

In the name of Christ. A - men.

Thanks be to God.

The Easter Dismissal

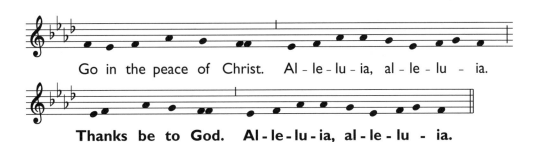

Go in the peace of Christ. Al - le - lu - ia, al - le - lu - ia.

Thanks be to God. Al - le - lu - ia, al - le - lu - ia.

or

Go in the peace of Christ. Al - le - lu - ia, al - le - - - lu - ia. ___

Thanks be to God. Al - le - lu - ia, al - le - - - lu - ia. ___

The Easter Dismissal

simple tone

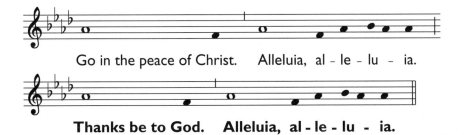

Go in the peace of Christ. Alleluia, al - le - lu - ia.

Thanks be to God. Alleluia, al - le - lu - ia.

Music: adapted from or based on traditional tones
© 2000 The Royal School of Church Music

The Greeting traditional language

The Lord be _ with you

and with thy spi - rit.

or

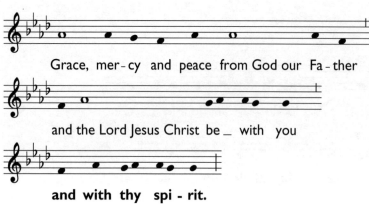

Grace, mer - cy and peace from God our Fa - ther

and the Lord Jesus Christ be _ with you

and with thy spi - rit.

The Greeting traditional language : simple tone

The Lord be with you

and with thy spi - rit.

or

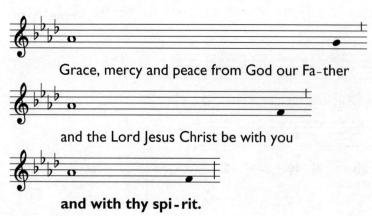

Grace, mercy and peace from God our Fa - ther

and the Lord Jesus Christ be with you

and with thy spi - rit.

For the Easter Greeting, see page 122.

The Collect

Prayer   end - ing   **A - men.**

Before and after the Gospel

traditional language

Hear the gospel of the Lord Jesus Christ according to *N.*   *or*   Mat-thew.

Glory be to thee, O Lord.

This is the gospel of the Lord.   **Praise be to thee, O Christ.**

Before and after the Gospel

traditional language : on major feast days

Hear the gospel of the Lord Jesus Christ according to *N.*   *or*   Mat-thew.

Glory be to thee, O Lord.

This is the gospel of the Lord.   **Praise be to thee, O Christ.**

The Peace

The peace of the Lord be al-ways with you.

and with thy spi - rit.

The Peace

traditional language : simple tone

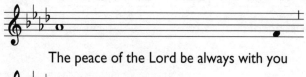

The peace of the Lord be always with you

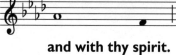

and with thy spirit.

For the Dismissal and Easter Dismissal see pages 124 and 125.

Order Two : Before and after the Gospel

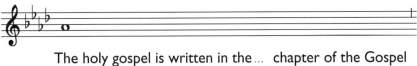

The holy gospel is written in the … chapter of the Gospel

according to Saint N , beginning at the … verse.

Glory be to thee, O Lord.

This is the gospel of Christ.   **Praise be to thee, O Christ.**

Order Two : Before and after the Gospel   on major feast days

The holy gospel is written in the … chapter of the Gospel

according to Saint N , beginning at the … verse.

Glory be to thee, O Lord.

This is the gospel of Christ.   **Praise be to thee, O Christ.**

Music: Traditional tones
© 2000 The Royal School of Church Music

Music for Eucharistic Prayers A – G

Dialogue

Sanctus and Benedictus

Acclamations

Responses

Conclusion

Music for Eucharistic Prayer H (complete setting)

Simple traditional chant

Dialogue

The Lord be with you   **and al-so with you.**

or

The Lord is here.   **His Spi-rit is with us.**

Lift up your hearts.   **We lift them to the Lord.**

Let us give thanks to the Lord our God.

It is right to give thanks and praise.

Sanctus and Benedictus

for ever praising you and *say - ing:*

Ho-ly, ho-ly, ho-ly Lord,

God of pow-er and might,

hea-ven and earth are full of your glo-ry.

Ho-san-na in the high-est.

Bless-ed is he who comes in the name of the Lord.

Ho-san-na in the high-est.

Acclamations

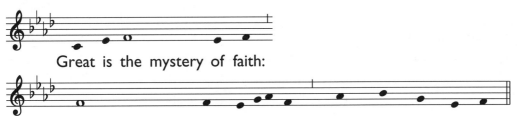

Great is the mystery of faith:

Christ has died: Christ is ris-en: Christ will come a-gain.

or

Praise to you, Lord Je – sus:

Dy-ing you des-troyed our death,

ri-sing you re-stored our life;

Lord Je-sus, come in glo-ry.

or

Christ is the bread of life:

When we eat this bread and drink this cup,

we proclaim your death, Lord Je-sus,

un-til you come in glo-ry.

or

Je-sus Christ is Lord:

Lord, by your cross and re-sur-rec-tion

you have set us free.

You are the Sa-viour of the world.

Conclusion

Prayers A, D, G

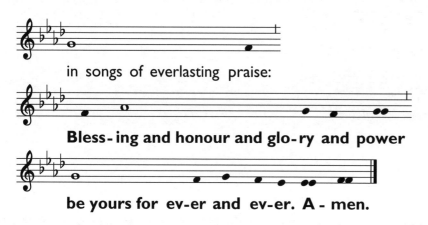

in songs of everlasting praise:

Bless-ing and honour and glo-ry and power

be yours for ev-er and ev-er. A - men.

Conclusion

Prayers B, C, E, F

for ev-er and ev-er. A - men.

Response Prayer A

To you be glo-ry and praise for ev-er.

Responses Prayer D

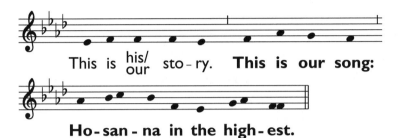

This is his/our sto-ry. **This is our song:**

Ho-san-na in the high-est.

Responses Prayer F

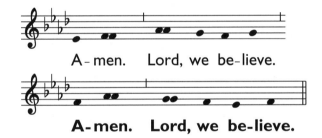

A-men. Lord, we be-lieve.

A-men. Lord, we be-lieve.

A-men. Come, Lord Je-sus.

A-men. Come, Lord Je-sus.

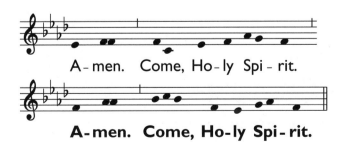

A-men. Come, Ho-ly Spi-rit.

A-men. Come, Ho-ly Spi-rit.

As an alternative in Prayer F, just the second part of each response may be sung twice.

Music: adapted from or based on traditional tones and chant
© 2000 The Royal School of Church Music

Authentic traditional tone

Dialogue

The Lord be with you **and al-so with you.**

or

The Lord is here. **His Spi-rit is with us.**

Lift ___ up your hearts. **We lift them to the Lord.**

Let us give thanks to the Lord our God.

It is right to give thanks and praise.

Sanctus and Benedictus

for ever prais-ing you and *say - ing:*

Ho-ly, ho-ly, ho-ly Lord,

God of pow-er and might,

hea-ven and earth are full of your glo-ry.

Ho-san-na in the high-est.

Bless-ed is he who comes in the name of the Lord.

Ho-san-na in the high-est.

Acclamations

Great is the mystery of faith:

Christ has died: Christ is ris-en: Christ will come a-gain.

or

Praise to you, Lord Je-sus:

Dy-ing you des-troyed our death, ris-ing you re-stored our life:

Lord Je-sus, come in glo-ry.

or

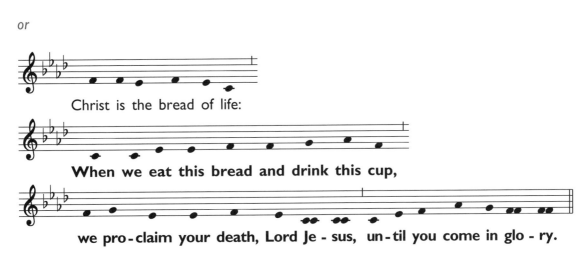

Christ is the bread of life:

When we eat this bread and drink this cup,

we pro-claim your death, Lord Je-sus, un-til you come in glo-ry.

or

Je-sus Christ is Lord:

Lord, by your cross and re-sur-rec-tion you have set us free.

You are the Sa-viour of the world.

Conclusion

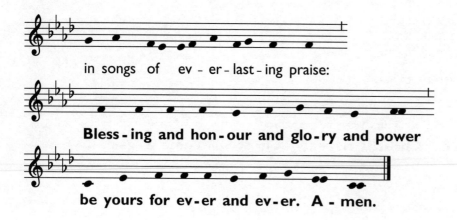

in songs of ev – er – last – ing praise:

Bless - ing and hon - our and glo - ry and power

be yours for ev- er and ev- er. A - men.

Conclusion

for ev – er and ev – er. A - men.

Response

To you be glo-ry and praise for ev-er.

Responses for Prayers D and F may be found on page 135.

Music: adapted from and based on traditional tones and chant

Modern chant

Dialogue

The Lord be with you **and al - so with you.**

or

The Lord is here. **His Spi - rit is with us.**

Lift up your hearts. **We lift them to the Lord.**

Let us give thanks to the Lord our God.

It is right to give thanks and praise.

Sanctus and Benedictus

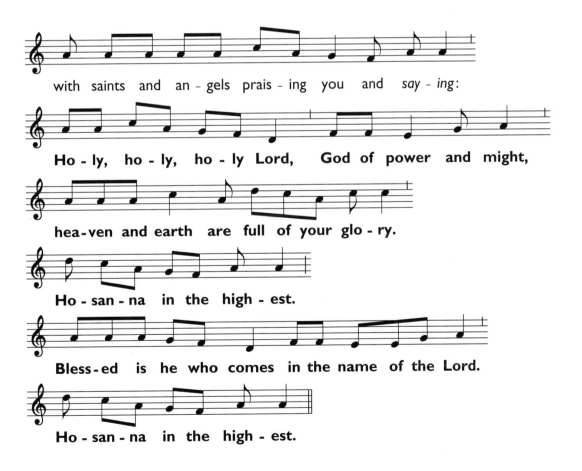

with saints and an - gels prais - ing you and *say - ing*:

Ho - ly, ho - ly, ho - ly Lord, God of power and might,

hea-ven and earth are full of your glo - ry.

Ho - san - na in the high - est.

Bless - ed is he who comes in the name of the Lord.

Ho - san - na in the high - est.

Acclamations

Great is the mys-tery of faith:

Christ has died: Christ is ri-sen:

Christ will come a-gain.

or

Praise to you, Lord Je-sus:

Dy-ing you des-troyed our death,   ris-ing you re-stored our life;

Lord Je-sus, come in glo-ry.

or

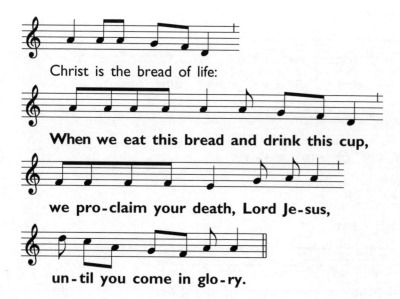

Christ is the bread of life:

When we eat this bread and drink this cup,

we pro-claim your death, Lord Je-sus,

un-til you come in glo-ry.

or

Je-sus Christ is Lord:

Lord, by your cross and re-sur-rec-tion you have set us free.

You are the Sa-viour of the world.

Conclusion

Prayers A, D, G

Bless-ing and hon-our and glo-ry and pow-er

be yours for ev-er and ev-er. A - men.

Conclusion

Prayers B, C, E, F

for ev-er and ev-er. A-men. A - men.

Responses

Sung three times before the Sanctus and once after the Acclamation.

To you be glo - ry and praise_ for ev - er.

Sung twice after the Sanctus.

To you be glo - ry and praise_ for ev - er.

Responses

This is his/our sto - ry. This is our song:

Ho - san - na in the high - est.

Responses

Sung twice.

A - men._ Lord, we be - lieve.

A - men. Lord, we be - lieve.

Sung twice.

A - men._ Lord, we be - lieve.

A - men. Lord, we be - lieve.

Each of the following responses is sung once.

A‑men. Come, Lord _ Je‑sus.

A‑men. Come, Lord _ Je‑sus.

A‑men. Come, Ho‑ly Spi‑rit.

A‑men. Come, Ho‑ly Spi‑rit.

A‑men. Come, Ho‑ly Spi‑rit.

A‑men. Come, Ho‑ly Spi‑rit.

As an alternative in Prayer F, just the second part of each response may be sung twice.

Music: John Harper
© 2000 The Royal School of Church Music

Eucharistic Prayer H   modern chant

The Lord be with you   **and al - so with you.**

or

The Lord is here.   **His Spi-rit is with us.**

Lift up your hearts.   **We lift them to the Lord.**

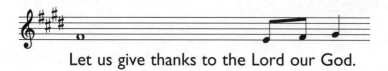

Let us give thanks to the Lord our God.

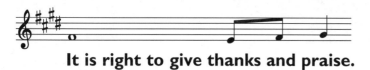

It is right to give thanks and praise.

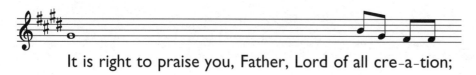

It is right to praise you, Father, Lord of all cre-a-tion;

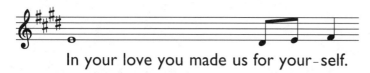

In your love you made us for your-self.

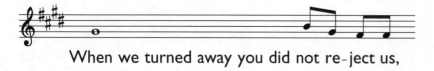

When we turned away you did not re-ject us,

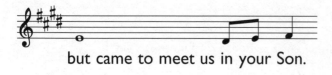

but came to meet us in your Son.

You embraced us as your chil-dren

and welcomed us to sit and eat with you.

In Christ you shared our life

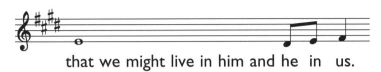

that we might live in him and he in us.

He opened wide his arms of love up-on the cross

and made for all the perfect sacri-fice for sin.

On the night he was betrayed, at supper with his friends

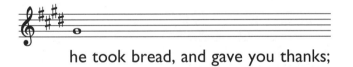

he took bread, and gave you thanks;

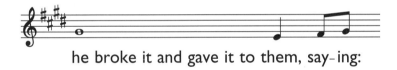

he broke it and gave it to them, say-ing:

Take, eat: this is my body which is given for you;

do this in remembrance of me.

Father, we do this in re-mem-brance of him:

his body is the bread of life.

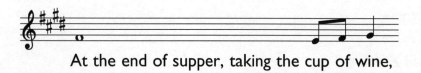

At the end of supper, taking the cup of wine,

he gave you thanks, and said:

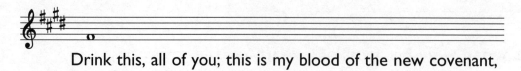

Drink this, all of you; this is my blood of the new covenant,

which is shed for you for the forgiveness of sins;

do this in remembrance of me.

Father, we do this in re-mem-brance of him:

his blood is shed for all.

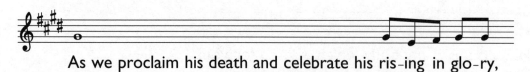

As we proclaim his death and celebrate his ris-ing in glo-ry,

send your Holy Spirit that this bread and wine

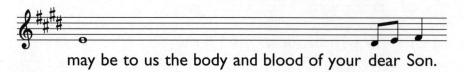

may be to us the body and blood of your dear Son.

As we eat and drink these ho-ly gifts

make us one in Christ, our ri-sen Lord.

With your whole Church through-out the world

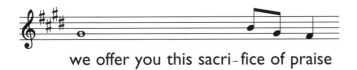

we offer you this sacri-fice of praise

and lift our voice to join the eternal song of hea-ven:

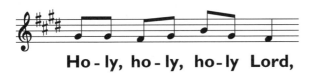

Ho-ly, ho-ly, ho-ly Lord,

God of power and might,

hea-ven and earth are full of your glo-ry.

Ho-san-na in the high-est.

Music: John Harper
© 2000 The Royal School of Church Music

Special Settings of Eucharistic Prayers A, B, D, F and G

Dialogue

Sanctus and Benedictus

Acclamations

Responses

Conclusion

Eucharistic Prayer A

Dialogue

In strict time ♩ = 100

The Lord be with you **and** al - so with you.

Lift up your hearts. **We** lift them to the Lord.

Let us give thanks to the Lord our God.

It is **right** to give thanks and praise.

Response

sung three times before the Sanctus

To you be glo - ry and praise for ___ ev - er.

Music: John Harper

Sanctus and Benedictus

Response

sung twice before the Acclamation

Acclamations

Great is the mys-te-ry of faith:

Christ has died: Christ is ri-sen: Christ will __

1st time
come __ a-gain. __   come __ a-gain.
last time   D.S.

or

Praise to you, Lord Jesus:

Dying you destroyed our death,

rising you restored our life: Lord

Jesus, come in glory.

or

Christ is the bread of life:

When we eat this bread and drink this cup,

we pro - claim your death, Lord__ Je - sus, __

__ un - til you come in__ glo - ry. _____

or

Je - sus Christ is Lord:

Lord, by your cross and re - sur - rec - tion

you have set ___ us free. You are the

Sa - viour of the world.

Response

sung once before the Conclusion

To you be glo - ry and praise for ___ ev - er.

Conclusion

Bless - ing and hon - our and glo - ry and power be

yours for ev - er and ev - er. _____ A -

- - - - men.

Eucharistic Prayer B

Dialogue

The Lord be with you   **and al-so with you.**

or

The Lord is here.   **His Spi-rit is with us.**

Lift up your hearts.   **We lift them to the Lord.**

Let us give thanks to the Lord our God.

It is right to give thanks and praise.

Sanctus and Benedictus

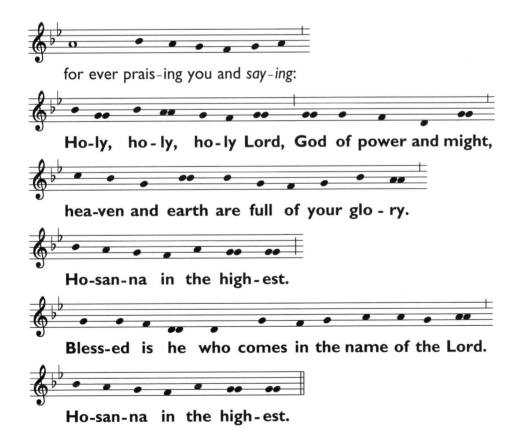

for ever prais-ing you and *say-ing*:

Ho-ly,   ho-ly,   ho-ly Lord, God of power and might,

hea-ven and earth are full of your glo - ry.

Ho-san-na in the high-est.

Bless-ed is he who comes in the name of the Lord.

Ho-san-na in the high-est.

Music: adapted from and based on a French tone
© 2000 The Royal School of Church Music

Acclamations

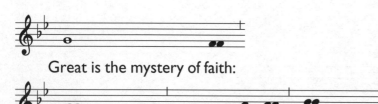

Great is the mystery of faith:

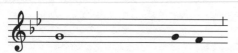

Christ has died: Christ is ris-en: Christ will come a-gain.

or

Praise to you, Lord Je-sus:

Dy-ing you des-troyed our death, ris-ing you re-stored our life:

Lord Je-sus, come in glo-ry.

or

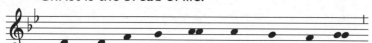

Christ is the bread of life:

When we eat this bread and drink this cup,

we pro-claim your death, Lord Je-sus, un-til you come in glo-ry.

or

Jesus Christ is Lord:

Lord, by your cross and re-sur-rec-tion you have set us free.

You are the Sa-viour of the world.

Conclusion

for ev-er and ev-er. **A - - men.** *or* **A-men.**

Eucharistic Prayer D

Dialogue

$\quad$ = 80

The Lord be with you **and al - so with you.**

or The Lord is here. **His Spi - rit is with us.**

Lift up your hearts. **We lift them to the Lord.**

Let us give thanks _____ to the Lord our God. **It is**

The introduction is optional. The upper line can form the basis of an ongoing vocal ostinato when the prayer is unaccompanied.

The accompaniment provides the basis for idiomatic adaptation or improvisation.

Music: John Harper

right _____ to give thanks and praise. It is right _____ to give

thanks and praise.

Sanctus and Benedictus

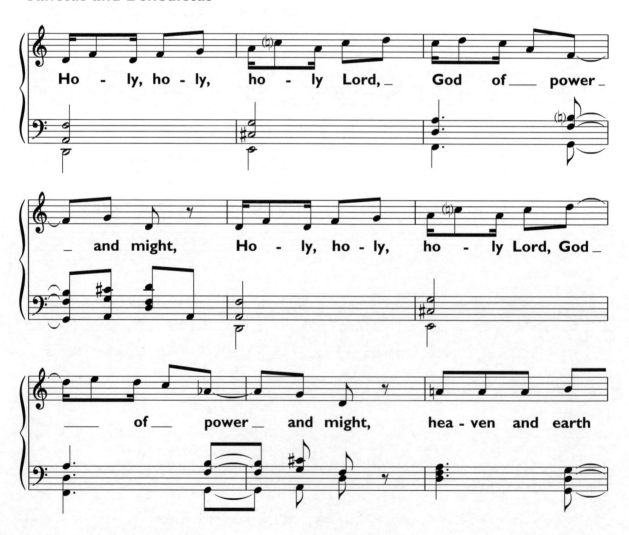

Ho - ly, ho - ly, ho - ly Lord, _ God of ___ power _

_ and might, Ho - ly, ho - ly, ho - ly Lord, God _

_____ of _ power _ and might, hea - ven and earth

are full of your glo - ry. ___ Ho - san - na,

ho - san - na, ho - san - na in the high - est. ___

Ho - san - na, ho - san - na, ho - san - na in the

high - est. ___ Bless - ed is he who comes in the

name of ___ the Lord. Ho - san - na,

Response

'This is his story' sung twice after the Sanctus.

'This is our story' sung twice before the Conclusion.

- san - na in the high - est.__

Conclusion

Bless - ing and hon - our, glo - ry and power be

yours for ev - er and ev - er.__ A - - men.

A - - men.__ A - - men. A - men.__

for ev - er. A - - men.__

Eucharistic Prayer D

second setting

Dialogue

The Lord __ be with you **And al - so with you.**

or

The Lord __ is here. **His Spi - rit is with us.**

Lift up your hearts. **We lift ___ them __ to the Lord.**

Let us give thanks to the Lord __ our God

It is right __ to give thanks and praise.

Sanctus and Benedictus

We join with them in hea - ven's song:

Ho - ly, ho - ly, ho - ly Lord, God of pow - er and might,

hea - ven and earth are full of your glo - ry.

Ho - san - na ___ in the high - est.

Bless-ed is he who comes in the name of the Lord.

Ho - san - na ___ in the high - est.

Refrain   sung twice after the Sanctus

This is his sto - ry.

This is our song: Ho - san - na ___ in the high - est.

Refrain   sung twice before the Conclusion

This is our sto - ry.

This is our song: Ho - san - na ___ in the high - est.

Conclusion

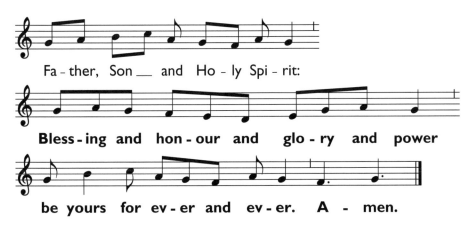

Fa - ther, Son ___ and Ho - ly Spi - rit:

Bless - ing and hon - our and glo - ry and power

be yours for ev - er and ev - er. A - men.

A steady dotted-crotchet pulse should be felt throughout, though the style should be free and flowing.

Music: John Harper, derived from a Latin Sanctus melody
© 2000 The Royal School of Church Music

Eucharistic Prayer D   **167**

Eucharistic Prayer F

first setting

Dialogue

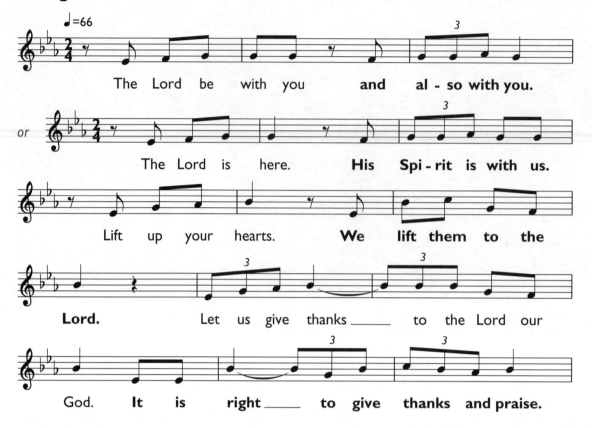

The Lord be with you **and** al - so with you.

or The Lord is here. **His Spi - rit is with us.**

Lift up your hearts. **We** lift them to the

Lord. Let us give thanks to the Lord our

God. **It is right** to give thanks and praise.

Sanctus and Benedictus

evermore prais - ing you and *say - ing*:

Ho - ly, ho - ly, ho - ly Lord,

God of pow - er and might, hea - ven and earth are

full of your glo - ry. Ho - san - na in the

high - est. Ho - san - na in the

high - est. **Bless - ed is** he who comes

in the name of __ the Lord. Ho - san - na in the
high - est. __ Ho - san - na in __ the high - est.

Response

sung four times after the Sanctus

A - men. Lord, we be - lieve.

Response

sung once

A - men. Come, __ Lord __ Je - sus.

Response

sung twice

A - men. A - men. Come, Ho - ly
Spi - rit. __ Come, Ho - ly Spi - rit.

Conclusion

for ev - er and ev - er.
A - - men. A - - men.

A - - - men.

Optional Drones

to sound through the prayer

Music: John Harper © 2000 The Royal School of Church Music

Eucharistic Prayer F

Dialogue

Music: John Harper, derived from 'Go down, Moses' © 2000 The Royal School of Church Music

Sanctus and Benedictus

Ho - ly, ho - ly, ho - - ly Lord, _____ God _

_ of power _ and _____ might, _

hea - ven and earth are full _ of your glo - ry. Ho -

san - na in _____ the _____ high - est. _____

Bless - ed is he who comes in the name, _____ who

comes in the name of the Lord.

Ho - san - na, _____ ho - san - na in the high - est, _____ ho -

san - na in _____ the _____ high - est. _____

This simple harmonic framework may be used as a basis for the accompaniment.
The appropriate phrase is identified by a number in the margin.

Response

sung four times after the Sanctus

A - men.   A - men.   Lord,   we   be - lieve. _____

Lord,   we   be - - lieve. ____

Response

sung once

A - men.   A - men.   Come, ____   Lord   Je - sus. ____

Lord   Je - sus, _____   come. ___

Response

sung twice

A - men.   A - men.   Come, _____   Ho - ly Spi - rit. _____

Ho - ly   Spi - rit, _____   come. __

Conclusion

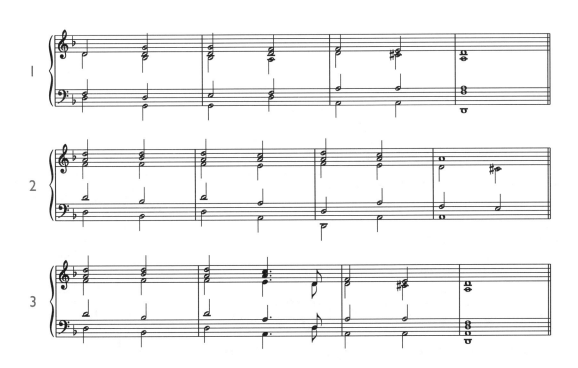

Eucharistic Prayer G

Dialogue

The Lord be with you   **And al - so with you.**

or

The Lord is here.   **His Spi - rit is with us.**

Lift up your hearts   **We lift them to the Lord.**

Let us give thanks to the Lord our God

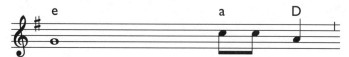

It is right to give thanks and praise.

Sanctus and Benedictus

we may find a voice to sing your praise:

Holy, holy, ho - ly Lord, God of power and might,

heaven and earth are full of your glo - ry.

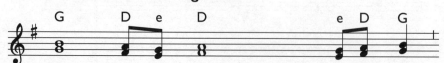

Ho-san-na in the high - est.

Blessed is he who comes in the name of the Lord.

Ho-san-na in the high - est.

Acclamations

Great is the my-stery of faith:

Christ has died: Christ is ri - sen: Christ will come a - gain.

or

Praise to you, Lord Je - sus:

Dying you des - troyed our death,

rising you res - tored our life;

Lord Je - sus, come in glo - ry.

or

Christ is the bread of life:

When we eat this bread and drink this cup

we proclaim your death, Lord Je - sus,

un - til you come in glo - ry.

or

Jesus Christ is Lord:

Lord, by your your cross and re-sur-rec-tion

you have set us free.

You are the Sa-viour of the world.

Conclusion

in songs of ever-last-ing praise:

Blessing and honour and glo-ry and power

be yours for ev-er and ev-er.   A-men.

The chord letters above the stave indicate harmonies to be sung or played. Lower case indicates minor. If the harmonies are sung, the basses should sing the lettered notes, and other voices should sing the notated music at their own pitch.

Music: John Harper

Eucharistic Prayer G

Dialogue

The Lord be with you and al - so with you.

or

The Lord is here. His Spi - rit is with us.

Lift up your hearts We lift them to the Lord.

Let us give thanks to the Lord our God.

It is right to give thanks and praise.

Sanctus and Benedictus

Ho - ly, ho - ly, ho - ly Lord, God of

power and might, heav'n and earth are full of your

glo - ry. Ho - san - na in the high - est.

Bless - ed is he who comes in the name of the Lord. Ho -

san - na in the high - est.

Acclamations

Great is the mystery of faith:

♩ = 54

Christ has died: Christ is ris-en: Christ will come a - gain.

or

Praise to you Lord Je‑sus:

Dy – ing you des – troyed our death, ris – ing you re – stored our life: Lord Je – sus, come in glo – ry.

or

Christ is the bread of life:

When we eat this bread and drink this cup we pro – claim your death, Lord Je – sus, un – til you come in glo – ry.

or

Jesus Christ is Lord:

Lord, by your cross and re - sur - rec - tion you have set us free. You are the Sa - viour of the world.

Conclusion

Bless - ing and hon - our and glo - ry and power be ___ yours for ev - er and ev - er A - - men.

This setting may be sung in unison, or in two parts where shown in bold. The accompaniment in small notes is optional, and may also be adapted for singing by tenors and basses.

Music: John Harper
© 2000 The Royal School of Church Music

Eucharistic Prayer G

Dialogue

A The Lord be with you   **and al - so with you.**

or

The Lord is here.   **His Spi - rit is with us.**

B Lift   up your hearts.   **We lift them to the Lord.**

C Let us give thanks to the Lord our God.

It is right to give thanks and praise.

Sanctus and Benedictus

we may find a voice to sing your praise:

H **Ho - ly, ho - ly, ho - ly Lord, God of pow'r and might,**

heav'n and earth are full of your glo - ry.

Ho - san - na in the high - est.

H **Bless - ed is he who comes in the name of the Lord.**

J **Ho - san - na in the high - est.**

Letters in the left margin indicate the chord to be used when the prayer is accompanied.

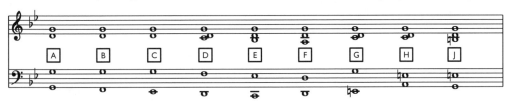

A   B   C   D   E   F   G   H   J

Acclamations

F Great is the mys-te-ry of faith:

G **Christ has died:**

H **Christ is ris-en:**

J **Christ will come a-gain.**

or

F Praise to you, Lord Je-sus:

G **Dying you des-troyed our death,**

H **rising you re-stored our life:**

J **Lord Jesus, come in glo-ry.**

or

F Christ is the bread of life:

G **When we eat this bread and drink this cup**

H **we proclaim your death, Lord Je-sus,**

J **until you come in glo-ry.**

or

F — Je-sus Christ is Lord:

G — Lord, by your cross and re-sur-rec-tion

H — you have set us free.

J — You are the Sa-viour of the world.

Conclusion

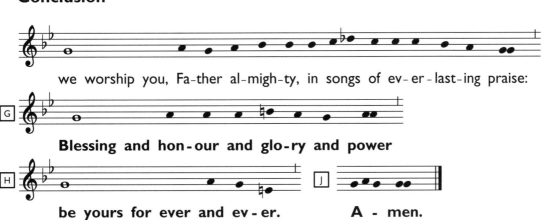

we worship you, Fa-ther al-migh-ty, in songs of ev-er-last-ing praise:

G — Blessing and hon-our and glo-ry and power

H — be yours for ever and ev-er. J — A - men.

Accompaniment

Letters in the left margin indicate the chord to be used when the prayer is accompanied.

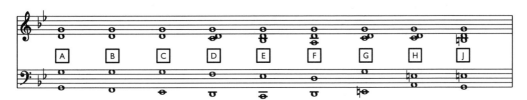

A B C D E F G H J

Music: Peter Moger
© 2000 The Royal School of Church Music

Eucharistic Prayer G   **183**

Eucharistic Prayers A and C

simple chant : traditional language

Dialogue

The Lord be with you **and with thy spi - rit.**

or

The Lord is here. **His Spi-rit is with us.**

Lift up your hearts. **We lift them up un-to the Lord.**

Let us give thanks un – to the Lord our God.

It is meet and right so to do.

Sanctus and Benedictus

evermore praising thee and *say – ing:*

Ho - ly, ho - ly, ho - ly Lord God of hosts,

hea-ven and earth are full of thy glo - ry.

Glo-ry be to thee, O Lord most high.

Bless-ed is he that com-eth in the name of the Lord.

Ho - san - na in the high - est.

Acclamation

Great is the mystery of faith:

Christ has died: Christ is ris - en: Christ will come a-gain.

or

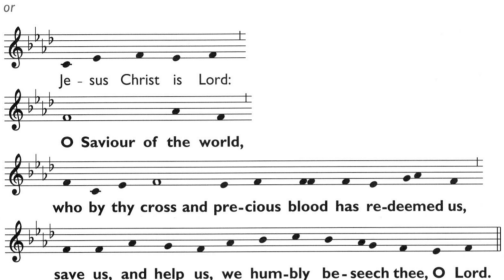

Je - sus Christ is Lord:

O Saviour of the world,

who by thy cross and pre-cious blood has re-deemed us,

save us, and help us, we hum-bly be-seech thee, O Lord.

Conclusion

world with - out end. **A - men.**

Eucharistic Prayers A and C

authentic chant : traditional language

Dialogue

The Lord be with you **and with thy spi-rit.**

or

The Lord is here. **His Spi-rit is with us.**

Lift __ up your hearts. **We lift them up un-to the Lord.**

Let us give thanks un - to the Lord our God.

It is meet and right so to do.

Sanctus and Benedictus

evermore prais - ing thee and *say-ing*:

Ho - ly, ho - ly, ho - ly Lord God of hosts,

hea-ven and earth are full of thy glo - ry.

Glo-ry be to thee, O Lord most high.

Bless-ed is he that com-eth in the name of the Lord.

Ho - san - na in the high - est.

Acclamations

Great is the mystery of faith:

Christ has died: Christ is ris-en: Christ will come a-gain.

or

Je-sus Christ is Lord:

O Sa-viour of the world,

who by thy cross and pre-cious blood hast re-deemed us,

save us, and help us,

we hum-bly be-seech thee, O Lord.

Conclusion

world with-out end. **A-men.**

Music: adapted from and based on traditional tones and chant

Eucharistic Prayers A and C

modern chant : traditional language

Dialogue

The Lord be with you **and with thy spi - rit.**

or

The Lord is here. **His Spi - rit is with us.**

Lift up your hearts. **We lift them up un - to the Lord.**

Let us give thanks un - to the Lord our God.

It is meet and right so to do.

Sanctus and Benedictus

ev - er - more prais - ing thee and *say - ing:*

Ho - ly, ho - ly, ho - ly Lord God of hosts,

hea-ven and earth are full of thy glo - ry.

Ho - san - na in the high - est.

Bless-ed is he that com - eth in the name of the Lord.

Ho - san - na in the high - est.

Acclamations

Great is the mys-tery of faith:

Christ has died: Christ is ri-sen:

Christ will come a-gain.

or

Je-sus Christ is Lord:

O Sa-viour of the world,

who by thy cross and pre-cious blood hast re-deemed us,

save us, and help us,   we hum-bly be-seech thee, O Lord.

Conclusion

world with-out end.   A-men.   A - men.

Music: John Harper
© 2000 The Royal School of Church Music

¶ *Part Three*

Anthology of Music for A Service of the Word

¶ Anthology of Music for A Service of the Word

There is a range of texts available for use in A Service of the Word, and great flexibility in the choice of texts from that range and elsewhere. Most of what is included in this anthology relates specifically to Morning, Evening and Night Prayer, though all of it may be used in A Service of the Word. The main body of the anthology provides alternative settings of the majority of the sung texts, and especially the special psalms and canticles. The final section of this anthology consists of music settings for the whole of Morning, Evening and Night Prayer.

Additionally, materials from the Anthology of Music for the Holy Communion may be suitable at A Service of the Word, especially Kyrie, Gloria in excelsis, Creed, Responses to the Intercessions, and Lord's Prayer. You will also be able to draw on the selection of psalms and canticles that forms the final part of the volume, and which includes the 14 seasonal canticles for Morning and Evening Prayer.

Musical style

The musical style of this part of the volume is distinct. Many of the texts are quite long, and many will be used by smaller groups of worshippers. The aim has been to provide for those who wish to sing these texts, reflecting their song-like nature, but maintaining a simple treatment. Each of the main texts is set in three ways:

- with a simple harmonised chant, often in only two parts, and always singable as a unison line without accompaniment;
- with a refrain for all to sing – the main text may be sung by a cantor or choral group, or by all;
- with a substitute metrical text.

The musical styles reflect ancient and modern, Eastern and Western, though the style is more reflective than the music for Holy Communion.

The three Gospel canticles and the Te Deum each include a setting of the traditional form of the text.

Ways of singing

The plainsong and other melodies are best sung unaccompanied, or perhaps with a melody instrument (or instruments) doubling the chant. The melodic strength and purpose can easily be weakened by organ harmonies. If organ support is needed then it is best provided by sustaining a drone based on the reciting note, or by playing the melody alone – perhaps in octaves.

The settings in two or three parts may be sung in unison (with or without an accompaniment). Where they are sung in parts, each should choose the part which suits their voice, and sing in the appropriate octave of their voice. Any accompaniment should double the voice parts.

The four-part settings may again be sung in unison, with or without accompaniment, though they sound best when sung in parts. With growing confidence many congregations may be able to 'feel' the harmony after a while.

In every case the flow of the text is paramount: that implies no rushing as well as no dragging. These settings may benefit from that calm and unhurried purposefulness which characterises the best of monastic worship.

Texts may be sung all the way through by all present, or shared between cantor and people, choral group and people, or between two groups of all present. The way in which it is done will not only reflect the resources available, but also familiarity. In the early stages it may be helpful for a cantor or choral group to sing more of the text while everyone gains familiarity with the melody and any harmony. Then everyone can take a greater share over the weeks and months as they gain in both familiarity and confidence.

Songs for Morning Prayer

There are two lively settings of the Benedicite – one in the shorter form, the other with a metrical text. Two other settings of Benedicite offer different treatment of the shorter and full texts. A similar group of settings is provided for Venite (Psalm 95), Jubilate (Psalm 100), and the Easter Anthems, which can be used at the beginning of Morning Prayer, or at other appropriate occasions. There are also four settings of the Gospel canticle, Benedictus. The metrical versions of Venite, Jubilate and Benedictus may be sung to other appropriate hymn tunes in the same metre. Additional settings of Venite and Benedictus are included in the setting of Morning Prayer in the last part of the anthology. All of these song texts are pointed for use with Anglican chant at the end of the volume.

Songs for Evening Prayer

There are four settings of the ancient hymn, Phos hilaron – a Song of the Light, one for each of the commended translations (including the well-known setting by Stainer), and a third metrical text with alternative new tunes. There are three settings of Verses from Psalm 141 and one of the Verses from Psalm 104 for the beginning of Evening Prayer. These are followed by five settings of the Gospel canticle, Magnificat, including a setting based on a Russian chant, one for the traditional text, and a metrical translation with several alternative tunes. Again, additional settings of Psalm 141 and Magnificat are included in Evening Prayer towards the end of the section. The Magnificat is also pointed for use with Anglican chant at the end of the volume.

Canticle for Night Prayer

Five settings of Nunc dimittis here can be supplemented by the music for the whole service found towards the end of this part. These include a simple, through-composed setting, as well as chanted settings, a setting of the traditional text, and a metrical version. The modern Nunc dimittis text is pointed for use with Anglican chant at the end of the volume.

Other materials

There are four settings of Te Deum, including one based on the ancient plainsong tones, but much simplified, one with simple chants, one with the traditional text, and a metrical setting. There is a hymn-like setting of the Affirmation of Faith based on Ephesians 3, two settings of the Trisagion, a chanted form of the Beatitudes (with optional refrain), and simple tones for the Litany.

Chants for the Responsory after the Reading(s), the Lord's Prayer, and various dialogues may be found in the settings Morning, Evening and Night Prayer discussed below.

Psalms and canticles for use in the Liturgy of the Word are found in Part Four of the volume.

Music for Morning, Evening and Night Prayer

Sung as a whole, these settings (which do not attempt to offer provision for every option of the text) may be more appropriate at a second or third service on a Sunday, rather than at a principal parish service. They may also be useful for use on quiet days or at times of preparation and penitence.

A reflective setting of each of these offices is provided. Some of the music draws directly on the plainsong tradition, but is bold in providing a simple form of the chants. Much of it is newly composed but draws on some of the characteristics of the chant in the use of simple melodic decoration of stable reciting notes.

Extracts from these services can be used in other contexts. The opening dialogue or the responsory after the readings may be used in combination with settings from elsewhere in the anthology.

Benedicite – a Song of Creation I

Refrain

1 Bless the Lord   all you works of the Lord:

sing his praise and ex - alt him for ev - er.

2 Bless the Lord you hea-vens: *Refrain*

3 Bless the Lord you an - gels of the Lord: *Refrain*

4 Bless the Lord   all peo - ple on earth: *Refrain*

5 O peo - ple of God   bless __ the Lord: *Refrain*

6 Bless the Lord   you priests of the Lord: *Refrain*

7 Bless the Lord you ser - vants of the Lord: *Refrain*

8 Bless the Lord   all you of up - right spi - rit:

bless the Lord   you that are ho - ly and hum - ble in heart;

bless the Fa - ther, the Son   and the Ho - ly Spi - rit: *Refrain*

Music: John Harper
© 2000 The Royal School of Church Music

Benedicite – a Song of Creation 2

Con moto ♩. = 72

Piano (or Organ)

mf

Bless the Lord all you works of the Lord: sing his

praise and ex – alt him for ev – er. Bless the Lord _____ you ___

hea – vens: sing his praise and ex – alt him for ev – er.

* 'Sing his praise and exalt him for ever' may be sung by everybody as a refrain throughout.

Bless the Lord you an - gels ___ of the Lord: sing his
praise and ex - alt him for ev — er. Bless the Lord all peo — ple
on ___ earth: sing his praise and ex - alt him for ev — er.
O ___ peo - ple of God bless ___ the Lord: sing his

mp più legato

mp

p

Lord you that are ho-ly and hum-ble in heart: bless the Fa-ther, the Son, and the Ho-ly Spi-rit: sing his praise and ex-alt him for ev - er, sing his praise and ex-alt him for ev - - - er.

Music: Alan Smith
© Alan Smith

Benedicite   199

Benedicite – a Song of Creation 3

1 Bless the Lord all you works of the Lord:

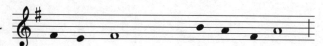

sing his praise and ex-alt him for ever.

2 Bless the Lord you heavens:

Refrain

sing his praise and ex-alt him for ev - er.

3 Bless the Lord you angels of the Lord: bless the Lord all you his hosts;

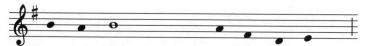

bless the Lord you waters a-bove the heavens: *Refrain*

4 Bless the Lord sun and moon: bless the Lord you stars of heaven;

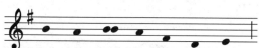

bless the Lord all rain and dew: *Refrain*

5 Bless the Lord all winds that blow: bless the Lord you fire and heat;

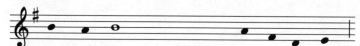

bless the Lord scorching wind and bit-ter cold: *Refrain*

6 Bless the Lord dews and fall-ing snows: bless the Lord you nights and days;

bless the Lord light and dark-ness: *Refrain*

Music: John Harper

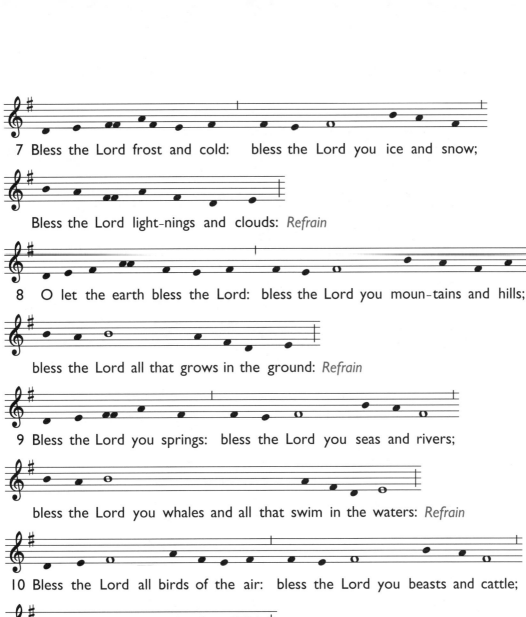

7 Bless the Lord frost and cold: bless the Lord you ice and snow;

Bless the Lord light-nings and clouds: *Refrain*

8   O let the earth bless the Lord: bless the Lord you moun-tains and hills;

bless the Lord all that grows in the ground: *Refrain*

9 Bless the Lord you springs: bless the Lord you seas and rivers;

bless the Lord you whales and all that swim in the waters: *Refrain*

10 Bless the Lord all birds of the air: bless the Lord you beasts and cattle;

bless the Lord all people on earth: *Refrain*

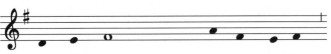

11   O peo-ple of God bless the Lord: bless the Lord you priests of the Lord:

bless the Lord you servants of the Lord: *Refrain*

12 Bless the Lord all you of up-right spi-rit:

bless the Lord you that are holy and hum-ble in heart;

bless the Father, the Son and the Ho-ly Spirit: *Refrain*

Benedicite – a Song of Creation 4

The text of each verse of this unison setting is printed on separate staves.

Music: Paul Stubbings
© Paul Stubbings

Venite 1 – a Song of Triumph

Psalm 95, shorter version

1 O come, let us sing to the Lord; let us heartily re-joice in the rock of our sal-vation.

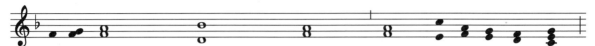

2 Let us come into his presence with thanksgiving and be glad in him with psalms.

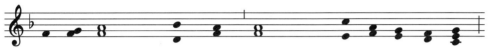

3 For the Lord is a great God and a great king a-bove all gods.

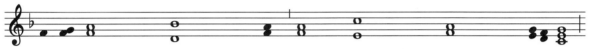

4 In his hand are the depths of the earth and the heights of the mountains are his also.

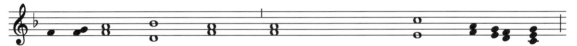

5 The sea is his, for he made it, and his hands have moulded the dry land.

6 Come, let us worship and bow down and kneel before the Lord our Maker.

7 For he is our God; we are the people of his pasture and the sheep of his hand.

Glo-ry to the Father and to the Son and to the Ho-ly Spirit;

as it was in the be-ginning is now and shall be for ever. A - men.

Music: John Harper
© 2000 The Royal School of Church Music

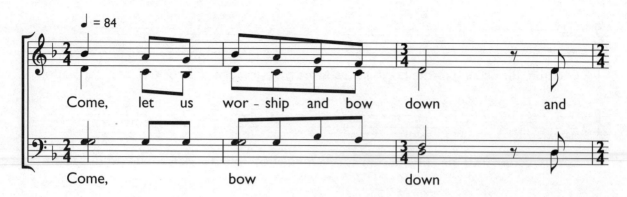

Come, let us wor-ship and bow down and
Come, bow down

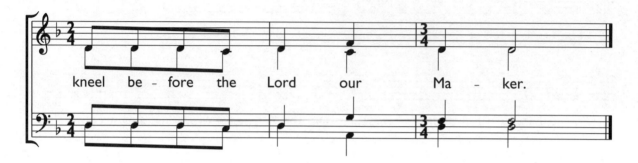

kneel be-fore the Lord our Ma-ker.

1 O come, let us sing to ' the Lord; ♦
 let us heartily rejoice in the rock of ' our salvation.

2 Let us come into his presence ' with thanksgiving ♦
 and be glad in ' him with psalms.

3 For the Lord is a ' great God ♦
 and a great king a'bove all gods.

4 In his hand are the depths of ' the earth ♦
 and the heights of the mountains ' are his also.

5 The sea is his, for he ' made it, ♦
 and his hands have moulded ' the dry land.

6 Come, let us worship and ' bow down ♦
 and kneel before the ' Lord our Maker.

7 For he is ' our God; ♦
 we are the people of his pasture and the sheep ' of his hand.

Music: John Harper
© 2000 The Royal School of Church Music

8 O that today you would listen to ¹ his voice: ♦
'Harden not your hearts as at Meribah,
on that day at Massah ¹ in the wilderness,

9 'When your forebears tested me, and put me to ¹ the proof, ♦
though they had ¹ seen my works.

10 'Forty years long I detested that generation ¹ and said, ♦
"This people are wayward in their hearts;
they do not ¹ know my ways."

11 'So I swore in ¹ my wrath, ♦
"They shall not enter in¹to my rest." '

Glory to the Father and to ¹ the Son
and to the ¹ Holy Spirit;

as it was in the beginning ¹ is now
and shall be for ev¹er. Amen.

Venite – a Song of Triumph 3

Psalm 95, metrical text LM

Come with all joy to sing to God Our sav – ing Rock, the liv – ing Lord;

In glad thanks-giv-ing seek his face With songs of vic - to - ry and grace.

1 Come with all joy to sing to God Our sav-ing Rock, the liv – ing Lord;

In glad thanks-giv-ing seek his face With songs of vic - to - ry and grace.

Words: Christopher Idle
© Christoper Idle / Jubilate Hymns
First tune: 'Mediæ Noctis', Unknown
Second tune: 'Mein' Seel', O Gott', Michael Praetorius

1 Come with all joy to sing to God
   Our saving rock, the living Lord;
   In glad thanksgiving seek his face
   With songs of victory and grace.

2 In holiness and light arrayed
   Above all gods that we have made
   He is the one almighty king,
   And his the glory that we sing.

3 The earth is his from east to west,
   From ocean-floor to mountain-crest;
   He made the seas and formed the lands,
   He shaped the islands by his hands.

4 Come near to worship, come with faith,
   Bow down to him who gives us breath:
   God is our shepherd, he alone;
   We are his people, all his own.

   verses 5 and 6 may be omitted

5 But if you hear God's voice today
   Do not reject what he will say:
   When Israel wandered from God's path
   They suffered forty years of wrath.

6 That generation went astray,
   They did not want to know his way;
   They put their saviour to the test,
   And saw his power, but lost their rest.

7 So to the God of earth and heaven,
   The Father, Spirit, Son, be given
   Praise now, as praise has ever been
   And ever shall be praise. Amen.

This text may be sung to other LM tunes.

O be joyful in the Lord, all the earth;

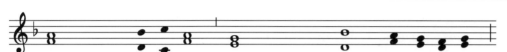

serve the Lord with gladness   and come before his pres-ence with a song.

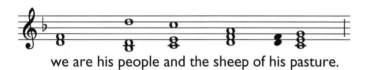

Know that the Lord is good;   it is he that has made us and we are his;

we are his people and the sheep of his pasture.

Enter his gates with thanksgiving   and his courts with praise;

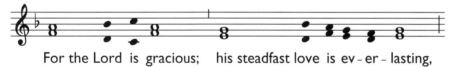

give thanks to him and bless his name.

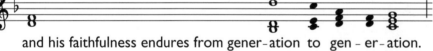

For the Lord is gracious;   his steadfast love is ev-er-lasting,

and his faithfulness endures from gener-ation to gen-er-ation.

Glory to the Father and to the Son   and to the Ho-ly Spirit;

as it was in the beginning is now   and shall be for ever. A-men.

Music: John Harper
© 2000 The Royal School of Church Music

Jubilate – a Song of Joy 2

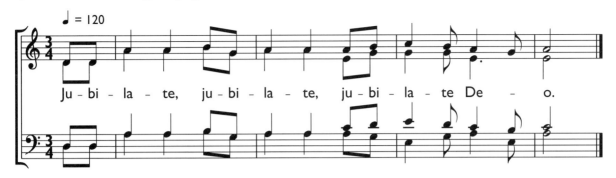

Ju – bi – la – te, ju – bi – la – te, ju – bi – la – te De – o.

1 O be joyful in the Lord, all ' the earth; ♦
serve the Lord ' with gladness
and come before his presence ' with a song.

2 Know that the Lord ' is God; ♦
it is he that has made us and we ' are his;
we are his people and the sheep ' of his pasture.

3 Enter his gates ' with thanksgiving
and his courts ' with praise; ♦
give thanks to him and ' bless his name.

4 For the Lord ' is gracious;
his steadfast love is ev'erlasting, ♦
and his faithfulness endures from generation to ' generation.

Glory to ' the Father
and to ' the Son
and to the ' Holy Spirit;

as it was in ' the be|ginning ' is now
and shall be for ev'er. Amen.

Music: John Harper
© 2000 The Royal School of Church Music

Jubilate – a Song of Joy 3

1 Come, re-joice be-fore your ma-ker All you peo-ples of the earth;

Serve the Lord your God with glad-ness, Come be-fore him with a song!

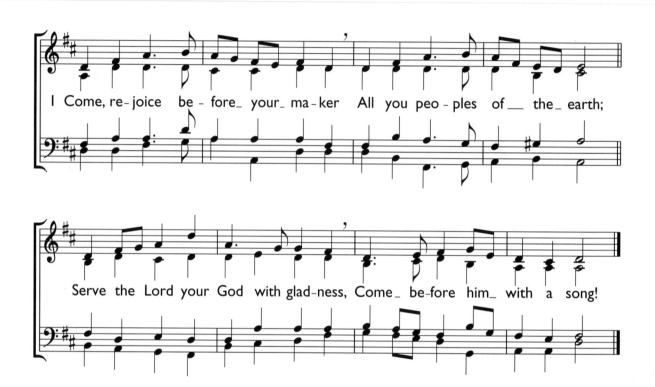

1 Come, re-joice be-fore your ma-ker All you peo-ples of the earth;

Serve the Lord your God with glad-ness, Come be-fore him with a song!

2 Know for certain that Jehovah
Is the true and only God:
We are his, for he has made us;
We are sheep within his fold.

3 Come with grateful hearts before him,
Enter now his courts with praise;
Show your thankfulness towards him,
Give due honour to his name.

4 For the Lord our God is gracious,
Everlasting in his love;
And to every generation
His great faithfulness endures.

5 Praise and honour to the Father,
Praise and honour to the Son,
Praise and honour to the Spirit,
Ever Three and ever One.

Words: Michael Baughen (Doxology by St Dominic's Convent, Stone)
© Michael Baughen / Jubilate Hymns
First tune: 'Neath', Mount Saint Bernard Abbey
Second tune: 'Shipston', melody collected by Lucy Broadwood (1858-1929),
and adapted by Ralph Vaughan Williams (1872-1958)
from The English Hymnal by permission of Oxford University Press.

The Easter Anthems 1

Christ our passover has been sacrificed for us: so let us ce-le-brate the feast,

not with the old leaven of cor-ruption and wickedness:

but with the unleavened bread of sin-cerity and truth.

Christ once raised from the dead dies no more: death has no more do-min-ion over him.

In dying he died to sin once for all: in living he lives to God.

See yourselves therefore as dead to sin: and alive to God in Jesus Christ our Lord.

Christ has been raised from the dead: the first fruits of those who sleep.

For as by man came death: by man has come also the resurrection of the dead;

for as in Adam all die: even so in Christ shall all be made a-live.

Glory to the Fa-ther and to the Son   and to the Ho-ly Spirit.

as it was in the be-ginning is now   and shall be for ever. A-men.

Music: John Harper
© 2000 The Royal School of Church Music

The Easter Anthems 2

A 1 Christ our passover has been sacrificed ' for us: ♦
so let us celebrate ' the feast,

B 2 not with the old leaven of corruption ' and wickedness: ♦
but with the unleavened bread of sincerity ' and truth.

A 3 Christ once raised from the dead dies ' no more: ♦
death has no more dominion o'ver him.

B 4 In dying he died to sin once ' for all: ♦
in living he lives ' to God.

C 5 See yourselves therefore as dead ' to sin: ♦
and alive to God in Jesus ' Christ our Lord.

A 6 Christ has been raised from ' the dead: ♦
the first fruits of those ' who sleep.

B 7 For as by man ' came death: ♦
by man has come also the resurrection of ' the dead;

C 8 for as in Adam ' all die: ♦
even so in Christ shall all be ' made alive.

A Glory to the Father and to ' the Son
and to the Holy ' Spirit;

B as it was in the beginning ' is now
and shall be for ever. ' Amen.

Music: John Harper
© 2000 The Royal School of Church Music

Benedictus – the Song of Zechariah 1

1 Blessèd be the Lord the ' God of Israel, ♦
  who has come to his people and ' set them free.

2 He has raised up for us a ' mighty Saviour, ♦
  born of the house of his ' servant David.

3 Through his holy prophets God ' promised of old ♦
  to save us from our enemies, from the hands of ' all that hate us,

4 To show mercy ' to our ancestors, ♦
  and to remember his ' holy covenant.

5 This was the oath God swore to our ' father Abraham: ♦
  to set us free from the hands ' of our enemies,

6 Free to worship ' him without fear, ♦
  holy and righteous in his sight   all the days ' of our life.

7 And you, child, shall be called the prophet ' of the Most High, ♦
  for you will go before the Lord to pre'pare his way,

8 To give his people knowledge ' of salvation ♦
  by the forgiveness of ' all their sins.

9 In the tender compas'sion of our God ♦
  the dawn from on high shall ' break upon us,

10 To shine on those who dwell in darkness and the ' shadow of death, ♦
   and to guide our feet into the ' way of peace.

   Glory to the Father ' and to the Son
   and to the ' Holy Spirit;

   as it was in the be'ginning is now
   and shall be for ev'er. Amen.

Music: John Harper
© 2000 The Royal School of Church Music

Benedictus – the Song of Zechariah 2

Bless-ed be the Lord ____ the God of Is-rael, who has come _ to his peo-ple _ and set them free. ___ He has raised up for us a migh - ty Sa - viour, _ born _ of the house of his ser - vant Da - vid.

3 Through his holy prophets God promised ' of old ♦
    to save us from our enemies,
        from the hands of all ' that hate us,

4 To show mercy to ' our ancestors, ♦
    and to remember his ho'ly covenant.

5 This was the oath God swore to our fa'ther Abraham: ♦
    to set us free from the hands of ' our enemies,

6 Free to worship him with'out fear, ♦
    holy and righteous in his sight
        all the days of ' our life.

Refrain

7 And you, child, shall be called the prophet of the ' Most High, ♦
    for you will go before the Lord to prepare ' his way,

8 To give his people knowledge of ' salvation ♦
    by the forgiveness of all ' their sins.

9 In the tender compassion of ' our God ♦
    the dawn from on high shall break up'on us,

10 To shine on those who dwell in darkness and the shadow ' of death, ♦
    and to guide our feet into the way ' of peace.

Refrain

    Glory to the Father and to ' the Son
    and to the Ho'ly Spirit;
    as it was in the beginning ' is now
    and shall be for ever. ' Amen.

Refrain

Music: John Harper
© 2000 The Royal School of Church Music

Benedictus – the Song of Zechariah 3

traditional text

1   Bless-ed be the Lord God of Israel :

for he hath visited, and re-deemed his people;

2   And hath raised up a mighty sal-vation for us :

in the house of his ser-vant David;

3   As he spake by the mouth of his ho-ly Prophets :

which have been since the world be-gan;

4   That we should be saved from our enemies :

and from the hands of all that hate us;

5   To per-form the mercy promised to our forefathers :

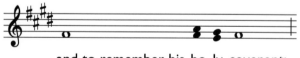

and to remember his ho-ly covenant;

6   To per-form the oath which he sware to our forefa-ther Abraham :

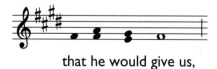

that he would give us,

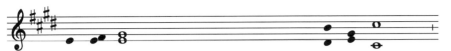

7   That we being delivered out of the hands of our enemies :

might serve him with-out fear,

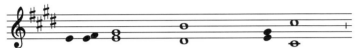

8   in ho-liness and righteousness be-fore him :

all the days of our life.

9   And thou, child, shalt be called the Prophet of the Highest :

for thou shalt go before the face of the Lord to pre-pare his ways;

10   To give knowledge of salvation unto his people :

for the remission of their sins;

11 Through the tender mercy of our God :

whereby the dayspring from on high hath visited us;

12   To give light to them that sit in darkness, and in the shadow of death :

and to guide our feet into the way of peace.

Glo-ry   be to the Father, and to the Son :

and to the Ho-ly Ghost;

as it was in the beginning, is now, and ev-er shall be :

world with-out end. A-men.

Benedictus – the Song of Zechariah 4a

metrical text DCM

I Now bless the God of Is-ra-el who comes in love and power,

Who rai-ses from the roy-al house de-liv'-rance in __ this hour.

Through ho-ly pro-phets God has sworn to __ free us __ from a - larm,

To __ save us from the __ hea-vy hand of __ all who wish us harm.

2 Remembering the covenant, God rescues us from fear,
That we might serve in holiness and peace from year to year.
And you, my child, shall go before, to preach, to prophesy,
That all may know the tender love, the grace of God most high.

3 In tender mercy, God will send the dayspring from on high,
Our rising sun, the light of life for those who sit and sigh.
God comes to guide our way to peace, that death shall reign no more.
Sing praises to the Holy One, O worship and adore.

‡ 4 To God the Father, fount of grace, through his beloved Son,
With God their Spirit, bond of love, be glory ever One.

Words: Ruth Duck © 1992 G.I.A. Publications Inc
Words of doxology: James Quinn SJ © 1968 James Quinn SJ and Geoffrey Chapman / Cassell plc
Music:'Kingsfold', English traditional melody collected by Lucy Broadwood (1858-1929),
and adapted by Ralph Vaughan Williams (1872-1958)
from The English Hymnal by permission of Oxford University Press.

Benedictus – the Song of Zechariah 4b

metrical text CM

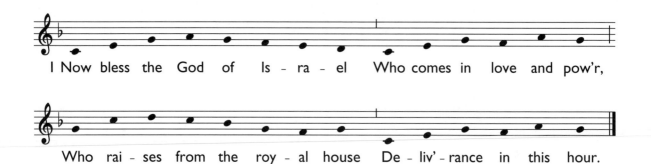

I Now bless the God of Is – ra – el Who comes in love and pow'r,

Who rai – ses from the roy – al house De – liv' – rance in this hour.

1 Now bless the God of Israel
Who comes in love and power,
Who raises from the royal house
Deliv'rance in this hour.

2 Through holy prophets God has sworn
To free us from alarm,
To save us from the heavy hand
Of all who wish us harm.

3 Remembering the covenant,
God rescues us from fear,
That we might serve in holiness
And peace from year to year.

3 And you, my child, shall go before,
To preach, to prophesy,
That all may know the tender love,
The grace of God most high.

4 In tender mercy, God will send
The dayspring from on high,
Our rising sun, the light of life
For those who sit and sigh.

5 God comes to guide our way to peace,
That death shall reign no more.
Sing praises to the Holy One,
O worship and adore.

6 To God the Father, fount of grace,
Through his beloved Son,
With God their Spirit, bond of love,
Be glory ever One.

Words: Ruth Duck
© 1992 G.I.A. Publications Inc
Music: 'Crux Christi', Charles Watson OSB © 1995 Charles Watson OSB

Phos hilaron – a Song of the Light 1

With movement

O joy - ful light, from the pure glo - ry of the e - ter - nal

hea - ven - ly Fa - ther, O ho - ly, bless-ed Je - sus Christ.

As we come to the set-ting of the sun and see the even-ing light,

we give thanks and praise to the Fa - ther and to the Son

and to the Ho - ly Spi - rit of God.

Wor-thy are you at all times to be sung with ho - ly voi-ces,

O Son of God, O giv - er of life,

and to be glo - ri - fied through all cre - a - tion.

Music: John Harper
© 2000 The Royal School of Church Music

Phos hilaron – a Song of the Light 2

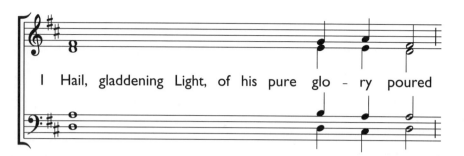

1 Hail, gladdening Light, of his pure glo - ry poured

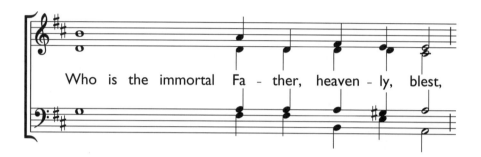

Who is the immortal Fa - ther, heaven - ly, blest,

Ho - li - est of ho - lies, Je - sus Christ _ our Lord.

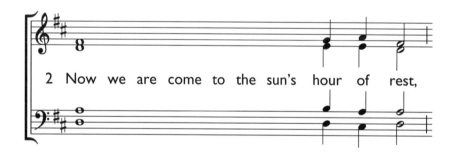

2 Now we are come to the sun's hour of rest,

The lights of eve - ning round us shine,

We hymn the Fa-ther, Son and Ho-ly Spi - rit div - ine.

3 Worthy are you at all times to be sung with un-de-fi-lèd tongue, Son of our God, giv-er of life, a - lone:____

There-fore in all the world your glo - ries, Lord, they own.

Words: Third-century Greek, translated John Keble, altered.
Music: 'Sebaste', John Stainer

Phos hilaron – a Song of the Light 3a

metrical text 8887

1 Light of gladness, Lord of glory,
  Jesus Christ our king most holy,
  Shine among us in your mercy:
  Earth and heaven join their hymn.

2 Let us sing at sun's descending
  As we see the lights of evening,
  Father, Son and Spirit praising
  With the holy seraphim.

3 Son of God, through all the ages
  Worthy of our holiest praises,
  Yours the life that never ceases,
  Light which never shall grow dim.

Words: Christopher Idle
© Christopher Idle / Jubilate Hymns
Music: 'Llaneilian', John Harper
© 2000 The Royal School of Church Music

Phos hilaron – a Song of the Light 3b

metrical text 8887

1 Light of gladness, Lord of glory,
   Jesus Christ our king most holy,
   Shine among us in your mercy:
   Earth and heaven join their hymn.

2 Let us sing at sun's descending
   As we see the lights of evening,
   Father, Son and Spirit praising
   With the holy seraphim.

3 Son of God, through all the ages
   Worthy of our holiest praises,
   Yours the life that never ceases,
   Light which never shall grow dim.

Words: Christopher Idle
© Christopher Idle / Jubilate Hymns
Music: 'Traeth yr Ora', John Harper
© 2000 The Royal School of Church Music

This hymn may also be sung to Quem pastores, *which is particularly suitable during Christmastide.*

Verses from Psalm 141 setting 1

Refrain

Let my prayer rise be-fore you as in - cense,

the lift - ing up of my hands as the even-ing sac - ri - fice.

Cantors

1 O Lord, I call to you; come ' to me quickly; ◆
hear my voice when I ' cry to you.

2 Set a watch before my ' mouth, O Lord, ◆
and guard the door ' of my lips.

Refrain

3 Let not my heart incline to any ' evil thing; ◆
let me not be occupied with ' evil doers.

4 But my eyes are turned to ' you, Lord God; ◆
in you I take refuge; do not leave ' me defenceless.

Refrain

Music: Alan Wilson
© 2000 Alan Wilson

* *Sustain this chord while the verse is sung*

Verses from Psalm 141 setting 2

Refrain

My prayers rise like ___ in- cense, my
hands like the eve - ning sac - ri - fice.

Verse

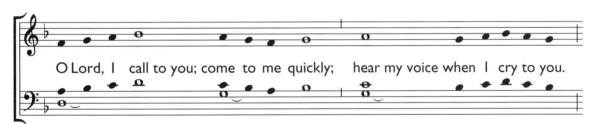

O Lord, I call to you; come to me quickly; hear my voice when I cry to you.

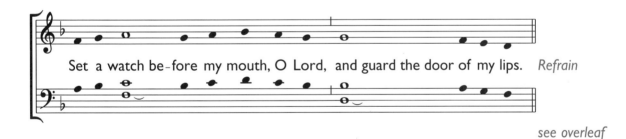

Set a watch be-fore my mouth, O Lord, and guard the door of my lips. *Refrain*

see overleaf

Music & words of the refrain: Arlo D Duba, arranged Geoff Weaver
© 1986 Arlo D Duba
Music of the verses: John Harper
© 2000 The Royal School of Church Music

Let not my heart incline to a-ny e-vil thing; let me not be occupied with e-vil do-ers.

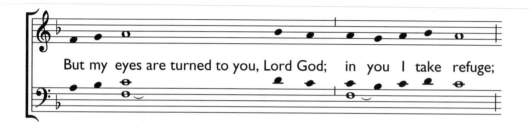

But my eyes are turned to you, Lord God; in you I take refuge;

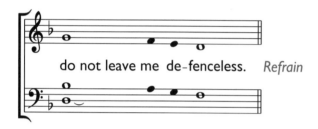

do not leave me de-fenceless. *Refrain*

Verses from Psalm 141 setting 3

Let my prayer rise be-fore you as in - cense, ___

the lift - ing up of my hands as the eve - ning sac - ri - fice. __

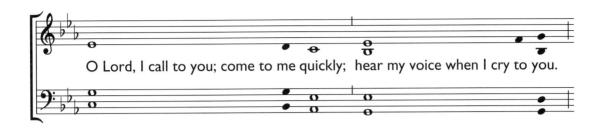

O Lord, I call to you; come to me quickly; hear my voice when I cry to you.

Set a watch before my mouth, O Lord, and guard the door of my lips. *Refrain*

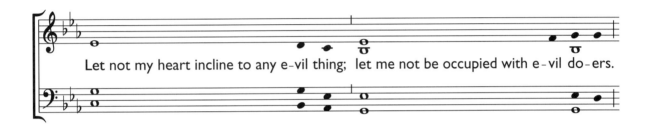

Let not my heart incline to any e-vil thing; let me not be occupied with e-vil do-ers.

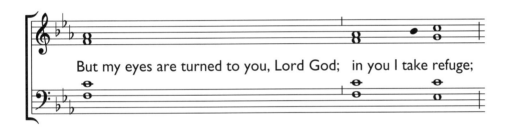

But my eyes are turned to you, Lord God; in you I take refuge;

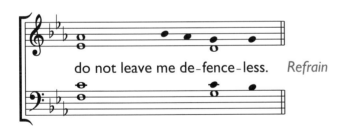

do not leave me de-fence-less. *Refrain*

Music: Paul Inwood, adapted

A further setting of Verses from Psalm 141 may be found in Evening Prayer, on page 277.

Verses from Psalm 104

Bless the Lord, O my soul. O Lord my God,
how ex - cel - lent is your great - ness!

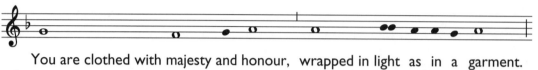

You are clothed with majesty and honour, wrapped in light as in a garment.

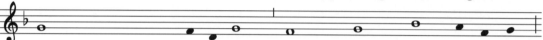

The sun knows the time for its setting. You make darkness that it may be night.

Refrain

O Lord, how manifold are your works!

In wisdom you have made them all; the earth is full of your creatures.

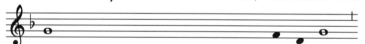

When you send forth your spirit, they are cre-ated,

and you re-new the face of the earth.

Refrain

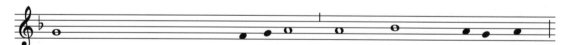

May the glory of the Lord en-dure for ever; may the Lord rejoice in his works;

I will sing to the Lord as long as I live;

I will make music to my God while I have my be-ing.

Refrain

Music: John Harper
© 2000 The Royal School of Church Music

Magnificat – the Song of Mary 1

♩ = 92

My soul proclaims the greatness of the Lord: _____
my spirit ___ rejoices ___ in God my Saviour.

A   ¶ My soul proclaims the greatness of the Lord:
            my spirit rejoices in ' God my saviour;
            he has looked with favour on his ' lowly servant.

B   ¶ From this day all generations will ' call me blessed;
            the Almighty has done great things for me:
                and holy ' is his name.

A   ¶ He has mercy on ' those who fear him:
            from generation to ' generation.

A   ¶ He has shown strength ' with his arm:
            and has scattered the proud in ' their conceit,

B   casting down the mighty ' from their thrones:
            and lifting ' up the lowly.

A   ¶ He has filled the hungry ' with good things:
            and sent the rich ' away empty.

A   ¶ He has come to the aid of his ' servant Israel:
            to remember his pro'mise of mercy,

B   the promise made ' to our ancestors,
            to Abraham and his chil'dren for ever.

A   Glory to the Father, and ' to the Son
            and to the ' Holy Spirit;

B   as it was in the begin'ning is now
            and shall be for ev'er. Amen.

Words: ELLC © 1988 ELLC
Music: John Harper
© 2000 The Royal School of Church Music

Magnificat – the Song of Mary 2

1 My soul proclaims the greatness of the Lord:
    my spirit rejoices in ' God my saviour;
  he has looked with favour on his ' lowly servant.

2 From this day all generations will ' call me blessed;
  the Almighty has done great things for me:
    and holy ' is his name.

3 He has mercy on ' those who fear him:
  from generation to ' generation.

4 He has shown ' strength with his arm:
  and has scattered the proud in ' their conceit,

5 Casting down the migh'ty from their thrones:
  and lifting ' up the lowly.

6 He has filled the hun'gry with good things:
  and sent the rich ' away empty.

7 He has come to the aid of his ' servant Israel:
  to remember his pro'mise of mercy,

8 The promise made ' to our ancestors,
  to Abraham and his chil'dren for ever.

  Glory to the Father, ' and to the Son
  and to the ' Holy Spirit;
  as it was in the be'ginning is now
  and shall be for ev'er. Amen.

Words: ELLC © 1988 ELLC
Music: Russian chant, adapted by John Harper
© 2000 The Royal School of Church Music

Magnificat – the Song of Mary 3

alternative chant

1 My soul proclaims the greatness of the Lord:
      my spirit rejoices in God my ' saviour;
      he has looked with favour on his ' lowly servant.

2 From this day all generations will call me ' blessed;
      the Almighty has done great things for me:
         and holy ' is his name.

3 He has mercy on those who ' fear him:
      from generation to ' generation.

4 He has shown strength with his ' arm:
      and has scattered the proud in ' their conceit,

5 Casting down the mighty from their ' thrones:
      and lifting ' up the lowly.

6 He has filled the hungry with ' good things:
      and sent the rich ' away empty.

7 He has come to the aid of his servant ' Israel:
      to remember his pro'mise of mercy,

8 The promise made to our ' ancestors,
      to Abraham and his chil'dren for ever.

      Glory to the Father, and to the ' Son
      and to the ' Holy Spirit;
      as it was in the beginning is ' now
      and shall be for ev'er. Amen.

Words: ELLC © 1988 ELLC
Music: Norman Warren
© Norman Warren

Magnificat – the Song of Mary 4

1   My soul doth magni-fy the Lord:

and my spirit hath rejoiced in God my Saviour.

2   For he hath re-garded:

the lowliness of his handmaiden.

3   For be-hold, from henceforth:

all generations shall call me blessed.

4   For he that is mighty hath magni-fied me:

and holy is his Name.

5   And his mercy is on them that fear him:

throughout all ge-ne-rations.

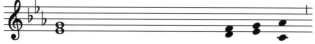

6   He hath shewed strength with his arm:

he hath scattered the proud in the imagination of their hearts.

7 He hath put down the mighty from their seat:

and hath exalted the hum- ble and meek.

8 He hath filled the hungry with good things:

and the rich he hath sent emp-ty a-way.

9 He re-membering his mercy   hath holpen his ser-vant Israel:

as he promised to our forefathers,   Abraham and his seed for ever.

Glory be to the Father, and to the Son:

and to the Ho-ly Ghost;

as it was in the beginning, is now, and ev-er shall be:

world without end. A - men.

Magnificat – the Song of Mary 5a

metrical text CM

Verses 1,3,5

1 With Ma – ry let my soul re-joice, ___

And praise God's ho – ly name ___

His sav – ing love from first to last, ___

From age to age, the same! ___

3 The rich our God will send away
   And feed the hungry poor
   The arms of love remain outstretched
   At mercy's open door.

5 All glory to the Father, Son
   And Spirit now proclaim;
   With Mary let the world rejoice
   And praise God's holy name!

4 So shall God's promise be fulfilled,
   To Israel firmly made:
   A child is born, a Son is given
   Whose crown will never fade.

Magnificat – the Song of Mary 5b

metrical text CM

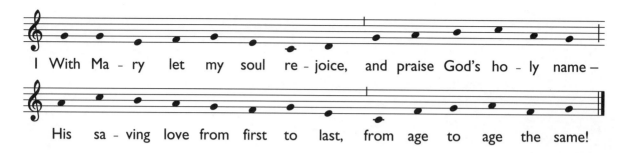

1 With Ma-ry let my soul re-joice, and praise God's ho-ly name –

His sa-ving love from first to last, from age to age the same!

Magnificat – the Song of Mary 5c

metrical text CM

1 With Ma-ry let my soul re-joice, And praise God's ho-ly name –

His sa-ving love from first to last, From age to age the same!

2 How strong his arm, how great his power!
The proud he will disown;
The meek and humble he exalts
To share his glorious throne

3 The rich our God will send away
And feed the hungry poor
The arms of love remain outstretched
At mercy's open door.

4 So shall God's promise be fulfilled,
To Israel firmly made:
A child is born, a Son is given
Whose crown will never fade.

5 All glory to the Father, Son
And Spirit now proclaim;
With Mary let the world rejoice
And praise God's holy name!

Words: David Mowbray © David Mowbray / Jubilate Hymns
Music of 5b: 'Anglicanus', The Anglican Office Book © 1981 The Communities' Consultative Council
Music of 5c: 'Oude Kerk', Dutch traditional melody, harmony John Harper
© 1995 Panel of Monastic Musicians

Nunc dimittis – the Song of Simeon 1

A light to re-veal you to the na-tions and the glo-ry of your peo-ple Is-ra-el.

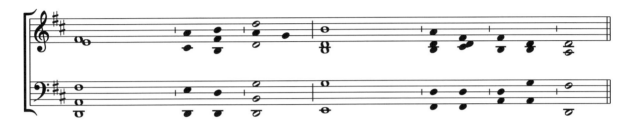

1 Now, Lord, you let your servant ' go in ' peace: ♦
your ' word has ' been ful'filled.

2 My own eyes have ' seen the sal'vation ♦
which you have prepared in the ' sight of ' every ' people;

3 A light to reveal you ' to the ' nations ♦
and the ' glory of your ' people ' Israel.

Glory to the Father and ' to the ' Son
and ' to the ' Holy ' Spirit;
as it was in the be'ginning is ' now
and shall be for ' ever. ' A'men.

Words: ELLC © 1988 ELLC
Music: Peter Moger
© Peter Moger

This setting may also be sung in D♭.

Nunc dimittis – the Song of Simeon 2

Now, Lord, ___ you let your ser-vant go in peace: your word has been ful – filled. My own eyes have seen the sal – va-tion which you have pre-pared in the sight of ev-'ry peo – ple; A light to re-veal you to the na – tions and the

Nunc dimittis – the Song of Simeon 3

1 Now, Lord, you let your servant ' go in ' peace: ◆
your word has ' been ful'filled.

2 My own eyes have ' seen the sal'vation ◆
which you have prepared in the sight of ' every ' people;

3 A light to reveal you ' to the ' nations ◆
and the glory of your ' people ' Israel.

Glory to the Father ' and to the ' Son
and to the ' Holy ' Spirit;
as it was in the be'ginning is ' now
and shall be for ' ever. A'men.

Words: ELLC © 1988 ELLC
Music: Norman Warren
© Norman Warren

Nunc dimittis – the Song of Simeon 4

traditional text

Lord, now lettest thou thy servant de-part in peace :

ac - cord - ing to thy word.

For mine eyes have seen thy sal-vation;

Which thou hast pre-pared : before the face of all people;

To be a light to lighten the Gentiles :

and to be the glory of thy peo-ple Israel.

Glory be to the Father, and to the Son :

and to the Ho-ly Ghost;

as it was in the beginning, is now, and ev - er shall be :

world with - out end. A-men.

Nunc dimittis – the Song of Simeon 5a metrical text 6565

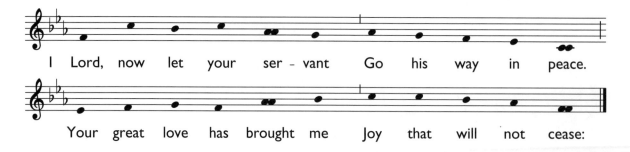

1 Lord, now let your ser - vant Go his way in peace.

Your great love has brought me Joy that will not cease:

Nunc dimittis – the Song of Simeon 5b metrical text 6565

1 Lord, now let your ser - vant Go his way in peace. __

Your great love has brought me Joy that will not cease:

2 For my eyes have seen him
Promised from of old,
Saviour of all people,
Shepherd of one fold.

3 Light of revelation
To the gentiles shown,
Light of Israel's glory
To the world made known.

4 Glory to the Father
And his only Son,
With the Holy Spirit
Ever Three in One.

Words: J E Seddon © Mrs M Seddon / Jubilate Hymns
Doxology: John Harper © 2000 The Royal School of Church Music
First tune: 'Llaniestyn', John Harper © 2000 The Royal School of Church Music
Second tune: 'Westhead', melody by Stanbrook Abbey © 1974 Stanbrook Abbey
Harmony by John Harper © 1995 Panel of Monastic Musicians

Te Deum laudamus I

We praise you, O God, we acclaim you as the Lord;

all creation worships you, the Father ev-er-last-ing.

To you all an-gels, all the powers of hea-ven,

the cherubim and se-ra-phim, sing in end-less praise:

Ho-ly, ho-ly, ho-ly Lord, God of power and might,

heaven and earth are full of your glo-ry.

The glorious company of ap-ost-les praise you.

The noble fellowship of pro-phets praise you.

The white-robed army of mar-tyrs praise you.

Throughout the world the holy Church ac-claims you:

Fa-ther, of ma-jes-ty un-boun-ded,

your true and only Son, worthy of all praise,

the Ho-ly Spi-rit, ad-vo-cate and guide.

You, Christ, are the King of glo-ry, the eternal Son of the Fa-ther.

When you took our flesh to set us free

you humbly chose the Vir-gin's womb.

You overcame the sting of death

and opened the kingdom of heaven to all be-liev-ers.

You are seated at God's right hand in glo-ry.

We believe that you will come and be our judge.

Come then, Lord, and help your peo-ple,

bought with the price of your own blood,

and bring us with your saints to glo-ry ev - er - last-ing.

The canticle may end here.

Save your people, Lord,   and bless your in he‑ri‑tance.

Govern and uphold them   now and al‑ways.

Day by day we bless you.   We praise your name for ev‑er.

Keep us today, Lord, from all sin.   Have mercy on us, Lord, have mer‑cy.

Lord, show us your love and mer‑cy,   for we have put our trust in you.

In you, Lord, is our hope: let us nev‑er be put to shame.

Words: ELLC © 1988 ELLC
Music: adapted from traditional chant © 2000 The Royal School of Church Music

Te Deum laudamus 2

chant 1

1 We praise you, O ' God, | we acclaim you ' as the Lord;
2 all creation ' worships you, | the Father ' everlasting.

3 To you all angels, all the powers of ' heaven,
the cherubim and seraphim, sing in ' endless praise:

4 Holy, holy, holy ' Lord, | God of ' power and might,
5 heaven and ' earth | are full ' of your glory.

6 The glorious company of apostles ' praise you.
The noble fellowship of ' prophets praise you.

7 The white-robed army of martyrs ' praise you.
Throughout the world the holy ' Church acclaims you:

8 Father, of majesty unbounded,
your true and only Son, worthy of all ' praise,
the Holy Spirit, advo'cate and guide.

chant 2

9 You, Christ, are the ' King of glory, | the eternal Son ' of the Father.

10 When you took our flesh to ' set us free
you humbly chose the ' Virgin's womb.

11 You overcame the ' sting of death
and opened the kingdom of heaven to ' all believers.

12 You are seated at God's right ' hand in glory.
We believe that you will come and ' be our judge.

13 Come then, Lord, and ' help your people,
bought with the price of ' your own blood,

14 and bring us ' with your saints | to glory ' everlasting.

The canticle may end here.

chant 1

15 Save your people, Lord, and bless your in'heritance.
Govern and uphold them ' now and always.

16 Day by day we ' bless you. | We praise your ' name for ever.

17 Keep us today, Lord, from all ' sin. | Have mercy on us, ' Lord, have mercy.

18 Lord, show us your love and ' mercy, | for we have put our ' trust in you.

19 In you, Lord, is our ' hope: | let us never be ' put to shame.

Words: ELLC © 1988 ELLC
Music: Norman Warren   © Norman Warren

Te Deum laudamus 3

Drone We praise thee, O God; we acknowledge thee to be the Lord.

All the earth doth wor-ship thee, the Father ev-er-last-ing.

To thee all angels cry a-loud, the heavens and all the powers there-in.

To thee cheru-bin and seraphin continual-ly do cry.

Holy, Ho-ly, Holy, Lord God of Sabaoth;

Heaven and earth are full of the majesty of thy glory.

The glorious company of the ap-os-tles praise thee.

The goodly fellowship of the pro-phets praise thee.

The noble army of mar-tyrs praise thee.

The holy Church throughout all the world doth ac-knowledge thee:

the Father of an in-fin-ite majesty;

thine honourable, true and on-ly Son;

also the Holy Ghost the Comforter.

Drone Thou art the King of glo-ry, O Christ.

Thou art the everlasting Son of the Father.

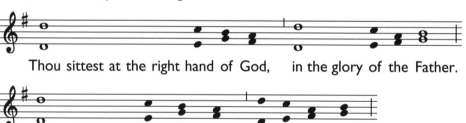

When thou tookest upon thee to de-liv-er man,

thou didst not abhor the Vir-gin's womb.

When thou hast overcome the sharp-ness of death,

thou didst open the kingdom of heaven to all be-lievers.

Thou sittest at the right hand of God,   in the glory of the Father.

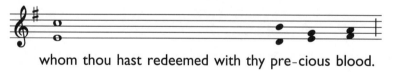

We believe that thou shalt come   to be our judge.

We therefore pray thee, help thy servants,

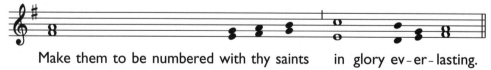

whom thou hast redeemed with thy pre-cious blood.

Make them to be numbered with thy saints   in glory ev-er-lasting.

Drone O Lord, save thy people and bless thine heritage.

Gov-ern them and lift them up for ever.

Day by day we magni-fy thee;

and we worship thy name, ever world with-out end.

Drone Vouch-safe, O Lord, to keep us this day with-out sin.

O Lord, have mer-cy up-on us, have mer-cy up-on us.

O Lord, let thy mercy light-en up-on us, as our trust is in thee.

O Lord, in thee have I trusted; let me never be con-founded.

Te Deum laudamus 4a

metrical text 8787D

I God, we praise you! God, we bless you! God, we name you sov'-reign Lord!

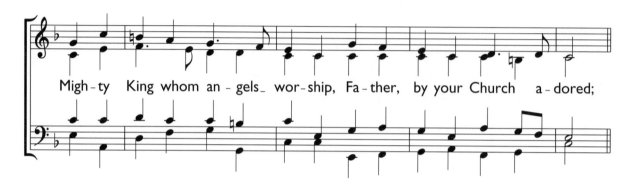

Migh-ty King whom an-gels wor-ship, Fa-ther, by your Church a-dored;

All cre-a-tion shows your glo-ry, heaven and earth draw near your throne

Sing-ing 'Ho-ly, ho-ly, ho-ly,' Lord of hosts, and God a-lone.

Words: Christopher Idle
© Christopher Idle / Jubilate Hymns
Music: 'Rustington', C H H Parry

In this setting pairs of verses of the text are sung to each verse of the tune.

Te Deum laudamus 4b

1 God, we praise you! God, we bless you! God, we name you sov'-reign Lord!

Migh - ty King whom an - gels wor - ship, Fa - ther, by your Church a - dored;

1 God, we praise you, God we bless you,
   God, we name you sovereign Lord!
   Mighty king whom angels worship,
   Father, by your Church adored:

2 All creation shows your glory,
   Heaven and earth draw near your throne
   Singing 'Holy, holy, holy,'
   Lord of hosts and God alone.

3 True apostles, faithful prophets,
   Saints who set their world ablaze,
   Martyrs, once unknown, unheeded,
   Join one growing song of praise,

4 While your Church on earth confesses
   One majestic Trinity:
   Father, Son, and Holy Spirit,
   God, our hope eternally.

5 Jesus Christ, the king of glory,
   Everlasting Son of God,
   Humble was your virgin mother,
   Hard the lonely path you trod:

6 By your cross is sin defeated,
   Hell confronted face to face,
   Heaven opened to believers,
   Sinners justified by grace.

7 Christ, at God's right hand victorious,
   You will judge the world you made;
   Lord, in mercy help your servants
   For whose freedom you have paid:

8 Raise us up from dust to glory,
   Guard us from all sin today;
   King enthroned above all praises,
   Save your people, God, we pray.

Words: Christopher Idle
© Christopher Idle / Jubilate Hymns
Music: 'Sixland', John Harper
© 1995 Panel of Monastic Musicians

Affirmation of Faith

We be-lieve in God the Fa-ther,

from whom ev-'ry fa-mil-y in hea-ven and on earth is named.

We be-lieve in God the Son,

who lives in our hearts through faith, and fills us with his love.

We be-lieve in God the Ho-ly Spi-rit,

who strength-ens us with pow-er from on high.

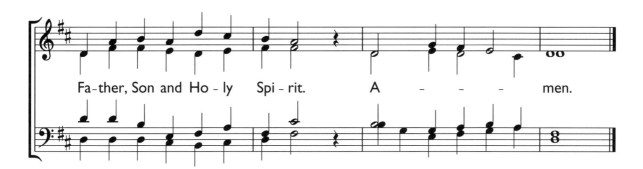

Words: Michael Perry, based on Ephesians 3
© Mrs B Perry / Jubilate Hymns
Music: John Harper
© 2000 The Royal School of Church Music

For other settings of the Creed, see pages 62 to 73.

Trisagion 1a

For use with high or low voices (or high and low voices together in 8 parts)

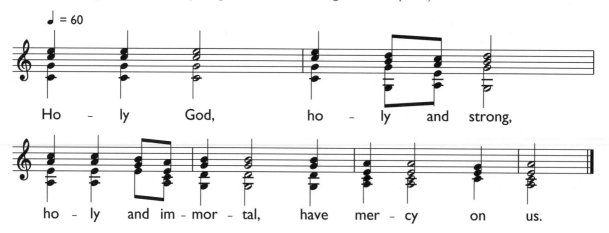

Ho - ly God, ho - ly and strong, ho - ly and im - mor - tal, have mer - cy on us.

Trisagion 1b

For use with congregation and/or small mixed choir

Ho - ly God, ho - ly and strong, ho - ly and im - mor - tal, have mer - cy on us.

Music: John Harper
© 2000 The Royal School of Church Music

Trisagion 2

Music: Richard Fabian
By permission of All Saints' Company

The Beatitudes

Re - joice and be glad for your re - ward is great in heaven.

Music: Peter Moger
© Peter Moger

1 Blessed are the ' poor in ' spirit,
   for theirs is the ' kingdom of ' heaven.

2 Blessed are ' those who ' mourn,
   for ' they shall be ' comforted.

3 Blessed ' are the ' meek,
   for they shall in'herit the ' earth.

4 Blessed are those who hunger and ' thirst after ' righteousness,
   for ' they shall be ' satisfied.

5 Blessed ' are the ' merciful,
   for ' they shall obtain ' mercy.

6 Blessed are the ' pure in ' heart,
   for ' they shall see ' God.

7 Blessed ' are the ' peacemakers,
   for they shall be called ' children of ' God.

8 Blessed are those who suffer persecution for ' righteousness' ' sake,
   for theirs is the ' kingdom of ' heaven.

Responses to the Litany

have mer - cy up - on us.

Good Lord, de - liv - er us.

Hear us, good Lord.

Lord, have mer - cy.

Holy God, holy and strong,

holy and im-mortal, have mer - cy up - on us.

Music: Traditional chant adapted by Robert Fielding
© Robert Fielding

'Holy God' may be sung in the harmonised version (Trisagion 1b) on page 260.

Music for Morning, Evening and Night Prayer

Music for Morning Prayer

The musical resources which follow should be used alongside the full text of Morning Prayer presented in Common Worship.

Preparation

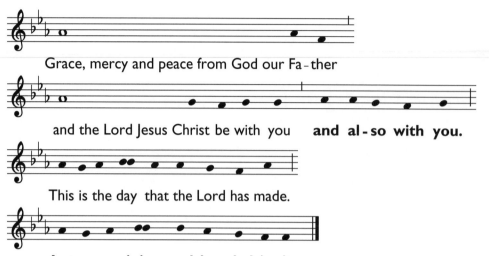

Grace, mercy and peace from God our Fa-ther

and the Lord Jesus Christ be with you   **and al-so with you.**

This is the day that the Lord has made.

Let us re-joice and be glad in it.

or

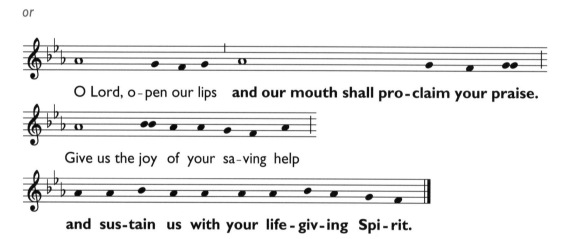

O Lord, o-pen our lips   **and our mouth shall pro-claim your praise.**

Give us the joy of your sa-ving help

and sus-tain us with your life-giv-ing Spi-rit.

Bless-ed is the Lord,   **for he has heard the voice of our prayer;**

therefore shall our hearts dance for joy

and in our song will we praise our God.

Prayer of Thanksgiving

Blessèd are you, Lord our God,   creator and redeem-er of all;

to you be glory and praise for ev - er.

From the waters of chaos you drew forth the world

and in your great love fashioned us in your im-age.

Now, through the deep wa-ters of death,

you have brought your people to new birth

by raising your Son to life in tri-umph.

May Christ your light ever dawn in our hearts

as we offer you our sacrifice of thanks and praise.

Blessèd be God, Fa-ther, Son and Ho-ly Spi-rit:

Bless-ed be God for ev - er.

1 O come, let us sing to the Lord;

let us heartily re‑joice in the rock of our sal‑vation.

2 Let us come into his pre‑sence with thanks‑giving

and be glad in him with psalms.

3 For the Lord is a great God   and a great king a‑bove all gods.

4 In his hands are the depths of the earth

and the heights of the mountains are his al‑so.

5 The sea is his, for he made it,   and his hands have moulded the dry land.

6 Come, let us worship and bow down   and kneel before the Lord our Ma‑ker.

7 For he is our God;

we are the people of his pas‑ture and the sheep of his hand.

Verses 8 to 11 may be omitted.

8   O that today you would listen to his voice:

'Harden not your hearts as at Me-ri-bah,

as on that day at Massah in the wil-der-ness,

9 'When your forbears tested me, and put me to the proof,

though they had seen my works

10 'Forty years I detested that generation and said,

"This people are wayward in their hearts;   they do not know my ways."

11 'So I swore in my wrath, "They shall not enter into my rest."'

Glo-ry to the Father and to the Son   and to the Ho-ly Spi-rit;

as it was in the beginning is now   and shall be for ev-er. A-men.

Further settings of the Venite and other opening songs may be found in the Anthology of Music for A Service of the Word.

The Word of God

Seasonal psalms and canticle may be found in the Anthology of Psalms and Canticles.

Responsory

A-wake, O sleep - er, and a - rise from the dead,

And Christ shall give you life.

A-wake, O sleep - er, and a - rise from the dead,

And Christ shall give you life.

You have died   and your life is hid with Christ in God.

A-wake, O sleep - er, and a - rise from the dead,

Set your minds on things that are a - bove.

not on things that are on the earth.

And Christ shall give you life.

When Christ our life ap - pears you will ap - pear with him in glo - ry.

A-wake, O sleep - er, and a - rise from the dead,

and Christ shall give you life.

The Gospel Canticle   Benedictus – the Song of Zechariah

¶ Bless – ed be the Lord the God of Is – rael,

who has come to his peo – ple and set them free.

¶ He has raised up for us a migh – ty Sa – viour,

born of the house of his ser – vant Da – vid.

¶ Through his holy prophets God promised of old

to save us from our e – ne – mies, from the hands of all that hate us,

To show mercy to our an – ces – tors, and to remember his ho – ly cov – en – ant.

¶ This was the oath God swore to our father A – bra – ham:

to set us free from the hands of our e – ne – mies,

Free to worship him with – out fear,

holy and righteous in his sight all the days of our life.

continued overleaf

¶ And you, child, shall be called the prophet of the Most High,

for you will go before the Lord to pre-pare his way,

To give his people knowledge of sal-va-tion

by the forgiveness of all their sins.

¶ In the tender compassion of our God

the dawn from on high shall break up-on us

To shine on those who dwell in dark-ness and the shadow of death,

and to guide our feet into the way of peace.

¶ Glo-ry to the Father and to the Son   and to the Ho-ly Spi-rit;

as it was in the beginning is now and shall be for ev-er.   A-men.

The Lord's Prayer

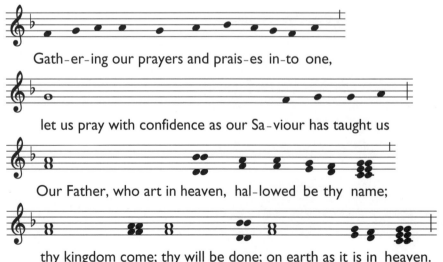

Gath-er-ing our prayers and prais-es in-to one,

let us pray with confidence as our Sa-viour has taught us

Our Father, who art in heaven, hal-lowed be thy name;

thy kingdom come; thy will be done; on earth as it is in heaven.

Give us this day our dai-ly bread.

And forgive us our tres-pass-es, as we forgive those who tres-pass a-gainst us.

And lead us not into temp-ta-tion; but deliver us from e-vil

For thine is the king-dom, the power, and the glo-ry

for ev-er and ev-er. A - men.

A modern language version of this setting of the Lord's Prayer may be found in Evening Prayer on page 280. Other settings may be found in the Anthology of Music for the Holy Communion, pages 94 to 100.

The Conclusion

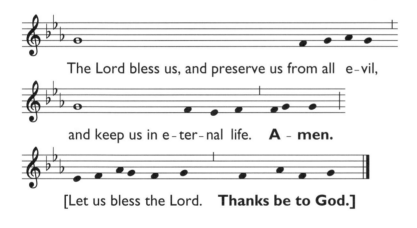

The Lord bless us, and preserve us from all e-vil,

and keep us in e-ter-nal life. **A - men.**

[Let us bless the Lord. **Thanks be to God.**]

or

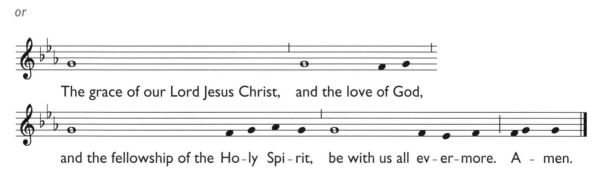

The grace of our Lord Jesus Christ, and the love of God,

and the fellowship of the Ho-ly Spi-rit, be with us all ev-er-more. A - men.

or The Peace, which may be found at the end of Evening Prayer on page 281.

Music: composed and adapted by John Harper
© 2000 The Royal School of Church Music

Music for Evening Prayer

The musical resources which follow should be used alongside the full text of Evening Prayer presented in Common Worship.

Preparation

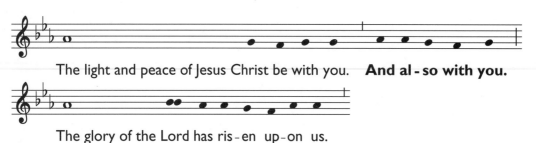

The light and peace of Jesus Christ be with you.   **And al‑so with you.**

The glory of the Lord has ris‑en up‑on us.

Let us re‑joice and sing God's praise for ev - er.

Prayer of Thanksgiving

Blessèd are you, sovereign God, our light and our sal‑va‑tion;

to you be glory and praise for ev - er.

You led your peo‑ple to free‑dom

by a pillar of cloud by day and a pillar of fire by night.

May we who walk in the light of your pre‑sence

acclaim your Christ, ris‑ing vic‑tor‑ious,

as he banishes all darkness from our hearts and minds.

Blessèd be God,   Fa‑ther, Son and Ho‑ly Spi‑rit:

Bless - ed be God for ev - er.

Verses from Psalm 141

Let my prayer rise before you as incense,

the lifting up of my hands as the evening sacrifice.

O Lord, I call to you; come to me quickly; hear my voice when I cry to you.

Set a watch before my mouth, O Lord, and guard the door of my lips.

Let my prayer rise before you as incense,

the lifting up of my hands as the evening sacrifice.

Let not my heart incline to any evil thing;

let me not be occupied with evil doers.

But my eyes are turned to you, Lord God; in you I take refuge;

do not leave me defenceless.

Let my prayer rise before you as incense,

the lifting up of my hands as the evening sacrifice.

Further settings of Phos hilaron, Verses from Psalm 141 and Verses from Psalm 104 may be found in the Anthology of Music for A Service of the Word, pages 225 to 234.

The Word of God

Seasonal psalms and canticle may be found in the Anthology of Psalms and Canticles.
Alternatively, the psalms and canticle may be read, and this doxology sung in unison, or as a canon.

To God the Fa – ther, God the Son, And God the Spi – rit, ev – er One,

All hon – our, praise and glo – ry be From age to age e – ter – nal – ly.

Responsory

The Lord is my light and my sal-va-tion; the Lord is the strength of my life.

The Lord is my light and my sal-va-tion; the Lord is the strength of my life.

The light shines in the dark-ness and the dark-ness has not o-ver-come it.

the Lord is the strength of my life.

Glo – ry to the Fa-ther, and to the Son, and to the Ho – ly Spi – rit.

The Lord is my light and my sal-va-tion; the Lord is the strength of my life.

The Gospel Canticle

¶ My soul proclaims the greatness of the Lord: my spirit rejoices in God my sa-viour;

he has looked with favour on his low-ly ser-vant.

¶ From this day all generations will call me bless-ed;

the Almighty has done great things for me: and ho-ly is his name.

¶ He has mercy on those who fear him: from genera-tion to gen-er-a-tion.

¶ He has shown strength with his arm: and has scattered the proud in their con-ceit,

casting down the mighty from their thrones: and lift-ing up the low-ly.

¶ He has filled the hun-gry with good things: and sent the rich a-way emp-ty.

¶ He has come to the aid of his ser-vant Is-rael: to remember his pro-mise of mer-cy,

the promise made to our an-ces-tors, to Abraham and his chil-dren for ev - er.

¶ Glo-ry to the Father and to the Son and to the Ho-ly Spi-rit;

as it was in the begin-ning is now and shall be for ev - er. A-men.

The Lord's Prayer

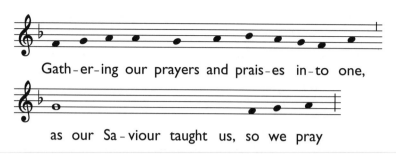

Gath-er-ing our prayers and prais-es in-to one,

as our Sa-viour taught us, so we pray

Our Father in heaven, hallowed be your name,

your kingdom come, your will be done, on earth as in heaven.

Give us today our dai-ly bread.

Forgive us our sins as we forgive those who sin a-gainst us.

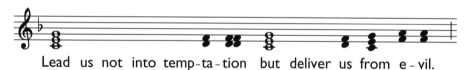

Lead us not into temp-ta-tion but deliver us from e-vil.

For the kingdom, the power, and the glo-ry are yours

now and for ev-er. A-men.

A traditional language version of this setting of the Lord's Prayer may be found in Morning Prayer on page 274. Other settings may be found in the Anthology of Music for the Holy Communion, pages 94 to 100.

The Conclusion

May the peace of God, which passes all un-der-stand-ing,

keep our hearts and minds in Christ Je - sus.   **A - men.**

The peace of the Lord be al-ways with you.

And also with you.

(Let us offer each other a sign of peace, God's seal on our prayers.)

or The Blessing or The Grace, found at the end of Morning Prayer on page 275.

Music: composed and adapted by John Harper
© 2000 The Royal School of Church Music

Music for Night Prayer

The musical resources which follow should be used alongside the full text of Night Prayer presented in Common Worship.

The Preparation

O God, make speed to save us. **O Lord, make haste to help us.**

Glory to the Fa-ther and to the Son and to the Ho-ly Spi-rit;

as it was in the begin-ning is now and shall be for ever. A-men.

Al - le - lu - ia.

Hymn

ferial tone

1 Be-fore the end-ing of the day, Cre-a-tor of the world, we pray

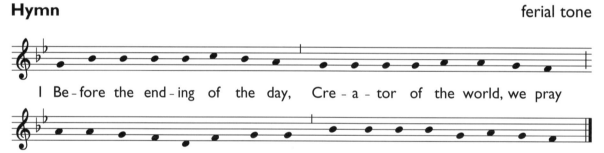

That you, with stead-fast love, would keep Your watch a-round us while we sleep.

2 From evil dreams defend our sight,
From fears and terrors of the night;
Tread underfoot our deadly foe
That we no sinful thought may know.

3 O Father, that we ask be done
Through Jesus Christ, your only Son;
And Holy Spirit, by whose breath
Our souls are raised to life from death.

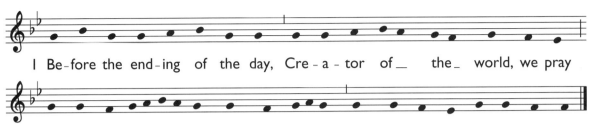

1 Be-fore the end-ing of the day, Cre-a-tor of _ the _ world, we pray

That you, with stead - fast love, would keep_ Your watch a-round us while we sleep.

2 From evil dreams defend our sight,
From fears and terrors of the night;
Tread underfoot our deadly foe
That we no sinful thought may know.

3 O Father, that we ask be done
Through Jesus Christ, your only Son;
And Holy Spirit, by whose breath
Our souls are raised to life from death.

The Word of God

Psalm 4

1 Answer me when I call, O God of my ' righteousness; ♦
you set me at liberty when I was in trouble;
have mercy on ' me and hear my prayer.

2 How long will you nobles dishonour my ' glory; ♦
how long will you love vain things and seek ' after falsehood?

3 But know that the Lord has shown me his marvellous ' kindness; ♦
when I call upon the Lord, ' he will hear me.

4 Stand in awe, and ' sin not; ♦
commune with your own heart upon your ' bed, and be still.

5 Offer the sacrifices of ' righteousness ♦
and put your ' trust in the Lord.

6 There are many that say, 'Who will show us ' any good?' ♦
Lord, lift up the light of your counten'ance upon us.

7 You have put gladness ' in my heart, ♦
more than when their corn and ' wine and oil increase.

8 In peace I will lie down ' and sleep, ♦
for it is you Lord, only, who make me ' dwell in safety.

Psalm 91

1 Whoever dwells in the shelter of the ' Most High ♦
and abides under the shadow of ' the Almighty,

2 Shall say to the Lord, 'My refuge and my ' stronghold, ♦
my God, in ' whom I put my trust.'

3 For he shall deliver you from the snare of the ' fowler ♦
and from the ' deadly pestilence.

4 He shall cover you with his wings
and you shall be safe under his ' feathers; ♦
his faithfulness shall be your ' shield and buckler.

5 You shall not be afraid of any terror ' by night, ♦
nor of the ar'row that flies by day;

6 Of the pestilence that stalks in ' darkness, ♦
nor of the sickness that des'troys at noonday.

7 Though a thousand fall at your side
and ten thousand at ' your right hand, ♦
yet it shall ' not come near you.

8 Your eyes have only ' to behold ♦
to see the reward ' of the wicked.

9 Because you have made the Lord your ' refuge ♦
and the Most ' High your stronghold,

10 There shall no evil happen ' to you, ♦
neither shall any ' plague come near your tent.

11 For he shall give his angels charge ' over you, ♦
to keep ' you in all your ways.

12 They shall bear you ' in their hands, ♦
lest you dash your ' foot against a stone.

13 You shall tread upon the lion and ' adder; ♦
the young lion and the serpent you shall ' trample underfoot.

14 Because they have set their love upon me,
therefore will I de'liver them; ♦
I will lift them up, be'cause they know my name.

15 They will call upon me and I will ' answer them; ♦
I am with them in trouble,
I will deliver them and bring ' them to honour.

16 With long life will I satis'fy them ♦
and show them ' my salvation.

Psalm 134

1 Come, bless the Lord, all you servants ' of the Lord, ♦
you that by night stand in the ' house of the Lord.

2 Lift up your hands towards the ' sanctuary ♦
and ' blëss the Lord.

3 The Lord who made heaven ' and earth ♦
give you blessing ' out of Zion.

Glory to the Father and ' to the Son
and to the ' Holy Spirit;
as it was in the beginning ' is now
and shall be for ' ever. Amen.

Responsory

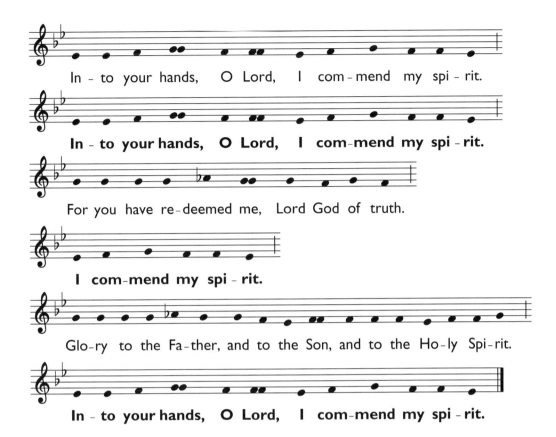

In – to your hands,   O Lord,   I com – mend my spi – rit.

In – to your hands,   O Lord,   I com – mend my spi – rit.

For you have re – deemed me,   Lord God of truth.

I com – mend my spi – rit.

Glo – ry to the Fa – ther, and to the Son, and to the Ho – ly Spi – rit.

In – to your hands,   O Lord,   I com – mend my spi – rit.

Keep me as the apple of your eye.   *or* eye. _____

Hide me under the shadow of your wings.   *or* **wings.** _____

The Gospel Canticle   Nunc dimittis – the Song of Simeon

Antiphon

Save us, O Lord, while wak-ing, and guard us while sleep-ing,

that a-wake we may watch with Christ and a-sleep may rest in peace.

Canticle

1 Now, Lord, you let your ser-vant go in peace:

your word has been ful-filled.

2 My own eyes have seen the sal-va-tion

which you have prepared in the sight of ev'-ry peo-ple;

3 A light to re-veal you to the na-tions

and the glory of your peo-ple Is-rael.

Glo-ry to the Fa-ther and to the Son and to the Ho-ly Spi-rit;

as it was in the begin-ning is now and shall be for ev-er. A-men.

Antiphon

Save us, O Lord, while wak-ing, and guard us while sleep-ing,

that a-wake we may watch with Christ and a-sleep may rest in peace.

The Collect

Prayer   end-ing   **A - men.**

Versions of the Lord's Prayer may be found in Morning Prayer (page 274), Evening Prayer (page 280) and in the Anthology of Music for the Holy Communion (pages 94 to 100).

The Conclusion

In peace, we will lie down and sleep;

For you alone, Lord, make us dwell in safe - ty.

Abide with us, Lord Je - sus,

For the night is at hand and the day is now past.

As the night-watch looks for the morn - ing,

So do we look for you, O Christ.

The Lord bless us and watch over us;

the Lord make his face shine upon us and be gracious to us;

the Lord look kindly on us and give us peace.   **A - men.**

Music: adapted from traditional chant
© 2000 The Royal School of Church Music

¶ *Part Four*

Anthology of Psalms and Canticles

Psalms and scriptural songs (i.e. canticles) are specified throughout the Lectionary for use at both Holy Communion and at A Service of the Word, including Morning, Evening and Night Prayer. It is impossible to include all the psalms and canticles in this volume. What is offered here is a selection of psalms and canticles for the principal seasons of the year. This selection includes 27 psalms and 14 canticles. In addition there are eight 'psalm songs' – metrical psalms in a lyrical style with refrain.

The psalms and canticles are grouped by season, though their use need not necessarily restricted to the season in which they are placed. The pattern of distribution can be observed in the Table of Psalms and Canticles by Season and Service on page 412.

The Gospel canticles and further psalms which have a special place in Morning, Evening and Night Prayer supplement this selection, and are found in Part Three of the volume, *Anthology of Music for A Service of the Word*.

Guidance on singing the psalms and canticles is included below, and in the Notes near the beginning of the book, on page 8.

Singing the *Common Worship* texts of the psalms and canticles

Psalms and canticles are translated in irregular prose in *Common Worship*, and this means that there is no easy and accessible way of singing them: a melody that will work well for one verse just will not fit the next. Therefore these texts require a musical setting which accommodates the irregular pattern of the text, and uses a form of melody which can be remembered.

Different ways of chanting are offered which, with preparation and patience, can engage everyone in singing. There are two settings of each psalm and canticle, so that there is always a choice of the way of chanting.

Four ways of chanting psalms and canticles are offered.

A simple form of plainsong
The eight ancient psalm tones have been simplified, and their treatment regularised so that the melody remains unchanged from verse to verse. Each of the eight psalm tones is allocated to a specific season, with two tones for Ordinary Time. Some tones have more notes than others, so they are not necessarily interchangeable.

On ways of singing the psalms, the use of refrains, and interpreting pointing, see below.

Anglican chant
Anglican chant derived originally from harmonised versions of plainsong tones (generally with the tone in a middle voice). Now it is regularised and independent of the plainsong. It has been the normative Anglican way of singing the prose texts of psalms since the late seventeenth century.

All the chants selected here are 'single' (i.e. the melody is sung to a single verse, whereas 'double' chants extend over two verses). They have reciting notes which are comfortable for most people to sing without strain, and the melodic patterns are straightforward. For those who wish to use a repertory of double chants, the sign ‡ has been included to indicate verses where it is necessary to repeat the second part of the chant to accommodate an odd number of verses.

'Cantor chants'
These chants originated as tones for solo cantor with optional gentle accompaniment, but they can be sung in harmony where there is the resource and the skill. The chant is sung over two verses; occasionally it is necessary to repeat the second part of the chant where there is an odd number of verses in the psalm or section of the psalm. This is indicated by the sign ‡.

Simple chants
These chants reduce the Anglican principle to the bare minimum – a reciting chord with an ending chord in the first part of the verse, and then a reciting note with two concluding chords in the second part of the verse. They can be sung in unison or in harmony, with or without accompaniment. For a church unused to singing the psalms and canticles they offer a very simple and almost foolproof solution.

Appendix of pointed texts

There is an appendix of frequently-used texts pointed for use with Anglican chant.

Using the refrains

Common Worship does not include texts for refrains, but suitable refrains have been suggested here. They need to be used with purpose: it is little help if a congregation is offered no more than the text of the refrain and remains unaware of the main thrust of the text of the psalm.

It is common these days to refer to the psalm after the first reading in Holy Communion as 'the responsorial psalm'. It is responsorial because it is sung in response to the first reading, not because it has a refrain or response for the people to sing. The whole psalm is therefore the response, and where possible it is good for all to share in the whole text.

In the plainsong and cantor chant settings there is a composed refrain. In the Anglican and simple chant settings there is a pointed version to be sung to the same chant as the rest of the psalm.

The refrain can be used in several ways. It can be sung at the beginning and end of the psalm only, allowing a focus for the psalm text but not interrupting the main text. Or it can be sung repetitively through the psalm – either after every two verses, or every four verses, or where the natural breaks in the psalm text occur. At the beginning of the psalm it is a good idea for a cantor or choral group to sing the refrain before it is repeated by everyone; thereafter it is best just to sing the refrain once with everyone.

The doxology

The rubric at the beginning of the *Common Worship* psalter indicates that the doxology 'Glory to the Father' is sung at the end of every psalm, section of a psalm, or group of psalms. The doxology is included at the end of every psalm and canticle in the selection. However, it is customary to omit the doxology at the end of the psalm after the first reading at Holy Communion.

Encouraging the singing of psalms and canticles

Ideally the psalms and canticles are songs 'owned' and sung by all God's people. If everyone is to sing the psalm text with confidence they need to be familiar with the text, with the rhythm of the text, and with the chant. That may well define a successive process of familiarisation over several weeks: hearing the psalm read as a spoken text, reciting the psalm together as a spoken text, hearing the psalm sung by a single voice or small group which has prepared it, and finally singing the psalm together. Developing this confidence in psalm singing is very important: psalms sung tentatively and badly are demoralising for the singers and painful for the listener.

There are several other ways of singing the psalms. In the case of the plainsong, Anglican and simple chants, verses may be sung alternately – first by a cantor or small group, then by all; but where the psalm is familiar the singing might be shared between one half of the assembly and the other, all singing the doxology. This method is also suitable in the 'single' form of the cantor chants, where the whole melody is sung through in one verse.

The 'double' cantor chants may be sung by everyone all the way through, by alternate verses (when everyone knows the melody of the whole chant). When the refrain is used there is always the option of using a cantor for the verses, and the refrain for all assembled. This may be the best solution on occasions when there are large numbers of visitors at service. However, it is worth emphasising ownership of the whole psalm text by all present.

Even quite experienced choral groups sing unfamiliar psalms with greater flow, cohesion and confidence when they sing in unison. In the early stages it is good to sing psalms in unison (and even unaccompanied) until the flow is established; then move on to singing in harmonies.

Interpreting the text layout and the pointing

The text of the psalter in *Common Worship* is presented in a way which should assist recitation. In most cases a verse consists of two lines, with a red diamond ♦ to indicate the mid-point where there is a short pause or break. Where there are three or more lines, the indented line is also followed by a break, but shorter than at the mid-point. For the most part commas within a line of a verse should be ignored; the syllable before the comma might be lengthened, but the recitation should not be fragmented by the 'tyranny' of the comma.

In singing the text these same principles apply, as does the need to keep the recitation moving forward. The articulation of the text is paramount. It needs always to be musical, and never turgid.

The four methods of chanting each have their own scheme of pointing, all based on the use of similar signs. Signs are printed in red. They must not become obstacles which stop the flow of the chanting!

I A simple form of plainsong

Each tone begins with an intonation – the notes in square brackets at the beginning of the tone. This intonation is used only in verse one in psalms and psalm canticles. (It is used in all verses of a Gospel Canticle.)

A single sign ' is used to indicate where the note is changed. Change from the reciting note immediately after the sign. Sing each syllable after the sign to the next note of the tone. If there is an additional syllable at the end of the verse or half verse, sing it to the last note of the tone (i.e. two syllables to the last note where necessary). The note after the sign will rarely be placed on a stressed syllable. The pointing takes account of the stress in the chant.

A written-out version of three verses from Psalm 98 illustrates the principle.

The psalm tone appears in this form on page 348:

and the psalm verses are pointed like this:

1   Sing to the Lord a ' new song, ♦
    for he has done ' marvellous things.

3   The Lord has made known his sal'vation; ♦
    his deliverance has he openly shown in the sight ' of the nations.

6   Make music to the Lord ' with the lyre, ♦
    with the lyre and the ' voice of melody.

These verses are sung as follows:

verse 1, sung with the intonation

Sing to the Lord a ' new song, ♦ for he has done ' mar-vel-lous things.

verse 3, which follows the normal tone pattern

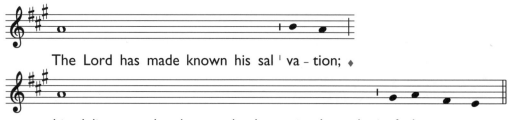

The Lord has made known his sal ' va – tion; ♦

his deliverance has he openly shown in the sight ' of the na – tions.

and verse 6, where it is necessary to repeat the last note of the tone – in this case at both the half verse, and at the end of the verse.

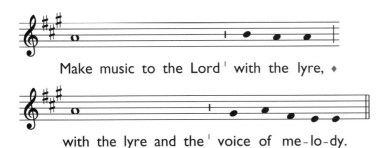

Make music to the Lord ' with the lyre, ◆

with the lyre and the ' voice of me‑lo‑dy.

It is customary to take a long breath at the mid-point of each verse. The note after the vertical dash is normally stressed in the first part of this tone (tone 8), but not in the second part. The patterns of English sometimes result in a weak syllable on a stressed note. In verse 6, for instance, the stress is on 'Lord', before the dash.

2 Anglican chant

The vertical dashes ' in the text correspond with those in the chant. Where there are three syllables between two dashes the first two are normally sung to the first chord of the bar, the last to the second chord of the bar. The exception occurs where there is a 'dot' · after the first syllable: always change to the second chord after the dot. Occasionally there is a single syllable between two dashes; then both chords are sung to this syllable. The chants are distributed seasonally, and are all 'single'. For those wishing to use 'double' chants, the sign ‡ indicates a verse where it is necessary to repeat the second half of the chant.

3 Cantor chants

These chants are presented in two forms, 'single' and 'double'. The double chant is sung over two verses; occasionally it is necessary to repeat the second part of the chant where there is an odd number of verses in the psalm or section of the psalm. This is indicated by the sign ‡.

As in Anglican chant, the vertical dashes in the text correspond with those in the chant. Where there are three syllables between two dashes the first two are normally sung to the first note after the dash, the last to the second note. The exception occurs where there is a 'dot' · after the first syllable: always change to the second note after the dot. Occasionally there is a single syllable between two dashes; then both notes are sung to this syllable.

4 Simple chants

The conventions of Anglican and Cantor chants apply here too (see above), but there are only five or six chords. A single sign ' indicates the point at which the chord changes.

Further guidance on the presentation of notation and on singing pointed texts may be found at the beginning of the volume, page 8.

Psalm Songs

Eight psalm songs are included for use during the main seasons of the year. Since the sixteenth century, psalms have been translated into metre, integrating them more readily with the vernacular traditions of Western song. In some denominations metrical psalms have been part of their worship since those times, in others they have been more recent. The Anglican Church has only recently started to substitute liturgical psalm texts by metrical translations (though of course many have been used within the hymn repertory), and the selection here responds to that practice. They are particularly suited to special occasions. Overuse or over-embellishment may destroy their freshness and strength.

Advent

Psalm 80

1   Hear, O Shepherd ' of Israel, ♦
       you that led Joseph ' like a flock;

2   Shine forth, you that are enthroned upon ' the cherubim, ♦
       before Ephraim, Benjamin and Ma'nasseh.

3   Stir up ' your mighty strength ♦
       and come to our sal'vation.

4   Turn us ' again, O God; ♦
       show the light of your countenance, and we ' shall be saved.

5   O ' Lord God of hosts, ♦
       how long will you be angry at your ' people's prayer?

6   You feed them with ' the bread of tears; ♦
       you give them abundance of ' tears to drink.

7   You have made us the derision of ' our neighbours, ♦
       and our enemies laugh us ' to scorn.

8   Turn us again, ' O God of hosts; ♦
       show the light of your countenance, and we ' shall be saved.

9   You brought a vine out ' of Egypt; ♦
       you drove out the nations and ' planted it.

10   You made room ' around it, ♦
       and when it had taken root, it ' filled the land.

11   The hills were covered with ' its shadow ♦
       and the cedars of God ' by its boughs.

12   It stretched out its bran'ches to the Sea ♦
       and its tendrils to the ' River.

13   Why then have you bro'ken down its wall, ♦
       so that all who pass by pluck ' off its grapes?

14   The wild boar out of the wood ' tears it off, ♦
       and all the insects of the field de'vour it.

15   Turn again, ' O God of hosts, ♦
       look down from heaven ' and behold;

16   Cherish this vine which your right hand ' has planted, ♦
       and the branch that you made so strong ' for yourself.

17   Let those who burnt it with fire, ' who cut it down, ♦
       perish at the rebuke of your ' countenance.

18   Let your hand be upon the man at ' your right hand, ♦
       the son of man you made so strong ' for yourself.

19   And so will we not ' go back from you; ♦
       give us life, and we shall call up'on your name.

20   Turn us again, O ' Lord God of hosts; ♦
       show the light of your countenance, and we ' shall be saved.

       Glory to the Father ' and to the Son
       and to the Holy ' Spirit;
       as it was in the begin'ning is now
       and shall be for ever. ' Amen.

Optional Refrain

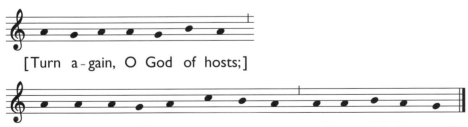

[Turn a-gain, O God of hosts;]

Show the light of your coun-ten-ance: and we shall be saved.

Music: adapted from traditional chant, tone 4
© 2000 The Royal School of Church Music

Psalm 80

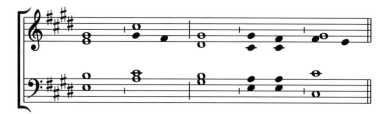

1 Hear, O Shepherd of ' Israel, ♦
you that led Joseph ' like a ' flock;

2 Shine forth, you that are enthroned upon the ' cherubim, ♦
before Ephraim, Benjamin ' and Ma'nasseh.

3 Stir up your mighty ' strength ♦
and come to ' our sal'vation.

4 Turn us again, O ' God; ♦
show the light of your countenance, and ' we shall be ' saved.

5 O Lord God of ' hosts, ♦
how long will you be angry at your ' people's ' prayer?

6 You feed them with the bread of ' tears; ♦
you give them abundance of ' tears to ' drink.

7 You have made us the derision of our ' neighbours, ♦
and our enemies ' laugh us to ' scorn.

8 Turn us again, O God of ' hosts; ♦
show the light of your countenance, and ' we shall be ' saved.

9 You brought a vine out of ' Egypt; ♦
you drove out the ' nations and ' planted it.

10 You made room a'round it, ♦
and when it had taken root, it ' filled the ' land.

11 The hills were covered with its ' shadow ♦
and the cedars of ' God by its ' boughs.

12 It stretched out its branches to the ' Sea ♦
and its tendrils ' to the ' River.

13 Why then have you broken down its ' wall, ♦
so that all who pass by ' pluck off its ' grapes?

14 The wild boar out of the wood tears it ' off, ♦
and all the insects of the ' field de'vour it.

15 Turn again, O God of ' hosts, ♦
look down from heaven ' and be'hold;

16 Cherish this vine which your right hand has ' planted, ♦
and the branch that you made so ' strong for your'self.

17 Let those who burnt it with fire, who cut it ' down, ♦
perish at the re'buke of your ' countenance.

18 Let your hand be upon the man at your ' right hand, ♦
the son of man you made so ' strong for your'self.

19 And so will we not go ' back from you; ♦
give us life, and we shall ' call upon your ' name.

20 Turn us again, O Lord God of ' hosts; ♦
show the light of your countenance, and ' we shall be ' saved.

Glory to the Father and to the ' Son
and to the ' Holy ' Spirit;
as it was in the beginning is ' now
and shall be for ' ever. A'men.

Optional Refrain

Turn us again, O God of ' hosts; ♦
show the light of your countenance, and ' we shall be ' saved.

or

Show the light of your ' countenance, | and ' we shall be ' saved.

Chant: Norman Warren
© Norman Warren

Psalm 122

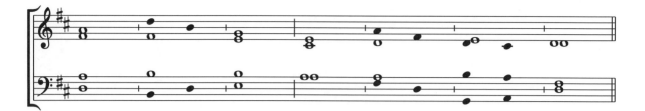

1 I was glad when they ' said to ' me, ♦
   'Let us ' go · to the ' house of the ' Lord.'

2 And now our ' feet are ' standing ♦
   within your ' gates, ' O Je'rusalem;

3 Jerusalem, ' built as a ' city ♦
   that is at ' unity ' in it'self.

4 Thither the tribes go up, the ' tribes of the ' Lord, ♦
   as is decreed for Israel,
      to give ' thanks · to the ' name of the ' Lord.

‡ 5 For there are set the ' thrones of ' judgement, ♦
   the ' thrones of the ' house of ' David.

6 O pray for the ' peace of Je'rusalem: ♦
   'May they ' prosper who ' love ' you.

7 'Peace be wi'thin your ' walls ♦
   and tran'quillity with'in your ' palaces.'

8 For my kindred and com'panions' ' sake, ♦
   I will ' pray that ' peace be ' with you.

9 For the sake of the house of the ' Lord our ' God, ♦
   I will ' seek to ' do you ' good.

Glory to the Father and ' to the ' Son
and ' to the ' Holy ' Spirit;
as it was in the be'ginning is ' now
and shall be for ' ever. ' A'men.

Optional Refrain

I was glad when they ' said to ' me: ♦
'Let us ' go · to the ' house of the ' Lord.'

Chant: Frederick A G Ouseley

Psalm 122

1 I was glad when they ' said to ' me, ◆
  'Let us go to the ' house of the ' Lord.'

2 And now our ' feet are ' standing ◆
  within your gates, ' O Je'rusalem;

3 Jerusalem, ' built as a ' city ◆
  that is at unity ' in it'self.

4 Thither the tribes go up, the ' tribes of the ' Lord, ◆
  as is decreed for Israel,
    to give thanks to the ' name of the ' Lord.

‡ 5 For there are set the ' thrones of ' judgement, ◆
  the thrones of the ' house of ' David.

6 O pray for the ' peace of Je'rusalem: ◆
  'May they ' prosper who ' love you.

7 'Peace be with'in your ' walls ◆
  and tranquillity with'in your ' palaces.'

8 For my kindred and com'panions' ' sake, ◆
  I will pray that ' peace be ' with you.

9 For the sake of the house of the ' Lord our ' God, ◆
  I will seek to ' do you ' good.

Glory to the Father ' and to the ' Son
and to the ' Holy ' Spirit;
as it was in the be'ginning is ' now
and shall be for ' ever. A'men.

Optional Refrain

I was glad when they said to me, 'Let us go to the house of the Lord.'

Music: Peter Moger
© 2000 Peter Moger

Psalm 126

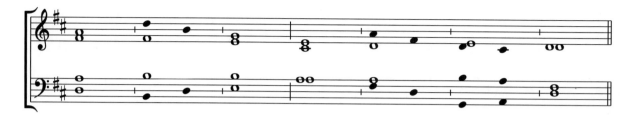

1 When the Lord restored the ' fortunes of ' Zion, ♦
  then were ' we like ' those who ' dream.

2 Then was our mouth ' filled with ' laughter ♦
  and our ' tongue with ' songs of ' joy.

3 Then said they a'mong the ' nations, ♦
  'The Lord has ' done great ' things for ' them.'

4 The Lord has indeed done ' great things for ' us, ♦
  and ' therefore ' we re'joiced.

5 Restore again our ' fortunes, O ' Lord, ♦
  as the ' river beds ' of the ' desert.

6 Those who ' sow in ' tears ♦
  shall ' reap with ' songs of ' joy.

‡ 7 Those who go out weeping, ' bearing the ' seed, ♦
  will come back with shouts of joy,
      ' bearing their ' sheaves ' with them.

Glory to the Father and ' to the ' Son
and ' to the ' Holy ' Spirit;
as it was in the be'ginning is ' now
and shall be for ' ever. ' A'men.

Optional Refrain

The Lord has done ' great things for ' us, ♦
and ' therefore ' we re'joice.

Chant: Frederick A G Ouseley

Psalm 126

1 When the Lord restored the ' fortunes of ' Zion, ♦
   then were we like ' those who ' dream.

2 Then was our mouth ' filled with ' laughter ♦
   and our tongue with ' songs of ' joy.

3 Then said they a'mong the ' nations, ♦
   'The Lord has done ' great things for ' them.'

4 The Lord has indeed done ' great things for ' us, ♦
   and therefore ' we re'joiced.

5 Restore again our ' fortunes, O ' Lord, ♦
   as the river beds ' of the ' desert.

6 Those who ' sow in ' tears ♦
   shall reap with ' songs of ' joy.

‡ 7 Those who go out weeping, ' bearing the ' seed, ♦
   will come back with shouts of joy,
      bearing their ' sheaves ' with them.

Glory to the Father ' and to the ' Son
and to the ' Holy ' Spirit;
as it was in the be'ginning is ' now
and shall be for ' ever. A'men.

Optional Refrain

The Lord has done great things for us; there-fore we re- joice.

Music: Peter Moger
© 2000 Peter Moger

A Song of the Wilderness

1 The wilderness and the dry land ' shall rejoice, ♦
  the desert shall blossom and ' burst into song.

2 They shall see the glory ' of the Lord, ♦
  the ma'jesty of our God.

3 Strengthen the ' weary hands, ♦
  and make ' firm the feeble knees.

4 Say to the anxious, 'Be strong, fear not,
      your God is coming with ' judgement, ♦
  coming with judge'ment to save you.'

5 Then shall the eyes of the blind be ' opened, ♦
  and the ears ' of the deaf unstopped;

6 Then shall the lame leap ' like a hart, ♦
  and the tongue of the ' dumb sing for joy.

7 For waters shall break forth in the ' wilderness, ♦
  and streams ' in the desert;

8 The ransomed of the Lord shall return with ' singing, ♦
  with everlasting ' joy upon their heads.

9 Joy and gladness ' shall be theirs, ♦
  and sorrow and sigh'ing shall flee away.

  Glory to the Father and ' to the Son
  and to the ' Holy Spirit;
  as it was in the beginning ' is now
  and shall be for ' ever. Amen.

Isaiah 35.1,2b-4a,4c-6,10

Optional Refrain

The ran-somed of the Lord shall re-turn,

and sor-row and sigh-ing shall flee a-way.

Music: adapted from traditional chant, tone 5
© 2000 The Royal School of Church Music

A Song of the Wilderness

1 The wilderness and the dry land shall re'joice, ♦
the desert shall blossom and ' burst into ' song.

2 They shall see the glory of the ' Lord, ♦
the majesty ' of our ' God.

3 Strengthen the weary ' hands, ♦
and make firm the ' feeble ' knees.

4 Say to the anxious, 'Be strong, fear not,
your God is coming with ' judgement, ♦
coming with ' judgement to ' save you.'

5 Then shall the eyes of the blind be ' opened, ♦
and the ears of the ' deaf un'stopped;

6 Then shall the lame leap like a ' hart, ♦
and the tongue of the dumb ' sing for ' joy.

7 For waters shall break forth in the ' wilderness, ♦
and ' streams in the ' desert;

8 The ransomed of the Lord shall return with ' singing, ♦
with everlasting joy up'on their ' heads.

9 Joy and gladness shall be ' theirs, ♦
and sorrow and sighing shall ' flee a'way.

Glory to the Father and to the ' Son
and to the ' Holy ' Spirit;
as it was in the be'ginning is ' now
and shall be for ' ever. A'men.

Isaiah 35.1,2b-4a,4c-6,10

Optional Refrain

The ransomed of the Lord shall re'turn, ♦
and sorrow and sighing shall ' flee a'way.

Chant: Norman Warren
© Norman Warren

A Song of the Spirit

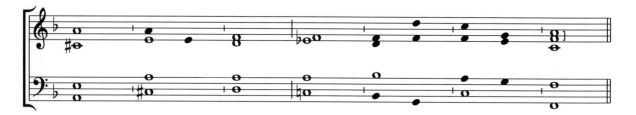

1 'Behold, I am coming soon', says the Lord,
    'and bringing my re'ward with ' me, ♦
    to give to everyone ac'cording ' to their ' deeds.

2 'I am the Alpha and the Omega, the first ' and the ' last, ♦
    the be'ginning ' and the ' end.'

3 Blessed are those who do God's commandments,
    that they may have the right to the ' tree of ' life, ♦
    and may enter into the ' city ' through the ' gates.

4 'I, Jesus, have sent my ' angel to ' you, ♦
    with this ' testimony for ' all the ' churches.

5 'I am the root and the ' offspring of ' David, ♦
    I am the ' bright ' morning ' star.'

6 'Come!' say the Spirit ' and the ' Bride; ♦
    'Come!' ' let each ' hearer re'ply!

7 Come forward, ' you who are ' thirsty, ♦
    let those who desire take the ' water of ' life · as a ' gift.

    Surely I am ' coming ' soon! ♦
    A'-men! ' Come, Lord ' Jesus!

Revelation 22.12-14, 16, 17

Optional Refrain

Surely I am ' coming ' soon! ♦
A'-men! ' Come, Lord ' Jesus!

Chant: Martindale Sidwell

A Song of the Spirit

1 'Behold, I am coming soon', says the Lord,
    'and bringing my re˙ward with ˙ me, ◆
  to give to everyone according ˙ to their ˙ deeds.

2 'I am the Alpha and the Omega, the first ˙ and the ˙ last, ◆
  the beginning ˙ and the ˙ end.'

3 Blessed are those who do God's commandments,
    that they may have the right to the ˙ tree of ˙ life, ◆
  and may enter into the city ˙ through the ˙ gates.

4 'I, Jesus, have sent my ˙ angel to ˙ you, ◆
  with this testimony for ˙ all the ˙ churches.

5 'I am the root and the ˙ offspring of ˙ David, ◆
  I am the bright ˙ morning ˙ star.'

6 'Come!' say the Spirit ˙ and the ˙ Bride; ◆
  'Come!' let each ˙ hearer re˙ply!

7 Come forward, ˙ you who are ˙ thirsty, ◆
  let those who desire take the water of ˙ life as a ˙ gift.

Surely I am ˙ coming ˙ soon! ◆
Amen! ˙ Come, Lord ˙ Jesus!

Revelation 22.12-14, 16, 17

Optional Refrain

Music: Peter Moger
© 2000 Peter Moger

Christmas

Psalm 96

1 Sing to the Lord a ' new song; ◆
  sing to the ' Lord, all the earth.

2 Sing to the Lord and ' bless his name; ◆
  tell out his salvation ' from day to day.

3 Declare his glory among the ' nations ◆
  and his wonders among ' all peoples.

4 For great is the Lord and greatly ' to be praised; ◆
  he is more to be feared ' than all gods.

5 For all the gods of the nations are but ' idols; ◆
  it is the Lord ' who made the heavens.

6 Honour and majesty are be'fore him; ◆
  power and splendour are in ' his sanctuary.

7 Ascribe to the Lord, you families of the ' peoples; ◆
  ascribe to the Lord ho'nour and strength.

8 Ascribe to the Lord the honour due ' to his name; ◆
  bring offerings and come in'to his courts.

9 O worship the Lord in the beauty of ' holiness; ◆
  let the whole earth tremble ' before him.

10 Tell it out among the nations that the ' Lord is king. ◆
   He has made the world so firm that it cannot be moved;
      he will judge the peoples ' with equity.

11 Let the heavens rejoice and let the ' earth be glad; ◆
   let the sea thunder and all that ' is in it;

12 Let the fields be joyful and all that is ' in them; ◆
   let all the trees of the wood shout for joy ' before the Lord.

13 For he comes, he comes to ' judge the earth; ◆
   with righteousness he will judge the world
      and the peo'ples with his truth.

   Glory to the Father and ' to the Son
   and to the Ho'ly Spirit;
   as it was in the beginning ' is now
   and shall be for ev'er. Amen.

Optional Refrain 1

Great is the Lord: and great-ly to be praised.

Optional Refrain 2

To you is born this day a sa-viour; who is Christ the Lord.

Music: adapted from traditional chant, tone 2
© 2000 The Royal School of Church Music

Psalm 96

1　Sing to the Lord a new ' song; ♦
　　sing to the Lord, ' all the ' earth.

2　Sing to the Lord and bless his ' name; ♦
　　tell out his salvation from ' day to ' day.

3　Declare his glory among the ' nations ♦
　　and his wonders a'mong all ' peoples.

4　For great is the Lord and greatly to be ' praised; ♦
　　he is more to be ' feared than all ' gods.

5　For all the gods of the nations are but ' idols; ♦
　　it is the Lord who ' made the ' heavens.

6　Honour and majesty are be'fore him; ♦
　　power and splendour are ' in his ' sanctuary.

7　Ascribe to the Lord, you families of the ' peoples; ♦
　　ascribe to the Lord ' honour and ' strength.

8　Ascribe to the Lord the honour due to his ' name; ♦
　　bring offerings and come ' into his ' courts.

9　O worship the Lord in the beauty of ' holiness; ♦
　　let the whole earth ' tremble be'fore him.

10　Tell it out among the nations that the Lord is ' king. ♦
　　He has made the world so firm that it cannot be moved;
　　　　he will judge the ' peoples with ' equity.

11　Let the heavens rejoice and let the earth be ' glad; ♦
　　let the sea thunder and ' all that is ' in it;

12　Let the fields be joyful and all that is ' in them; ♦
　　let all the trees of the wood shout for joy be'fore the ' Lord.

13　For he comes, he comes to judge the ' earth; ♦
　　with righteousness he will judge the world
　　　　and the peoples ' with his ' truth.

　　Glory to the Father and to the ' Son
　　and to the ' Holy ' Spirit;
　　as it was in the beginning is ' now
　　and shall be for ' ever. A'men.

Optional Refrain 1

Great is the ' Lord: | and greatly ' to be ' praised.

Optional Refrain 2

To you is born this day a ' saviour; | who is ' Christ the ' Lord.

Chant: John Harper
© 2000 The Royal School of Church Music

Psalm 97

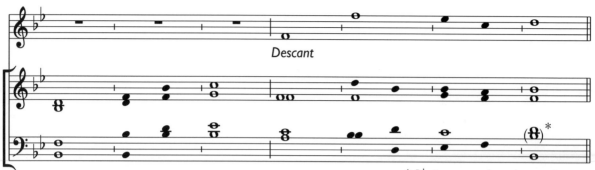

Descant

Bb in tenor when descant is sung

1 The Lord is king: let the ' earth re'joice; ♦
let the multitude ' of the ' isles be ' glad.

2 Clouds and darkness are ' round a'bout him; ♦
righteousness and justice are the foun'dation ' of his ' throne.

3 Fire ' goes be'fore him ♦
and burns up his ' enemies on ' every ' side.

4 His lightnings ' lit up the ' world; ♦
the ' earth ' saw it and ' trembled.

5 The mountains melted like wax at the ' presence · of the ' Lord, ♦
at the presence of the ' Lord of the ' whole ' earth.

6 The heavens de'clared his ' righteousness, ♦
and all the ' peoples have ' seen his ' glory.

7 Confounded be all who worship carved images
and delight in ' mere ' idols. ♦
Bow down be'fore him, ' all you ' gods.

8 Zion heard and was glad, and the daughters of ' Judah re'joiced, ♦
be'cause of your ' judgements, O ' Lord.

9 For you, Lord, are most high over ' all the ' earth; ♦
you are exalted ' far a'bove all ' gods.

10 The Lord loves those ' who hate ' evil; ♦
he preserves the lives of his faithful
and delivers them ' from the ' hand of the ' wicked.

11 Light has sprung up ' for the ' righteous ♦
and joy ' for the ' true of ' heart.

12 Rejoice in the ' Lord, you ' righteous, ♦
and give ' thanks to his ' holy ' name.

Glory to the Father and ' to the ' Son
and ' to the ' Holy ' Spirit;
as it was in the be'ginning is ' now
and shall be for ' ever. ' A'men.

Chant: Peter Hurford
© Peter Hurford

Optional Refrain 1

Zion hears ' and is ' glad, ◆
and the ' daughters of ' Judah re'joice.

Optional Refrain 2

The Lord is king, let the ' earth re'joice; ◆
give ' thanks to his ' holy ' name

Psalm 97

1 The Lord is king: let the ' earth re'joice; ◆
let the multitude of the ' isles be ' glad.

2 Clouds and darkness are ' round a'bout him; ◆
righteousness and justice are the foundation ' of his ' throne.

3 Fire ' goes be'fore him ◆
and burns up his enemies on ' every ' side.

4 His lightnings ' lit up the ' world; ◆
the earth ' saw it and ' trembled.

5 The mountains melted like wax at the ' presence · of the ' Lord, ◆
at the presence of the Lord of the ' whole ' earth.

6 The heavens de'clared his ' righteousness, ◆
and all the peoples have ' seen his ' glory.

7 Confounded be all who worship carved images
and de'light in mere ' idols. ◆
Bow down before him, ' all you ' gods.

8 Zion heard and was glad, and the daughters of ' Judah re'joiced, ◆
because of your ' judgements, O ' Lord.

9 For you, Lord, are most high over ' all the ' earth; ◆
you are exalted far a'bove all ' gods.

10 The Lord loves ' those who hate ' evil; ◆
he preserves the lives of his faithful
and delivers them from the ' hand of the ' wicked.

11 Light has sprung ' up for the ' righteous ◆
and joy for the ' true of ' heart.

12 Rejoice in the ' Lord, you ' righteous, ◆
and give thanks to his ' holy ' name.

Glory to the Father ' and to the ' Son
and to the ' Holy ' Spirit;
as it was in the be'ginning is ' now
and shall be for ' ever. A'men.

Music: Peter Moger
© 2000 Peter Moger

Optional Refrain for Christmas

Zion hears and is glad, and the daugh-ters of Ju-dah re-joice.

Optional Refrain for Eastertide and Transfiguration

The Lord is king: let the earth re - joice.

alternative chant

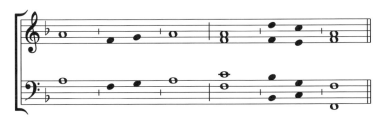

Psalm 147 (13–21)

13 Sing praise to the Lord, ' O Je'rusalem; ♦
   praise your ' God, ' O ' Zion;

14 For he has strengthened the ' bars of your ' gates ♦
   and has ' blest your ' children with'in you.

15 He has established peace ' in your ' borders ♦
   and satisfies ' you with the ' finest ' wheat.

16 He sends forth his command ' to the ' earth ♦
   and his ' word runs ' very ' swiftly.

17 He gives ' snow like ' wool ♦
   and ' scatters the ' hoarfrost like ' ashes.

18 He casts down his hailstones like ' morsels of ' bread; ♦
   who ' can en'dure his ' frost?

19 He sends forth his ' word and ' melts them; ♦
   he blows with his ' wind · and the ' waters ' flow.

20 He declares his ' word to ' Jacob, ♦
   his ' statutes and ' judgements to ' Israel.

‡ 21 He has not dealt so with any ' other ' nation; ♦
   they do not know his laws.
       ' Alle'lu'ia.

   Glory to the Father and ' to the ' Son
   and ' to the ' Holy ' Spirit;
   as it was in the be'ginning is ' now
   and shall be for ' ever. ' A'men.

Optional Refrain

The Word became flesh and ' dwelt a'mong us; ♦
and ' we have ' seen his ' glory.

Chant: Jonathan Battishill

Psalm 147 (13–21)

alternative chant

13 Sing praise to the Lord, ' O Je'rusalem; ♦
   praise your ' God, O ' Zion;

14 For he has strengthened the ' bars of your ' gates ♦
   and has blest your ' children with'in you.

15 He has established ' peace in your ' borders ♦
   and satisfies you with the ' finest ' wheat.

16 He sends forth his com'mand to the ' earth ♦
   and his word ' runs · very ' swiftly.

17 He gives ' snow like ' wool ♦
   and scatters the ' hoarfrost like ' ashes.

18 He casts down his hailstones like ' morsels of ' bread; ♦
   who can en'dure his ' frost?

19 He sends forth his ' word and ' melts them; ♦
   he blows with his wind and the ' waters ' flow.

20 He declares his ' word to ' Jacob, ♦
   his statutes and ' judgements to ' Israel.

‡ 21 He has not dealt so with any ' other ' nation; ♦
   they do not know his laws.
      ' Alle'luia.

Glory to the Father ' and to the ' Son
and to the ' Holy ' Spirit;
as it was in the be'ginning is ' now
and shall be for ' ever. A'men.

Optional Refrain

The Word be-came flesh and dwelt a - mong us.

Music: Peter Moger   © 2000 Peter Moger
Alternative chant: Timothy Hone   © 2000 Timothy Hone

A Song of the Messiah

1 The people who walked in darkness have seen a ' great light; ♦
  those who dwelt in a land of deep darkness,
    upon them ' the light has dawned.

2 You have increased their joy and given them great ' gladness; ♦
  they rejoiced before you as with joy at ' the harvest.

3 For you have shattered the yoke that ' burdened them; ♦
  the collar that lay heavy on ' their shoulders.

4 For to us a child is born and to us a ' son is given, ♦
  and the government will be upon ' his shoulder.

5 And his name will be called: Wonderful Counsellor;
    the ' Mighty God; ♦
  the Everlasting Father; ' the Prince of Peace.

6 Of the increase of his government ' and of peace ♦
  there ' will be no end,

7 Upon the throne of David and over his ' kingdom, ♦
  to establish and uphold it with justice ' and righteousness.

8 From this time forth and for ' evermore; ♦
  the zeal of the Lord of hosts ' will do this.

Glory to the Father and ' to the Son
and to the Ho'ly Spirit;
as it was in the beginning ' is now
and shall be for ev'er. Amen.

Isaiah 9.2,3b,4a,6,7

Optional Refrain

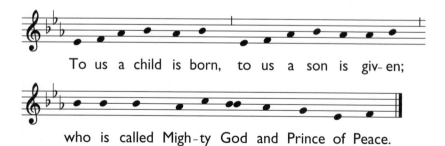

To us a child is born, to us a son is giv-en;

who is called Migh-ty God and Prince of Peace.

Music: adapted from traditional chant, tone 2
© 2000 The Royal School of Church Music

A Song of the Messiah

1 The people who walked in darkness have seen a great ' light; ♦
   those who dwelt In a land of deep darkness,
      upon them the ' light has ' dawned.

2 You have increased their joy and given them great ' gladness; ♦
   they rejoiced before you as with ' joy at the ' harvest.

3 For you have shattered the yoke that ' burdened them; ♦
   the collar that lay heavy ' on their ' shoulders.

4 For to us a child is born and to us a son is ' given, ♦
   and the government will be up'on his ' shoulder.

5 And his name will be called: Wonderful Counsellor;
      the Mighty ' God; ♦
   the Everlasting Father; the ' Prince of ' Peace.

6 Of the increase of his government and of ' peace ♦
   there will ' be no ' end,

7 Upon the throne of David and over his ' kingdom, ♦
   to establish and uphold it with ' justice and ' righteousness.

8 From this time forth and for ever'more; ♦
   the zeal of the Lord of ' hosts will ' do this.

   Glory to the Father and to the ' Son
   and to the ' Holy ' Spirit;
   as it was in the beginning is ' now
   and shall be for ' ever. A'men.

Isaiah 9.2,3b,4a,6,7

Optional Refrain

To us a child is born, to us a son is ' given; ♦
who is called Mighty God and ' Prince of ' Peace.

Chant: John Harper

A Song of Redemption

1 The Father has delivered us from the do'minion of ' darkness, ♦
  and transferred us to the kingdom of ' his be'loved ' Son;

2 In whom we ' have re'demption, ♦
  the for'giveness ' of our ' sins.

3 He is the image of the in'visible ' God, ♦
  the ' firstborn of ' all cre'ation.

4 For in him all things ' were cre'ated, ♦
  in heaven and on earth, ' visible ' and in'visible.

5 All things were created ' through him and ' for him, ♦
  he is before all things and in him ' all things ' hold to'gether.

6 He is the head of the ' body, the ' Church, ♦
  he is the beginning, the ' firstborn ' from the ' dead.

‡ 7 In him all the fullness of God was ' pleased to ' dwell; ♦
  and through him God was ' pleased to ' reconcile ' all things.

Glory to the Father and ' to the ' Son
and ' to the ' Holy ' Spirit;
as it was in the be'ginning is ' now
and shall be for ' ever. ' A'men.

Colossians 1.13-18a, 19, 20a

Optional Refrain

He is the image of the in'visible ' God: ♦
the ' first-born of ' all cre'ation.

Chant: Jonathan Battishill

A Song of Redemption

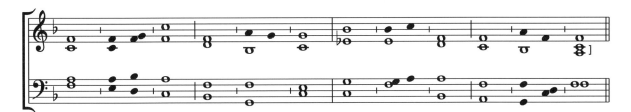

1   The Father has delivered us from the do|minion of ' darkness, ♦
     and transferred us to the kingdom of his be|loved ' Son;

2   In whom ' we have re|demption, ♦
     the forgiveness ' of our ' sins.

3   He is the image of the in|visible ' God, ♦
     the firstborn of ' all cre|ation.

4   For in him all things ' were cre|ated, ♦
     in heaven and on earth, visible ' and in|visible.

5   All things were created ' through him and ' for him, ♦
     he is before all things and in him all things ' hold to|gether.

6   He is the head of the ' body, the ' Church, ♦
     he is the beginning, the firstborn ' from the ' dead.

‡   7   In him all the fullness of God was ' pleased to ' dwell; ♦
     and through him God was pleased to ' reconcile ' all things.

Glory to the Father ' and to the ' Son
and to the ' Holy ' Spirit;
as it was in the be|ginning is ' now
and shall be for ' ever. A|men.

Colossians 1.13-18a, 19, 20a

Optional Refrain

Music: Peter Moger   © 2000 Peter Moger

Psalms and Canticles: Christmas   **317**

Epiphany

Psalm 19 (1–6)

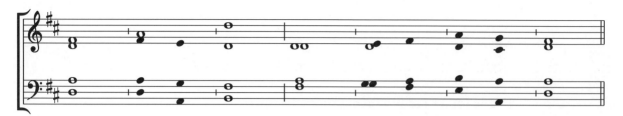

1 The heavens are telling the ' glory of ' God ♦
 and the ' firmament pro'claims his ' handiwork.

2 One day pours out its song ' to an'other ♦
 and one night unfolds ' knowledge ' to an'other.

3 They have neither ' speech nor ' language ♦
 and their ' voices ' are not ' heard,

4 Yet their sound has gone out into ' all ' lands ♦
 and their ' words · to the ' ends of the ' world.

5 In them has he set a tabernacle ' for the ' sun, ♦
 that comes forth as a bridegroom out of his chamber
  and rejoices as a ' champion to ' run his ' course.

6 It goes forth from the end of the heavens
  and runs to the very ' end a'gain, ♦
 and there is nothing ' hidden ' from its ' heat.

Glory to the Father and ' to the ' Son
and ' to the ' Holy ' Spirit;
as it was in the be'ginning is ' now
and shall be for ' ever. ' A'men.

Optional Refrain

Their sound has gone out into ' all ' lands ♦
and their ' words · to the ' ends of the ' world.

Chant: Edward J Hopkins

Psalm 19 (1-6)

1 The heavens are telling the ' glory of ' God ♦
   and the firmament pro'claims his ' handiwork.

2 One day pours out its song ' to an'other ♦
   and one night unfolds knowledge ' to an'other.

3 They have neither ' speech nor ' language ♦
   and their voices ' are not ' heard,

4 Yet their sound has gone out ' into all ' lands ♦
   and their words to the ' ends of the ' world.

5 In them has he set a tabernacle ' for the ' sun, ♦
   that comes forth as a bridegroom out of his chamber
       and rejoices as a champion to ' run his ' course.

6 It goes forth from the end of the heavens
       and runs to the very ' end a'gain, ♦
    and there is nothing hidden ' from its ' heat.

   Glory to the Father ' and to the ' Son
   and to the ' Holy ' Spirit;
   as it was in the be'ginning is ' now
   and shall be for ' ever. A'men.

Optional Refrain

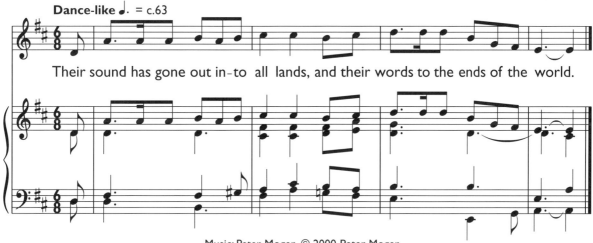

Their sound has gone out in-to all lands, and their words to the ends of the world.

Music: Peter Moger © 2000 Peter Moger

Psalm 72 (1–7, 11–15)

1 Give the king your judgements, ' O God, ♦
   and your righteousness to ' the son of a king.

2 Then shall he judge your people ' righteously ♦
   and your ' poor with justice.

3 May the mountains ' bring forth peace, ♦
   and the little hills righteousness ' for the people.

4 May he defend the poor among the ' people, ♦
   deliver the children of the needy and crush ' the oppressor.

5 May he live as long as the sun and ' moon endure, ♦
   from one generation ' to another.

6 May he come down like rain upon the ' mown grass, ♦
   like the showers ' that water the earth.

7 In his time shall righteousness ' flourish, ♦
   and abundance of peace
      till the moon ' shall be no more.

11 All kings shall fall down be'fore him; ♦
   all nations shall ' do him service.

12 For he shall deliver the poor that ' cry out, ♦
   the needy and those who ' have no helper.

13 He shall have pity on the ' weak and poor; ♦
   he shall preserve the lives ' of the needy.

14 He shall redeem their lives from oppression and ' violence, ♦
   and dear shall their ' blood be in his sight.

15 Long may he live;
      unto him may be given gold from ' Sheba; ♦
   may prayer be made for him continually
      and may they bless him ' all the day long.

Glory to the Father and ' to the Son
and to the ' Holy Spirit;
as it was in the beginning ' is now
and shall be for ' ever. Amen.

Optional Refrain

Kings shall fall down be-fore him;   all na-tions shall do him ser-vice.

Music: adapted from traditional chant, tone 1
© 2000 The Royal School of Church Music

Psalm 72 (1–7, 11–15)

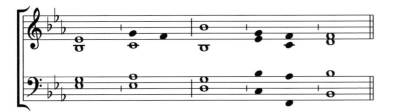

1   Give the king your judgements, O ' God, ♦
    and your righteousness to the ' son of a ' king.

2   Then shall he judge your people ' righteously ♦
    and your ' poor with ' justice.

3   May the mountains bring forth ' peace, ♦
    and the little hills righteousness ' for the ' people.

4   May he defend the poor among the ' people, ♦
    deliver the children of the needy and ' crush the op'pressor.

5   May he live as long as the sun and moon en'dure, ♦
    from one generation ' to an'other.

6   May he come down like rain upon the mown ' grass, ♦
    like the showers that ' water the ' earth.

7   In his time shall righteousness ' flourish, ♦
    and abundance of peace
        till the moon shall ' be no ' more.

11   All kings shall fall down be'fore him; ♦
    all nations shall ' do him ' service.

12   For he shall deliver the poor that cry ' out, ♦
    the needy and those who ' have no ' helper.

13   He shall have pity on the weak and ' poor; ♦
    he shall preserve the ' lives of the ' needy.

14   He shall redeem their lives from oppression and ' violence, ♦
    and dear shall their blood be ' in his ' sight.

15   Long may he live;
        unto him may be given gold from ' Sheba; ♦
    may prayer be made for him continually
        and may they bless him ' all the day ' long.

    Glory to the Father and to the ' Son
    and to the ' Holy ' Spirit;
    as it was in the beginning is ' now
    and shall be for ' ever. A'men.

Optional Refrain

Kings shall fall down down be'fore him; ♦
all nations shall ' do him ' service.

Chant: Norman Warren
© Norman Warren

A Song of the New Jerusalem

1 Arise, shine out, for your ' light has come, ♦
   the glory of the Lord is ris'ing upon you.

2 Though night still covers ' the earth, ♦
   and dark'ness the peoples;

3 Above you the Holy One a'rises, ♦
   and above you ' God's glory appears.

4 The nations will come to ' your light, ♦
   and kings to your ' dawning brightness.

5 Your gates will lie open con'tinually, ♦
   shut neither ' by day nor by night.

6 The sound of violence shall be heard no longer in ' your land, ♦
   or ruin and devastation with'in your borders.

7 You will call your walls, Sal'vation, ♦
   and ' your gates, Präise.

8 No more will the sun give you ' daylight, ♦
   nor moonlight ' shine upon you;

9 But the Lord will be your ever'lasting light, ♦
   your God will ' be your splendour.

10 For you shall be called the city ' of God, ♦
   the dwelling of the Holy ' One of Israel.

   Glory to the Father and ' to the Son
   and to the ' Holy Spirit;
   as it was in the beginning ' is now
   and shall be for ' ever. Amen.

Isaiah 60.1-3,11a,18,19,14b

Optional Refrain

Na - tions will come to your light,   and kings to your dawn - ing bright - ness.

Music: adapted from traditional chant, tone 6
© 2000 The Royal School of Church Music

A Song of the New Jerusalem

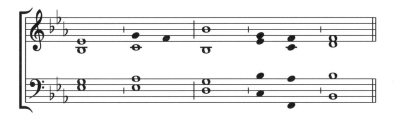

1 Arise, shine out, for your light has ' come, ♦
the glory of the Lord is ' rising up ' on you

2 Though night still covers the ' earth, ♦
and ' darkness the ' peoples;

3 Above you the Holy One a ' rises, ♦
and above you God's ' glory ap ' pears.

4 The nations will come to your ' light, ♦
and kings to your ' dawning ' brightness.

5 Your gates will lie open con ' tinually, ♦
shut neither by ' day nor by ' night.

6 The sound of violence shall be heard no longer in your ' land, ♦
or ruin and devastation with ' in your ' borders.

7 You will call your walls, Sal ' vation, ♦
and your ' gates, ' Praise.

8 No more will the sun give you ' daylight, ♦
nor moonlight ' shine up ' on you;

9 But the Lord will be your everlasting ' light, ♦
your God will ' be your ' splendour.

10 For you shall be called the city of ' God, ♦
the dwelling of the ' Holy One of ' Israel.

Glory to the Father and to the ' Son
and to the ' Holy ' Spirit;
as it was in the beginning is ' now
and shall be for ' ever. A ' men.

Isaiah 60.1-3,11a,18,19,14b

Optional Refrain

Nations will come to your ' light, ♦
and kings to your ' dawning ' brightness.

Chant: Norman Warren
© Norman Warren

A Song of Praise

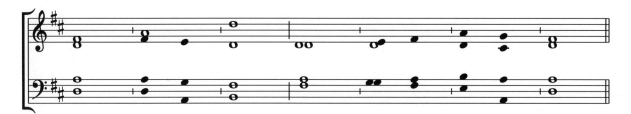

1 You are worthy, our ' Lord and ' God, ◆
to receive ' glory and ' honour and ' power.

2 For you have cre'ated ' all things, ◆
and by your ' will they ' have their ' being.

3 You are worthy, O Lamb, for ' you were ' slain, ◆
and by your blood you ransomed for God
saints from every ' tribe and ' language and ' nation.

4 You have made them to be a kingdom and priests
' serving our ' God, ◆
and they will ' reign with ' you on ' earth.

To the One who sits on the throne and ' to the ' Lamb ◆
be blessing and honour, glory and might,
for ever and ' ever. ' A'men.

Revelation 4.11; 5.9b, 10

This Canticle is also known as Glory and Honour.

Optional Refrain

You created ' all things, O ' God, ◆
and are ' worthy · of our ' praise for ' ever.

Chant: Edward J Hopkins

A Song of Praise

1 You are worthy, our ' Lord and ' God, ◆
   to receive glory and ' honour and ' power.

2 For you have cre'ated ' all things, ◆
   and by your will ' they have their ' being.

3 You are worthy, O Lamb, for ' you were ' slain, ◆
   and by your blood you ransomed for God
      saints from every tribe and ' language and ' nation.

4 You have made them to be a kingdom and priests
      ' serving our ' God, ◆
   and they will reign with ' you on ' earth.

   To the One who ' sits on the ' throne
   and ' to the ' Lamb
   be blessing and honour, ' glory and ' might,
   for ever and ' ever. A'men.

Revelation 4.11; 5.9b, 10

This Canticle is also known as Glory and Honour.

Optional Refrain

Music: Peter Moger
© 2000 Peter Moger

Lent and Passiontide

Psalm 22 (1–11, 23–31)

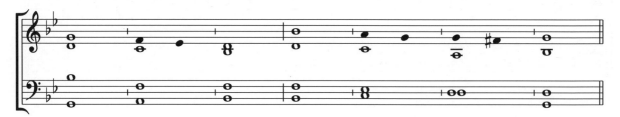

1   My God, my God, why have ' you for'saken me, ♦
     and are so far from my salvation,
        from the ' words of ' my dis'tress?

2   O my God, I cry in the daytime,
        but you ' do not ' answer; ♦
     and by night also, ' but I ' find no ' rest.

3   Yet you ' are the ' Holy One, ♦
     enthroned up'on the ' praises of ' Israel.

4   Our forebears ' trusted in ' you; ♦
     they ' trusted, and ' you de'livered them.

5   They cried out to you and ' were de'livered; ♦
     they put their trust in you ' and were ' not con'founded.

6   But as for me, I am a worm and ' no ' man, ♦
     scorned by all ' and des'pised by the ' people.

7   All who see me ' laugh me to ' scorn; ♦
     they curl their lips and ' wag their ' heads, ' saying,

8   'He trusted in the Lord; let ' him de'liver him; ♦
     let him deliver him, if ' he de'lights in ' him.'

9   But it is you that took me ' out of the ' womb ♦
     and laid me safe up'on my ' mother's ' breast.

10   On you was I cast ever since ' I was ' born; ♦
     you are my God even ' from my ' mother's ' womb.

‡   11   Be not far from me, for trouble is ' near at ' hand ♦
     and ' there is ' none to ' help.

Optional Refrain

My ' God, my ' God, ♦
why have ' you for'saken ' me?

Chant: William Croft

second part

23   Praise the Lord, ' you that ' fear him; ♦
     O seed of Jacob, glorify him;
         stand in awe of ' him, O ' seed of ' Israel.

24   For he has not despised nor abhorred the suffering of the poor;
         neither has he hidden his ' face ' from them; ♦
     but when they ' cried to ' him he ' heard them.

25   From you comes my praise in the great ' congre'gation; ♦
     I will perform my vows
         in the ' presence of ' those that ' fear you.

26   The poor shall eat ' and be ' satisfied; ♦
     those who seek the Lord shall praise him;
         their ' hearts shall ' live for ' ever.

27   All the ends of the earth
         shall remember and ' turn to the ' Lord, ♦
     and all the families of the ' nations shall ' bow be'fore him.

28   For the kingdom ' is the ' Lord's ♦
         and he ' rules ' over the ' nations.

29   How can those who sleep in the earth
         bow ' down in ' worship, ♦
     or those who go down to the ' dust ' kneel be'fore him?

30   He has saved my life for himself;
         my des'cendants shall ' serve him; ♦
     this shall be told of the Lord for ' gene'rations to ' come.

‡   31   They shall come and make known his salvation,
         to a people ' yet un'born, ♦
     declaring that ' he, the ' Lord, has ' done it.

     Glory to the Father and ' to the ' Son
     and ' to the ' Holy ' Spirit;
     as it was in the be'ginning is ' now
     and shall be for ' ever. ' A'men.

Optional Refrain

All the ' ends of the ' earth♦
shall ' turn to ' you, O ' Lord.

Chant: adapted from William Croft

Psalm 22 (1–11, 23–31)

1 My God, my God, why have ' you for'saken me, ♦
   and are so far from my salvation,
      from the words of ' my dis'tress?

2 O my God, I cry in the daytime,
      but you ' do not ' answer; ♦
   and by night also, but I ' find no ' rest.

3 Yet ' you are the ' Holy One, ♦
   enthroned upon the ' praises of ' Israel.

4 Our forebears ' trusted in ' you; ♦
   they trusted, and ' you de'livered them.

5 They cried out to you and ' were de'livered; ♦
   they put their trust in you and were ' not con'founded.

6 But as for me, I am a ' worm and no ' man, ♦
   scorned by all and des'pised by the ' people.

7 All who see me ' laugh me to ' scorn; ♦
   they curl their lips and wag their ' heads, ' saying,

8 'He trusted in the Lord; ' let him de'liver him; ♦
   let him deliver him, if ' he de'lights in him.'

9 But it is you that took me ' out of the ' womb ♦
   and laid me safe upon my ' mother's ' breast.

10 On you was I cast ever since ' I was ' born; ♦
   you are my God even from my ' mother's ' womb.

‡ 11 Be not far from me, for trouble is ' near at ' hand ♦
   and there is ' none to ' help.

Optional Refrain

Chant: Katherine Dienes © Katherine Dienes
Music of refrain: Peter Moger © 2000 Peter Moger

alternative chant

second part

23 Praise the Lord, ' you that ' fear him; ♦
  O seed of Jacob, glority him;
    stand in awe of him, O ' seed of ' Israel.

24 For he has not despised nor abhorred the suffering of the poor;
    neither has he hidden his ' face ' from them; ♦
  but when they cried to ' him he ' heard them.

25 From you comes my praise in the great ' congre'gation; ♦
  I will perform my vows
    in the presence of ' those that ' fear you.

26 The poor shall ' eat and be ' satisfied; ♦
  those who seek the Lord shall praise him;
    their hearts shall ' live for ' ever.

27 All the ends of the earth
    shall remember and ' turn to the ' Lord, ♦
  and all the families of the nations shall ' bow be'fore him.

28 For the kingdom ' is the ' Lord's ♦
  and he rules ' over the ' nations.

29 How can those who sleep in the earth
    ' bow down in ' worship, ♦
  or those who go down to the dust ' kneel be'fore him?

30 He has saved my life for himself;
    my des'cendants shall ' serve him; ♦
  this shall be told of the Lord for gene'rations to ' come.

‡ 31 They shall come and make known his salvation,
    to a people ' yet un'born, ♦
  declaring that he, the ' Lord, has ' done it.

  Glory to the Father ' and to the ' Son
  and to the ' Holy ' Spirit;
  as it was in the be'ginning is ' now
  and shall be for ' ever. A'men.

Optional Refrain

All the ends of the earth   shall turn to you, O Lord.   Lord.

Alternative chant: Norman Warren   © Norman Warren
Music of refrain: Peter Moger   © 2000 Peter Moger

Psalm 25 (1–10)

1 To you, O Lord, I lift up my soul;
    O my ' God, in you I trust; ♦
let me not be put to shame;
    let not my enemies ' triumph over me.

2 Let none who look to ' you be put to shame, ♦
but let the treacherous be shamed ' and frustrated.

3 Make me to ' know your ways, O Lord, ♦
and ' teach me your paths.

4 Lead me in your ' truth and teach me, ♦
for you are the God of my salvation;
    for you have I hoped ' all the day long.

5 Remember, Lord, your com'passion and love, ♦
for they are from ' everlasting.

6 Remember not the sins of my youth
    or ' my transgressions, ♦
but think on me in your goodness, O Lord,
    according ' to your steadfast love.

7 Gracious and ' upright is the Lord; ♦
therefore shall he teach ' sinners in the way.

8 He will guide the hum'ble in doing right ♦
and teach his way ' to the lowly.

9 All the paths of the Lord are ' mercy and truth ♦
to those who keep his covenant ' and his testi·monies.

10 For your ' name's sake, O Lord, ♦
be merciful to my ' sin, for it is great.

Glory to the Father ' and to the Son
and to the ' Holy Spirit;
as it was in the be'ginning is now
and shall be for ' ever. Amen.

Optional Refrain

The paths of the Lord are mer-cy and truth.

Music: adapted from traditional chant, tone 7
© 2000 The Royal School of Church Music

Psalm 25 (1–10)

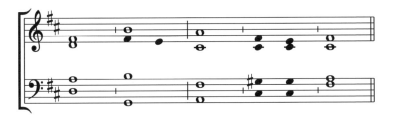

1 To you, O Lord, I lift up my soul;
   O my God, in you I ' trust; ♦
let me not be put to shame;
   let not my enemies ' triumph ' over me.

2 Let none who look to you be put to ' shame, ♦
but let the treacherous be ' shamed and frus'trated.

3 Make me to know your ways, O ' Lord, ♦
and ' teach me your ' paths.

4 Lead me in your truth and ' teach me, ♦
for you are the God of my salvation;
   for you have I hoped ' all the day ' long.

5 Remember, Lord, your compassion and ' love, ♦
for they are from ' ever'lasting.

6 Remember not the sins of my youth
   or my trans'gressions, ♦
but think on me in your goodness, O Lord,
   according to your ' steadfast ' love.

7 Gracious and upright is the ' Lord; ♦
therefore shall he teach sinners ' in the ' way.

8 He will guide the humble in doing ' right ♦
and teach his ' way to the ' lowly.

9 All the paths of the Lord are mercy and ' truth ♦
to those who keep his covenant ' and his ' testimonies.

10 For your name's sake, O ' Lord, ♦
be merciful to my sin, for ' it is ' great.

   Glory to the Father and to the ' Son
   and to the ' Holy ' Spirit;
   as it was in the beginning is ' now
   and shall be for ' ever. A'men.

Optional Refrain

The paths of the ' Lord ♦
are ' mercy and ' truth.

Chant: Norman Warren
© Norman Warren

Psalm 51 (1–13)

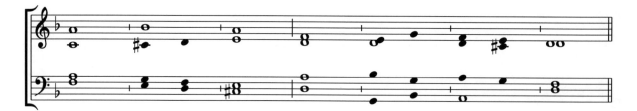

1 Have mercy on me, O God, in ' your great ' goodness; ♦
    according to the abundance of your compassion
        ' blot out ' my of'fences.

2 Wash me thoroughly ' from my ' wickedness ♦
    and ' cleanse me ' from my ' sin.

3 For I ac'knowledge my ' faults ♦
    and my ' sin is ' ever be'fore me.

4 Against you only ' have I ' sinned ♦
    and done what is ' evil ' in your ' sight,

‡   5 So that you are justified ' in your ' sentence ♦
    and ' righteous ' in your ' judgement.

6 I have been wicked even ' from my ' birth, ♦
    a sinner ' when my ' mother con'ceived me.

7 Behold, you desire truth ' deep with'in me ♦
    and shall make me understand wisdom
        ' in the ' depths of my ' heart.

8 Purge me with hyssop and I ' shall be ' clean; ♦
    wash me and I ' shall be ' whiter than ' snow.

9 Make me hear of ' joy and ' gladness, ♦
    that the bones you have ' broken ' may re'joice.

10 Turn your face ' from my ' sins ♦
    and ' blot out ' all my mis'deeds.

11 Make me a clean ' heart, O ' God, ♦
    and re'new a right ' spirit with'in me.

12 Cast me not away ' from your ' presence ♦
    and take not your ' holy ' spirit ' from me.

13 Give me again the joy of ' your sal'vation ♦
    and sustain me ' with your ' gracious ' spirit;

    Glory to the Father and ' to the ' Son
    and ' to the ' Holy ' Spirit;
    as it was in the be'ginning is ' now
    and shall be for ' ever. ' A'men.

Optional Refrain for Ash Wednesday

Wash me thoroughly ' from my ' wickedness ♦
and ' cleanse me ' from my ' sin.

Chant: John Goss

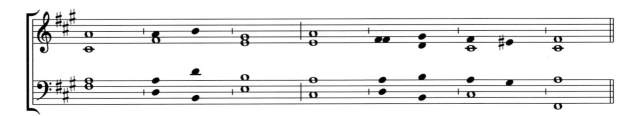

Optional Refrain for Lent

Make me a clean | heart, O | God ♦
and re|new a right | spirit with|in me.

Alternative chant: Thomas Kelway

Psalm 51 (1–13)

1 Have mercy on me, O God, in ' your great ' goodness; ♦
   according to the abundance of your compassion
       blot out ' my of'fences.

2 Wash me thoroughly ' from my ' wickedness ♦
   and cleanse me ' from my ' sin.

3 For I ac'knowledge my ' faults ♦
   and my sin is ' ever be'fore me.

4 Against you only ' have I ' sinned ♦
   and done what is evil ' in your ' sight,

‡ 5 So that you are justified ' in your ' sentence ♦
     and righteous ' in your ' judgement.

6 I have been wicked even ' from my ' birth, ♦
   a sinner when my ' mother con'ceived me.

7 Behold, you desire truth ' deep with'in me ♦
   and shall make me understand wisdom
       in the ' depths of my ' heart.

8 Purge me with hyssop and ' I shall be ' clean; ♦
   wash me and I shall be ' whiter than ' snow.

9 Make me hear of ' joy and ' gladness, ♦
   that the bones you have broken ' may re'joice.

10 Turn your ' face from my ' sins ♦
    and blot out ' all my mis'deeds.

11 Make me a clean ' heart, O ' God, ♦
    and renew a right ' spirit with'in me.

12 Cast me not a'way from your ' presence ♦
    and take not your holy ' spirit ' from me.

13 Give me again the joy of ' your sal'vation ♦
    and sustain me with your ' gracious ' spirit.

    Glory to the Father ' and to the ' Son
    and to the ' Holy ' Spirit;
    as it was in the be'ginning is ' now
    and shall be for ' ever. A'men.

Music: Peter Moger
© 2000 Peter Moger

Optional Refrain for Ash Wednesday

Wash me thor-ough-ly from my wick-ed-ness and _____ cleanse me from my _____ sin.

last time

Optional Refrain for Lent

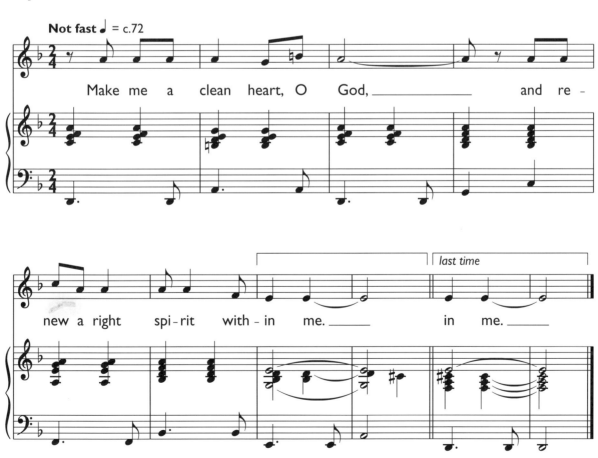

Make me a clean heart, O God, _____ and re-new a right spi-rit with-in me. _____ in me. _____

last time

Psalm 116 (10–17)

10 Höw shall ' I repay the Lord ♦
for all the benefits he has ' given to me?

11 I will lift up the cup ' of salvation ♦
and call upon the ' name of the Lord.

12 I will fulfil my ' vows to the Lord ♦
in the presence of ' all his people.

13 Precious in the ' sight of the Lord ♦
is the death of his ' faithful servants.

14 O Lord, I ' am your servant, ♦
your servant, the child of your handmaid;
you have ' freed me from my bonds.

15 I will offer to you a sacri'fice of thanksgiving ♦
and call upon the ' name of the Lord.

16 I will fulfil my ' vows to the Lord ♦
in the presence of ' all his people,

17 In the courts of the ' house of the Lord, ♦
in the midst of you, O Jerusalem.
' Alleluia.

Glory to the Father ' and to the Son
and to the ' Holy Spirit;
as it was in the be'ginning is now
and shall be for ' ever. Amen.

Optional Refrain

I will lift up the cup of sal-va-tion:

I will of-fer a sac-ri-fice of thanks-giv-ing.

Music: adapted from traditional chant, tone 7
© 2000 The Royal School of Church Music

Psalm 116 (10–17)

10 How shall I repay the ' Lord ♦
    for all the benefits he has ' given to ' me?

11 I will lift up the cup of sal ' vation ♦
    and call upon the ' name of the ' Lord.

12 I will fulfil my vows to the ' Lord ♦
    in the presence of ' all his ' people.

13 Precious in the sight of the ' Lord ♦
    is the death of his ' faithful ' servants.

14 O Lord, I am your ' servant, ♦
    your servant, the child of your handmaid;
        you have freed me ' from my ' bonds.

15 I will offer to you a sacrifice of ' thanksgiving ♦
    and call upon the ' name of the ' Lord.

16 I will fulfil my vows to the ' Lord ♦
    in the presence of ' all his ' people,

17 In the courts of the house of the ' Lord, ♦
    in the midst of you, O Jerusalem.
        ' Alle ' luia.

Glory to the Father and to the ' Son
and to the ' Holy ' Spirit;
as it was in the beginning is ' now
and shall be for ' ever. A ' men.

Optional Refrain

I will lift up the cup of sal ' vation ♦
I will offer to you a ' sacrifice of ' thanksgiving

Chant: John Harper
© 2000 The Royal School of Church Music

A Song of Humility

1 Come, let us re'turn to the Lord ♦
   who has torn us ' and will heal us.

2 God has ' stricken us ♦
   and will ' bind up our wounds.

3 After two days, he ' will revive us, ♦
   and on the third day will raise us up,
      that we may live ' in his presence.

4 Let us ' strive to know the Lord; ♦
   his appearing is as sure ' as the sunrise.

5 He will come to ' us like the showers, ♦
   like the spring rains that ' water the earth.

6 'O Ephraim, how ' shall I deal with you? ♦
   How shall I deal with ' you, O Judah?

7 'Your love for me is ' like the morning mist, ♦
   like the dew that goes ' early away.

8 'Therefore, I have hewn them ' by the prophets, ♦
   and my judgement goes ' forth as the light.

9 'For loyalty is my desire ' and not sacrifice, ♦
   and the knowledge of God rather ' than burnt offerings.'

   Glory to the Father ' and to the Son
   and to the ' Holy Spirit;
   as it was in the be'ginning is now
   and shall be for ' ever. Amen.

Hosea 6.1-6

Optional Refrain

Raise us up, O God, that we may live in your pre- sence.

Music adapted from traditional chant, tone 7
© 2000 The Royal School of Church Music

A Song of Humility

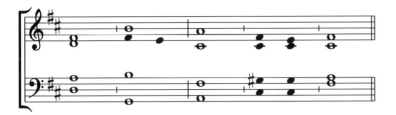

1 Come, let us return to the ' Lord ♦
   who has torn us ' and will ' heal us.

2 God has ' stricken us ♦
   and will ' bind up our ' wounds.

3 After two days, he will re'vive us, ♦
   and on the third day will raise us up,
      that we may ' live in his ' presence.

4 Let us strive to know the ' Lord; ♦
   his appearing is as ' sure as the ' sunrise.

5 He will come to us like the ' showers, ♦
   like the spring rains that ' water the ' earth.

6 'O Ephraim, how shall I ' deal with you? ♦
   How shall I deal with ' you, O ' Judah?

7 'Your love for me is like the morning ' mist, ♦
   like the dew that goes ' early a'way.

8 'Therefore, I have hewn them by the ' prophets, ♦
   and my judgement goes ' forth as the ' light.

9 'For loyalty is my desire and not ' sacrifice, ♦
   and the knowledge of God rather than ' burnt ' offerings.'

   Glory to the Father and to the ' Son
   and to the ' Holy ' Spirit;
   as it was in the beginning is ' now
   and shall be for ' ever. A'men.

Hosea 6.1-6

Optional Refrain

Therefore, I have hewn them by the ' prophets, ♦
and my judgement goes ' forth as the ' light.

Chant: Norman Warren
© Norman Warren

A Song of Christ the Servant

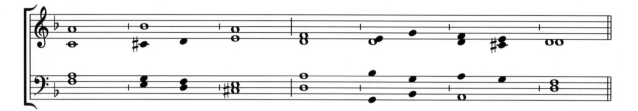

1   Christ suffered for you, leaving you ' an ex'ample, ♦
    that you should ' follow ' in his ' steps.

2   He committed no sin, no guile was ' found on his ' lips, ♦
    when he was reviled, he did ' not re'vile in ' turn.

3   When he suffered, he ' did not ' threaten, ♦
    but he trusted himself to ' God who ' judges ' justly.

4   Christ himself bore our sins in his body ' on the ' tree, ♦
    that we might die to ' sin and ' live to ' righteousness.

5   By his wounds, you have been healed,
      for you were ' straying like ' sheep, ♦
    but have now returned
      to the shepherd and ' guardian ' of your ' souls.

    Glory to the Father and ' to the ' Son
    and ' to the ' Holy ' Spirit;
    as it was in the be'ginning is ' now
    and shall be for ' ever. ' A'men.

1 Peter 2.21b-25

Optional Refrain

Christ bore our sins ' on the ' tree; ♦
by his ' wounds we ' have been ' healed.

Chant: John Goss

A Song of Christ the Servant

1 Christ suffered for you, leaving ' you an ex'ample, ♦
that you should follow ' in his ' steps.

2 He committed no sin, no guile was ' found on his ' lips, ♦
when he was reviled, he did not re'vile in ' turn.

‡ 3 When he suffered, he ' did not ' threaten, ♦
but he trusted himself to God who ' judges ' justly.

4 Christ himself bore our sins in his body ' on the ' tree, ♦
that we might die to sin and ' live to ' righteousness.

5 By his wounds, you have been healed,
for you were ' straying like ' sheep, ♦
but have now returned
to the shepherd and guardian ' of your ' souls.

Glory to the Father ' and to the ' Son
and to the ' Holy ' Spirit;
as it was in the be'ginning is ' now
and shall be for ' ever. A'men.

1 Peter 2.21b-25

alternative chant

Optional Refrain

♩ = 72

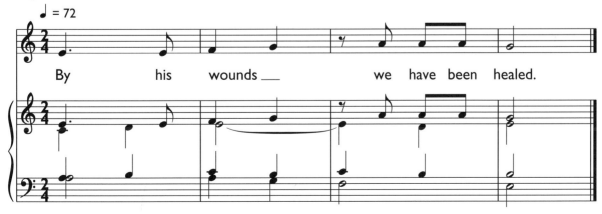

By his wounds ___ we have been healed.

Chant: Katherine Dienes   © Katherine Dienes
Alternative chant: Norman Warren   © 2000 Norman Warren
Music: Peter Moger   © 2000 Peter Moger

Easter

Psalm 23

1 The Lord ' is my ' shepherd; ♦
   therefore ' can I ' lack ' nothing.

2 He makes me lie down in ' green ' pastures ♦
   and leads me be'side ' still ' waters.

3 He shall re'fresh my ' soul ♦
   and guide me in the paths of righteousness ' for his ' name's ' sake.

4 Though I walk through the valley of the shadow of death,
       I will ' fear no ' evil; ♦
   for you are with me;
       your ' rod and your ' staff, they ' comfort me.

5 You spread a table before me
       in the presence of ' those who ' trouble me; ♦
   you have anointed my head with oil
       ' and my ' cup shall be ' full.

6 Surely goodness and loving mercy shall follow me
       all the ' days of my ' life, ♦
   and I will dwell in the ' house of the ' Lord for ' ever.

   Glory to the Father and ' to the ' Son
   and ' to the ' Holy ' Spirit;
   as it was in the be'ginning is ' now
   and shall be for ' ever. ' A'men.

Optional Refrain

Goodness and loving ' mercy shall ' follow me, ♦
and I will dwell in the ' house of the ' Lord for ' ever.

Chant: George A Macfarren

Psalm 23

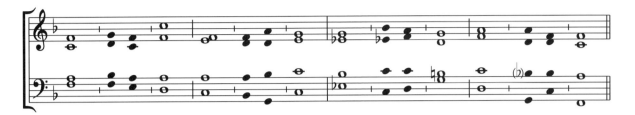

1 The Lord ˈ is my ˈ shepherd; ◆
   therefore ˈ can I lack ˈ nothing.

2 He makes me lie ˈ down in green ˈ pastures ◆
   and leads me beˈside still ˈ waters.

3 He shall reˈfresh my ˈ soul ◆
   and guide me in the paths of righteousness ˈ for his ˈ name's sake.

4 Though I walk through the valley of the shadow of death,
      I will ˈ fear no ˈ evil; ◆
   for you are with me;
      your rod and your ˈ staff, they ˈ comfort me.

5 You spread a table before me
      in the presence of ˈ those who ˈ trouble me; ◆
   you have anointed my head with oil
      and my ˈ cup shall be ˈ full.

6 Surely goodness and loving mercy shall follow me
      all the ˈ days of my ˈ life, ◆
   and I will dwell in the house of the ˈ Lord for ˈ ever.

   Glory to the Father ˈ and to the ˈ Son
   and to the ˈ Holy ˈ Spirit;
   as it was in the beˈginning is ˈ now
   and shall be for ˈ ever. Aˈmen.

Optional Refrain

I will dwell in the house of the Lord for ev – er.

Music: Peter Moger
© 2000 Peter Moger

Psalm 67

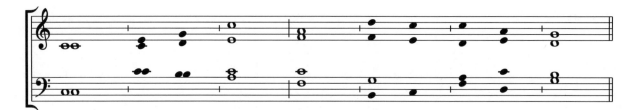

1   God be gracious to ' us and ' bless us ♦
    and make his ' face to ' shine up'on us,

2   That your way may be ' known upon ' earth, ♦
    your saving ' power a'mong all ' nations.

‡   3   Let the peoples ' praise you, O ' God; ♦
    let ' all the ' peoples ' praise you.

4   O let the nations re'joice and be ' glad, ♦
    for you will judge the peoples righteously
        and govern the ' nations ' upon ' earth.

5   Let the peoples ' praise you, O ' God; ♦
    let ' all the ' peoples ' praise you.

6   Then shall the earth bring ' forth her ' increase, ♦
    and God, our ' own ' God, will ' bless us.

7   God ' will ' bless us, ♦
    and all the ' ends of the ' earth shall ' fear him.

Glory to the Father and ' to the ' Son
and ' to the ' Holy ' Spirit;
as it was in the be'ginning is ' now
and shall be for ' ever. ' A'men.

Optional Refrain

Let the peoples ' praise you, O ' God, ♦
let ' all the ' peoples ' praise you.

Chant: Peter Hurford
© Peter Hurford

Psalm 67

1 God be gracious to ' us and ' bless us ◆
   and make his face to ' shine up'on us,

2 That your way may be ' known up'on earth, ◆
   your saving power a'mong all ' nations.

‡ 3 Let the peoples ' praise you, O ' God; ◆
   let all the ' peoples ' praise you.

4 O let the nations re'joice and be ' glad, ◆
   for you will judge the peoples righteously
       and govern the nations ' upon ' earth.

5 Let the peoples ' praise you, O ' God; ◆
   let all the ' peoples ' praise you.

6 Then shall the earth bring ' forth her ' increase, ◆
   and God, our own ' God, will ' bless us.

7 God ' will ' bless us, ◆
   and all the ends of the ' earth shall ' fear him.

   Glory to the Father ' and to the ' Son
   and to the ' Holy ' Spirit;
   as it was in the be'ginning is ' now
   and shall be for ' ever. A'men.

Optional Refrain

Psalm 93

1 The Lord is king and has put on glorious ap'parel; ♦
the Lord has put on his glory
        and gird'ed himself with strength.

2 He has made the whole ' world so sure ♦
that it ' cannot be moved.

3 Your throne has been established ' from of old; ♦
you are from ' everlasting.

4 The floods have lifted up, O Lord,
the floods have lifted ' up their voice; ♦
the floods lift ' up their pounding waves.

5 Mightier than the thunder of many waters,
        mightier than the breakers ' of the sea, ♦
the Lord on ' high is mightier.

6 Your testimonies are ' very sure; ♦
holiness adorns your house, O ' Lord, for ever.

Glory to the Father and ' to the Son
and to the ' Holy Spirit;
as it was in the beginning ' is now
and shall be for ' ever. Amen.

For Ascensiontide

Optional Refrain

The Lord is king   and has gird-ed him-self with strength.

Music: adapted from traditional chant, tone 8
© 2000 The Royal School of Church Music

Psalm 93

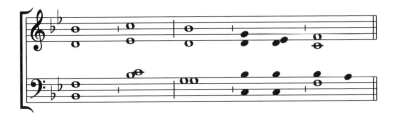

1 The Lord is king and has put on glorious ap'parel; ♦
   the Lord has put on his glory
     and girded him'self with ' strength.

2 He has made the whole world so ' sure ♦
   that it ' cannot be ' moved.

3 Your throne has been established from of ' old; ♦
   you are from ' ever'lasting.

4 The floods have lifted up, O Lord,
   the floods have lifted up their ' voice; ♦
   the floods lift up their ' pounding ' waves.

5 Mightier than the thunder of many waters,
   mightier than the breakers of the ' sea, ♦
   the Lord on ' high is ' mightier.

6 Your testimonies are very ' sure; ♦
   holiness adorns your house, O ' Lord, for ' ever.

   Glory to the Father and to the ' Son
   and to the ' Holy ' Spirit;
   as it was in the beginning is ' now
   and shall be for ' ever. A'men.

For Ascensiontide

Optional Refrain

The Lord is ' king ♦
and has girded him'self with ' strength.

Chant: Norman Warren
© Norman Warren

Psalm 98

1 Sing to the Lord a ' new song, ♦
for he has done ' marvellous things.

2 His own right hand and his ' holy arm ♦
have won for ' him the victory.

3 The Lord has made known his sal'vation; ♦
his deliverance has he openly shown in the sight ' of the nations.

4 He has remembered his mercy and faithfulness
towards the house of ' Israel, ♦
and all the ends of the earth have seen the sal'vation of our God.

5 Sound praises to the Lord, ' all the earth; ♦
break into singing ' and make music.

6 Make music to the Lord ' with the lyre, ♦
with the lyre and the ' voice of melody.

7 With trumpets and the sound ' of the horn ♦
sound praises be'fore the Lord, the King.

8 Let the sea thunder and all that ' fills it, ♦
the world and all that ' dwell upon it.

9 Let the rivers ' clap their hands ♦
and let the hills ring out together before the Lord,
for he ' comes to judge the earth.

10 In righteousness shall he ' judge the world ♦
and the peop'les with equity.

Glory to the Father and ' to the Son
and to the ' Holy Spirit;
as it was in the beginning ' is now
and shall be for ' ever. Amen.

Optional Refrain for Eastertide

The Lord has made known his vic-to-ry   in the sight of the na-tions.

Optional Refrain for Christmas

The Lord has made known his sal-va-tion   in the sight of the na-tions.

Music: adapted from traditional chant, tone 8
© 2000 The Royal School of Church Music

Psalm 98

1 Sing to the Lord a new ˈ song, ♦
   for he has done ˈ marvellous ˈ things.

2 His own right hand and his holy ˈ arm ♦
   have won for ˈ him the ˈ victory.

3 The Lord has made known his salˈvation; ♦
   his deliverance has he openly shown in the ˈ sight of the ˈ nations.

4 He has remembered his mercy and faithfulness
       towards the house of ˈ Israel, ♦
   and all the ends of the earth have seen the salvation ˈ of our ˈ God.

5 Sound praises to the Lord, all the ˈ earth; ♦
   break into singing ˈ and make ˈ music.

6 Make music to the Lord with the ˈ lyre, ♦
   with the lyre and the ˈ voice of ˈ melody.

7 With trumpets and the sound of the ˈ horn ♦
   sound praises before the ˈ Lord, the ˈ King.

8 Let the sea thunder and all that ˈ fills it, ♦
   the world and all that ˈ dwell upˈon it.

9 Let the rivers clap their ˈ hands ♦
   and let the hills ring out together before the Lord,
       for he comes to ˈ judge the ˈ earth.

10 In righteousness shall he judge the ˈ world ♦
   and the ˈ peoples with ˈ equity.

   Glory to the Father and to the ˈ Son
   and to the ˈ Holy ˈ Spirit;
   as it was in the beginning is ˈ now
   and shall be for ˈ ever. Aˈmen.

Optional Refrain for Eastertide

The Lord has made known his ˈ victory ♦
in the ˈ sight of the ˈ nations.

Optional Refrain for Christmas

The Lord has made known his salˈvation ♦
in the ˈ sight of the ˈ nations.

Chant: Norman Warren
© Norman Warren

Psalm 118 (14–29)

14 The Lord is my ' strength and my ' song, ♦
   and he has be'come ' my sa'lvation.

15 Joyful ' shouts of sa'lvation ♦
   sound from the ' tents ' of the ' righteous:

16 'The right hand of the Lord does mighty deeds;
     the right hand of the Lord ' raises ' up; ♦
   the right hand of the ' Lord does ' mighty ' deeds.'

17 I shall not ' die, but ' live ♦
   and de'clare the ' works of the ' Lord.

‡ 18 The Lord has ' punished me ' sorely, ♦
   but he has not ' given me ' over to ' death.

19 Open to me the ' gates of ' righteousness, ♦
   that I may enter ' and give ' thanks to the ' Lord.

20 This is the ' gate of the ' Lord; ♦
   the ' righteous shall ' enter ' through it.

21 I will give thanks to you, for ' you have ' answered me ♦
   and have be'come ' my sa'lvation.

22 The stone which the ' builders re'jected ♦
   has be'come the ' chief ' cornerstone.

‡ 23 This is the ' Lord's ' doing, ♦
   and it is ' marvellous ' in our ' eyes.

24 This is the day that the ' Lord has ' made; ♦
   we will re'joice ' and be ' glad in it.

25 Come, O Lord, and ' save us we ' pray. ♦
   Come, Lord, ' send us ' now pros'perity.

26 Blessed is he who comes in the ' name of the ' Lord; ♦
   we bless you ' from the ' house of the ' Lord.

27 The Lord is God; he has ' given us ' light; ♦
   link the pilgrims with cords
      ' right · to the ' horns of the ' altar.

28 You are my God and ' I will ' thank you; ♦
   you are my ' God and ' I will ex'alt you.

29 O give thanks to the Lord, for ' he is ' good; ♦
   his ' mercy en'dures for ' ever.

Glory to the Father and ' to the ' Son
and ' to the ' Holy ' Spirit;
as it was in the be'ginning is ' now
and shall be for ' ever. ' A'men.

Chant: Martindale Sidwell
Copyright Control

Optional Refrain

This is the day that the ' Lord has ' made ♦
we will re'joice ' and be ' glad in it.

Psalm 118 (14–29)

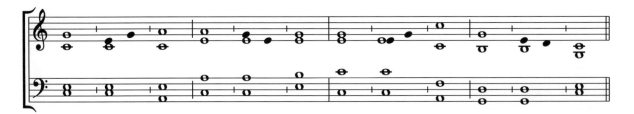

14　The Lord is my ' strength and my ' song, ♦
　　and he has be'come my sal'vation.

15　Joyful ' shouts of sal'vation ♦
　　sound from the ' tents of the ' righteous:

16　'The right hand of the Lord does mighty deeds;
　　　　the right hand of the Lord ' raises ' up; ♦
　　the right hand of the Lord does ' mighty ' deeds.'

17　I shall not ' die, but ' live ♦
　　and declare the ' works of the ' Lord.

‡　18　The Lord has ' punished me ' sorely, ♦
　　but he has not given me ' over to ' death.

19　Open to me the ' gates of ' righteousness, ♦
　　that I may enter and give ' thanks to the ' Lord.

20　This is the ' gate of the ' Lord; ♦
　　the righteous shall ' enter ' through it.

21　I will give thanks to you, for ' you have ' answered me ♦
　　and have be'come my sal'vation.

22　The stone which the ' builders re'jected ♦
　　has become the ' chief ' cornerstone.

‡　23　This is the ' Lord's ' doing, ♦
　　and it is marvellous ' in our ' eyes.

24　This is the day that the ' Lord has ' made; ♦
　　we will re'joice and be ' glad in it.

25　Come, O Lord, and ' save us we ' pray. ♦
　　Come, Lord, send us ' now pros'perity.

26　Blessed is he who comes in the ' name of the ' Lord; ♦
　　we bless you from the ' house of the ' Lord.

27　The Lord is God; he has ' given us ' light; ♦
　　link the pilgrims with cords
　　　　right to the ' horns of the ' altar.

28　You are my God and ' I will ' thank you; ♦
　　you are my God and ' I will ex'alt you.

29　O give thanks to the Lord, for ' he is ' good; ♦
　　his mercy en'dures for ' ever.

　　Glory to the Father ' and to the ' Son
　　and to the ' Holy ' Spirit;
　　as it was in the be'ginning is ' now
　　and shall be for ' ever. A'men.

Chant: Dom Gregory Murray OSB　©The Trustees of Downside Abbey
Music of refrain: Peter Moger　© 2000 Peter Moger

Optional Refrain

𝅘𝅥 = c.120

This is the day _____ that the Lord _ has made;
we will re - joice and be glad in it. _____

The Song of Moses and Miriam

1 I will sing to the Lord, who has ' triumphed ' gloriously, ♦
  the horse and his rider he has ' thrown ' into the ' sea.

2 The Lord is my ' strength and my ' song ♦
  and has be'come ' my sal'vation.

3 This is my God whom ' I will ' praise, ♦
  the God of my forebears ' whom I ' will ex'alt.

4 The Lord ' is a ' warrior, ♦
  the ' Lord ' is his ' name.

5 Your right hand, O Lord, is ' glorious in ' power: ♦
  your right hand, O ' Lord, ' shatters the ' enemy.

6 At the blast of your nostrils, the ' sea ' covered them; ♦
  they sank as ' lead · in the ' mighty ' waters.

7 In your unfailing ' love, O ' Lord, ♦
  you lead the people ' whom you ' have re'deemed.

8 And by your in'vincible ' strength ♦
  you will guide them ' to your ' holy ' dwelling.

‡ 9 You will bring them in and ' plant them, O ' Lord, ♦
  in the sanctuary ' which your ' hands have est'ablished.

Glory to the Father and ' to the ' Son
and ' to the ' Holy ' Spirit;
as it was in the be'ginning is ' now
and shall be for ' ever. ' A'men.

Exodus 15.1b-3,6,10,13,17

Optional Refrain

The Lord is my ' strength and my ' song, ♦
and has be'come ' my sal'vation.

Chant: Martindale Sidwell
Copyright Control

alternative chant

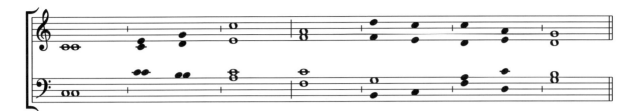

The Song of Moses and Miriam

1 I will sing to the Lord, who has ' triumphed ' gloriously, ♦
the horse and his rider he has thrown ' into the ' sea.

2 The Lord is my ' strength and my ' song ♦
and has be'come my sal'vation.

3 This is my God whom ' I will ' praise, ♦
the God of my forebears whom ' I will ex'alt.

4 The ' Lord is a ' warrior, ♦
the ' Lord is his ' name.

5 Your right hand, O Lord, is ' glorious in ' power: ♦
your right hand, O Lord, ' shatters the ' enemy.

6 At the blast of your nostrils, the ' sea ' covered them; ♦
they sank as lead in the ' mighty ' waters.

7 In your unfailing ' love, O ' Lord, ♦
you lead the people whom ' you have re'deemed.

8 And by your in'vincible ' strength ♦
you will guide them to your ' holy ' dwelling.

‡ 9 You will bring them in and ' plant them, O ' Lord, ♦
in the sanctuary which your ' hands have es'tablished.

Glory to the Father ' and to the ' Son
and to the ' Holy ' Spirit;
as it was in the be'ginning is ' now
and shall be for ' ever. A'men.

Exodus 15.1b-3,6,10,13,17

Music: Peter Moger
© 2000 Peter Moger

Optional Refrain

The Lord is my strength and my song: and has be-come my sal-va-tion.

A Song of Faith

1 Blessed be the God and ' Father ♦
of ' our Lord Jesus Christ!

2 By his great mercy we have been born anew to a ' living hope ♦
through the resurrection of Jesus ' Christ from the dead,

3 Into an inheritance that is imperishable, undefiled and un'fading, ♦
kept in ' heaven for you,

4 Who are being protected by the power of God
through faith for a sal'vation, ♦
ready to be revealed ' in the last time.

5 You were ransomed from the futile ways of your ' ancestors ♦
not with perishable things like ' silver or gold

6 But with the precious ' blood of Christ ♦
like that of a lamb ' without spot or stain.

7 Through him we have confidence in God,
who raised him from the dead and gave him ' glory, ♦
so that your faith and ' hope are set on God.

Glory to the Father and ' to the Son
and to the ' Holy Spirit;
as it was in the beginning ' is now
and shall be for ' ever. Amen.

1 Peter 1.3-5,18,19,21

Optional Refrain

God raised Christ from the dead, the Lamb with-out spot or stain.

Music: adapted from traditional chant, tone 8
© 2000 The Royal School of Church Music

A Song of Faith

1 Blessed be the God and ' Father ♦
of our Lord ' Jesus ' Christ!

2 By his great mercy we have been born anew to a living ' hope ♦
through the resurrection of Jesus Christ ' from the ' dead,

3 Into an inheritance that is imperishable, undefiled and un'fading, ♦
kept in ' heaven for ' you,

4 Who are being protected by the power of God
through faith for a sal'vation, ♦
ready to be revealed in the ' last ' time.

5 You were ransomed from the futile ways of your ' ancestors ♦
not with perishable things like ' silver or ' gold

6 But with the precious blood of ' Christ ♦
like that of a lamb without ' spot or ' stain.

7 Through him we have confidence in God,
who raised him from the dead and gave him ' glory, ♦
so that your faith and hope are ' set on ' God.

Glory to the Father and to the ' Son
and to the ' Holy ' Spirit;
as it was in the beginning is ' now
and shall be for ' ever. A'men.

I Peter 1.3-5,18,19,21

Optional Refrain

God raised Christ from the ' dead, ♦
the Lamb without ' spot or ' stain.

Chant: Norman Warren
© Norman Warren

Pentecost

Psalm 104 (26–36, 37b)

26 O Lord, how manifold ' are your ' works! ♦
In wisdom you have made them all;
    the ' earth is ' full of your ' creatures.

27 There is the sea, spread ' far and ' wide, ♦
and there move creatures beyond ' number, both ' small and ' great.

28 There go the ships, and there is ' that Le'viathan ♦
which you have ' made to ' play in the ' deep.

29 All of these ' look to ' you ♦
to give them their ' food in ' due ' season.

30 When you ' give it them, they ' gather it; ♦
you open your hand and ' they are ' filled with ' good.

31 When you hide your face ' they are ' troubled; ♦
when you take away their breath,
    they die and re'turn a'gain to the ' dust.

‡ 32 When you send forth your spirit, they ' are cre'ated, ♦
and you re'new the ' face of the ' earth.

33 May the glory of the Lord en'dure for ' ever; ♦
may the ' Lord re'joice in his ' works;

34 He looks on the earth ' and it ' trembles; ♦
he touches the ' mountains ' and they ' smoke.

35 I will sing to the Lord as ' long as I ' live; ♦
I will make music to my God ' while I ' have my ' being.

36 So shall my ' song ' please him ♦
while I re'joice ' in the ' Lord.

‡ 37b Bless the Lord, ' O my ' soul.
    Al' - le'lu'ia.

Glory to the Father and ' to the ' Son
and ' to the ' Holy ' Spirit;
as it was in the be'ginning is ' now
and shall be for ' ever. ' A'men.

Optional Refrain

Send forth your ' Spirit, O ' Lord, ♦
and re'new the ' face of the ' earth.

Chant: George J Elvey

Psalm 104 (26–36, 37b)

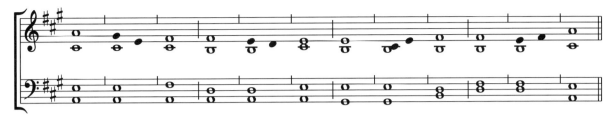

26 O Lord, how manifold ' are your ' works! ♦
In wisdom you have made them all;
    the earth is ' full of your ' creatures.

27 There is the sea, spread ' far and ' wide, ♦
and there move creatures beyond number, both ' small and ' great.

28 There go the ships, and there is ' that Le'viathan ♦
which you have made to ' play in the ' deep.

29 All of these ' look to ' you ♦
to give them their ' food in due ' season.

30 When you give it ' them, they ' gather it; ♦
you open your hand and they are ' filled with ' good.

31 When you hide your face ' they are ' troubled; ♦
when you take away their breath,
    they die and return a'gain to the ' dust.

‡ 32 When you send forth your spirit, ' they are cre'ated, ¨
and you renew the ' face of the ' earth.

33 May the glory of the Lord en'dure for ' ever; ♦
may the Lord re'joice in his ' works;

34 He looks on the ' earth and it ' trembles; ♦
he touches the mountains ' and they ' smoke.

35 I will sing to the Lord as ' long as I ' live; ♦
I will make music to my God while I ' have my ' being.

36 So shall ' my song ' please him ♦
while I re'joice in the ' Lord.

‡ 37b Bless the Lord, ' O my ' soul.
    Alle'lu'ia.

Glory to the Father ' and to the ' Son
and to the ' Holy ' Spirit;
as it was in the be'ginning is ' now
and shall be for ' ever. A'men.

Optional Refrain

Send forth your Spi-rit, O Lord,___ and re-new the face of the earth. ___

A Song of Ezekiel

1 I will take you from the ' nations, ◆
and gather you from ' all the countries.

2 I will sprinkle clean water up'on you, ◆
and you shall be clean from all ' your uncleannesses.

3 A new heart I will ' give you, ◆
and put a new ' spirit within you,

4 And I will remove from your body the ' heart of stone ◆
and give ' you a heart of flesh.

5 You shall be my ' people, ◆
and ' I will be your God.

Glory to the Father and ' to the Son
and to the ' Holy Spirit;
as it was in the beginning ' is now
and shall be for ' ever. Amen.

Ezekiel 36.24-26,28b

Optional Refrain

I will put a new spi - rit with - in you,   and you shall be my peo - ple.

Music: adapted from traditional chant, tone 5
© 2000 The Royal School of Church Music

A Song of Ezekiel

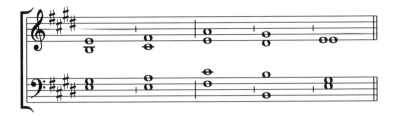

1 I will take you from the ' nations, ◆
   and gather you from ' all the ' countries.

2 I will sprinkle clean water up'on you, ◆
   and you shall be clean from ' all your un'cleannesses.

3 A new heart I will ' give you, ◆
   and put a new ' spirit with'in you,

4 And I will remove from your body the heart of ' stone ◆
   and give you a ' heart of ' flesh.

5 You shall be my ' people, ◆
   and I will ' be your ' God.

   Glory to the Father and to the ' Son
   and to the ' Holy ' Spirit;
   as it was in the beginning is ' now
   and shall be for ' ever. A'men.

Ezekiel 36.24-26,28b

Optional Refrain

I will put a new spirit with'in you, ◆
and you shall ' be my ' people.

Chant: John Harper
© 2000 The Royal School of Church Music

A Song of God's Children

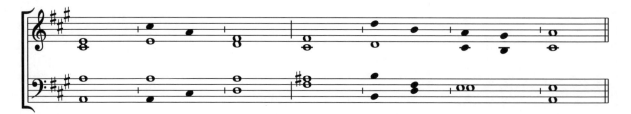

1 The law of the Spirit of life ' in Christ ' Jesus ♦
   has set us free from the ' law of ' sin and ' death.

2 All who are led by the Spirit of God are ' children of ' God; ♦
   for we have received the Spirit that enables us to ' cry, ' 'Abba, ' Father'.

3 The Spirit himself bears witness that we are ' children of ' God ♦
   and if God's ' children, then ' heirs of ' God;

4 If heirs of God, then fellow-'heirs with ' Christ; ♦
   since we suffer with him now, that we ' may be ' glorified ' with him.

5 These sufferings that we ' now en'dure ♦
   are not worth comparing to the glory ' that shall ' be re'vealed.

6 For the creation waits with ' eager ' longing ♦
   for the re'vealing · of the ' children of ' God.

   Glory to the Father and ' to the ' Son
   and ' to the ' Holy ' Spirit;
   as it was in the be'ginning is ' now
   and shall be for ' ever. ' A'men.

Romans 8.2,14,15b-19

Optional Refrain

The Spirit ' of the ' Father ♦
gives ' life · to the ' children of ' God.

Chant: George J Elvey

A Song of God's Children

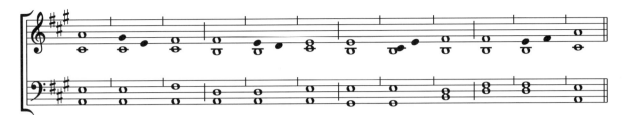

1 The law of the Spirit of ' life in Christ ' Jesus ♦
  has set us free from the law of ' sin and ' death.

2 All who are led by the Spirit of God are ' children of ' God; ♦
  for we have received the Spirit that enables us to cry, ' 'Abba, ' Father'.

3 The Spirit himself bears witness that we are ' children of ' God ♦
  and if God's children, then ' heirs of ' God;

4 If heirs of God, then fellow-'heirs with ' Christ; ♦
  since we suffer with him now, that we may be ' glorified ' with him.

5 These sufferings that ' we now en'dure ♦
  are not worth comparing to the glory that ' shall be re'vealed.

6 For the creation waits with ' eager ' longing ♦
  for the revealing of the ' children of ' God.

Glory to the Father ' and to the ' Son
and to the ' Holy ' Spirit;
as it was in the be'ginning is ' now
and shall be for ' ever. A'men.

Romans 8.2,14,15b-19

Optional Refrain

The Spi - rit __ of the Fa - ther __ gives life to the chil-dren of God. __

Chant: Dom Gregory Murray OSB   © The Trustees of Downside Abbey
Music: Peter Moger   © 2000 Peter Moger

Ordinary Time

Psalm 1

1 Blessed are they who have not walked
    in the counsel of the ' wicked, ♦
nor lingered in the way of sinners,
    nor sat in the assembly of ' the scornful.

2 Their delight is in the law of ' the Lord ♦
and they meditate on his law ' day and night.

3 Like a tree planted by streams of water
    bearing fruit in due season, with leaves that do not ' wither, ♦
whatever they do, it ' shall prosper.

4 As for the wicked, it is not ' so with them; ♦
they are like chaff which the wind ' blows away.

5 Therefore the wicked shall not be able to stand in the ' judgement, ♦
nor the sinner in the congregation of ' the righteous.

6 For the Lord knows the way of the ' righteous, ♦
but the way of the wicked ' shall perish.

Glory to the Father and to ' the Son
and to the Ho'ly Spirit;
as it was in the beginning ' is now
and shall be for ev'er. Amen.

Optional Refrain

The Lord knows the way of the right-eous, what-ev-er they do, it shall pros-per.

Music: adapted from traditional chant, tone 3
© 2000 The Royal School of Church Music

Psalm 1

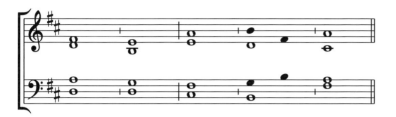

1 Blessed are they who have not walked
 in the counsel of the ' wicked, ♦
nor lingered in the way of sinners,
 nor sat in the assembly ' of the ' scornful.

2 Their delight is in the law of the ' Lord ♦
and they meditate on his law ' day and ' night.

3 Like a tree planted by streams of water
 bearing fruit in due season, with leaves that do not ' wither, ♦
whatever they do, ' it shall ' prosper.

4 As for the wicked, it is not so with ' them; ♦
they are like chaff which the wind ' blows a'way.

5 Therefore the wicked shall not be able to stand in the ' judgement, ♦
nor the sinner in the congregation ' of the ' righteous.

6 For the Lord knows the way of the ' righteous, ♦
but the way of the ' wicked shall ' perish.

 Glory to the Father and to the ' Son
 and to the ' Holy ' Spirit;
 as it was in the beginning is ' now
 and shall be for ' ever. A'men.

Optional Refrain

The Lord knows the way of the ' righteous: ♦
whatever they do, ' it shall ' prosper.

Chant: John Harper
© 2000 The Royal School of Church Music

Psalm 34 (1–10)

1 I will bless the ' Lord at ' all times; ♦
his praise shall ' ever be ' in my ' mouth.

2 My soul shall glory ' in the ' Lord; ♦
let the ' humble ' hear and be ' glad.

3 O magnify the ' Lord with ' me; ♦
let us ex'alt his ' name to'gether.

4 I sought the Lord ' and he ' answered me ♦
and de'livered me from ' all my ' fears.

5 Look upon him ' and be ' radiant ♦
and your faces ' shall not ' be a'shamed.

6 This poor soul cried, and the ' Lord ' heard me ♦
and ' saved me from ' all my ' troubles.

7 The angel ' of the ' Lord ♦
encamps around those who ' fear him ' and de'livers them.

8 O taste and see that the ' Lord is ' gracious; ♦
blessed is the ' one who ' trusts in ' him.

9 Fear the Lord, all ' you his ' holy ones, ♦
for those who ' fear him ' lack ' nothing.

10 Lions may lack and ' suffer ' hunger, ♦
but those who seek the Lord
lack ' nothing ' that is ' good.

Glory to the Father and ' to the ' Son
and ' to the ' Holy ' Spirit;
as it was in the be'ginning is ' now
and shall be for ' ever. ' A'men.

Optional Refrain

O taste and see that the ' Lord is ' gracious ♦
blessed is the ' one who ' trusts in ' him.

Chant: James Turle

alternative chant

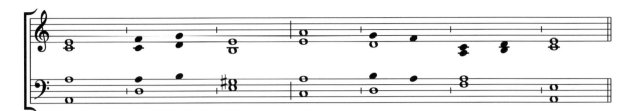

Psalm 34 (1–10)

1 I will bless the ' Lord at ' all times; ♦
his praise shall ever be ' in my ' mouth.

2 My soul shall ' glory · in the ' Lord; ♦
let the humble ' hear and be ' glad.

3 O magnify the ' Lord with ' me; ♦
let us exalt his ' name to'gether.

4 I sought the ' Lord and he ' answered me ♦
and delivered me from ' all my ' fears.

5 Look upon ' him and be ' radiant ♦
and your faces shall ' not be a'shamed.

6 This poor soul cried, and the ' Lord ' heard me ♦
and saved me from ' all my ' troubles.

7 The angel of the Lord encamps around ' those who ' fear him ♦
and de'livers ' them.

8 O taste and see that the ' Lord is ' gracious; ♦
blessed is the one who ' trusts in ' him.

9 Fear the Lord, all ' you his ' holy ones, ♦
for those who ' fear him lack ' nothing.

10 Lions may lack and ' suffer ' hunger, ♦
but those who seek the Lord
lack nothing ' that is ' good.

Glory to the Father ' and to the ' Son
and to the ' Holy ' Spirit;
as it was in the be'ginning is ' now
and shall be for ' ever. A'men.

Chant: Christopher Tambling   © Christopher Tambling
Alternative chant: Norman Warren   © Norman Warren
Music: Peter Moger   © 2000 Peter Moger

alternative chant

Optional Refrain

O taste and see that the Lord is gra - cious; bless-ed is the one who trusts in ___ him. *last time* trusts in ___ him.

Psalm 85 (8–13)

8 I will listen to what the Lord God ' will say, ♦
    for he shall speak peace to his people and to the faithful,
        that they turn not a'gain to folly.

9 Truly, his salvation is near to those who ' fear him, ♦
    that his glory may dwell ' in our land.

10 Mercy and truth are met to'gether, ♦
    righteousness and peace have ' kissed each other;

11 Truth shall spring up from ' the earth ♦
    and righteousness look ' down from heaven.

12 The Lord will indeed give all that ' is good, ♦
    and our land will ' yield its increase.

13 Righteousness shall go be'fore him ♦
    and direct his steps ' in the way.

Glory to the Father and to ' the Son
and to the ' Holy Spirit;
as it was in the beginning ' is now
and shall be for ev'er. Amen.

Optional Refrain

Show us your mer - cy, O Lord, and grant us your sal - va - tion.

Music: adapted from traditional chant, tone 1
© 2000 The Royal School of Church Music

Psalm 85 (8–13)

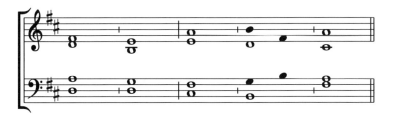

8 I will listen to what the Lord God will ' say, ♦
    for he shall speak peace to his people and to the faithful,
        that they turn not a'gain to ' folly.

9 Truly, his salvation is near to those who ' fear him, ♦
    that his glory may ' dwell in our ' land.

10 Mercy and truth are met to'gether, ♦
    righteousness and peace have ' kissed each ' other;

11 Truth shall spring up from the ' earth ♦
    and righteousness look ' down from ' heaven.

12 The Lord will indeed give all that is ' good, ♦
    and our land will ' yield its ' increase.

13 Righteousness shall go be'fore him ♦
    and direct his ' steps in the ' way.

    Glory to the Father and to the ' Son
    and to the ' Holy ' Spirit;
    as it was in the beginning is ' now
    and shall be for ' ever. A'men.

Optional Refrain

Show us your mercy, O ' Lord, ♦
and grant us ' your sal'vation.

Chant: John Harper
© 2000 The Royal School of Church Music

Psalm 119 (1–8)

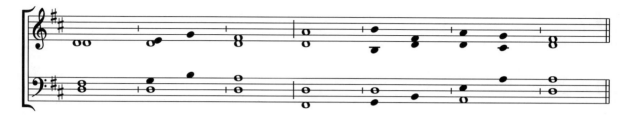

1 Blessed are those whose ' way is ' pure, ♦
  who ' walk · in the ' law of the ' Lord.

2 Blessed are those who ' keep his ' testimonies ♦
  and seek him ' with their ' whole ' heart,

3 Those who ' do no ' wickedness, ♦
  but ' walk in ' his ' ways.

4 You, O ' Lord, have ' charged ♦
  that we should ' diligently ' keep your com'mandments.

5 O that my ways were ' made so di'rect ♦
  that ' I might ' keep your ' statutes.

6 Then should I not be ' put to ' shame, ♦
  because I have ' regard for ' all your com'mandments.

7 I will thank you with an ' unfeigned ' heart, ♦
  when I have ' learned your ' righteous ' judgements.

8 I will ' keep your ' statutes; ♦
  O for'sake ' me not ' utterly.

  Glory to the Father and ' to the ' Son
  and ' to the ' Holy ' Spirit;
  as it was in the be'ginning is ' now
  and shall be for ' ever. ' A'men.

Optional Refrain

Blessed are those who walk in the ' law of the ' Lord; ♦
who seek him ' with their ' whole ' heart.

Chant: James Turle

Psalm 119 (1–8)

1 Blessed are those whose ' way is ' pure, ♦
who walk in the ' law of the ' Lord

2 Blessed are those who ' keep his ' testimonies ♦
and seek him with their ' whole ' heart,

3 Those who ' do no ' wickedness, ♦
but ' walk in his ' ways.

4 You, O ' Lord, have ' charged ♦
that we should diligently ' keep your com'mandments.

5 O that my ways were made ' so di'rect ♦
that I might ' keep your ' statutes.

6 Then should I not be ' put to ' shame, ♦
because I have regard for ' all your com'mandments.

7 I will thank you with an ' unfeigned ' heart, ♦
when I have learned your ' righteous ' judgements.

8 I will ' keep your ' statutes; ♦
O for'sake me not ' utterly.

Glory to the Father ' and to the ' Son
and to the ' Holy ' Spirit;
as it was in the be'ginning is ' now
and shall be for ' ever. A'men.

Optional Refrain

Bless - ed are those who walk in the law of the Lord.

Chant melody: Robert Fielding   © Robert Fielding
Music: Peter Moger   © 2000 Peter Moger

Psalm 121

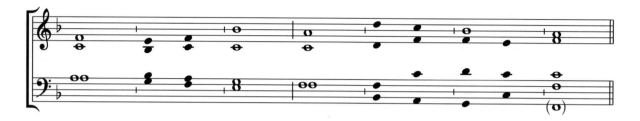

1 I lift up my eyes ' to the ' hills; ◆
   from ' where is my ' help to ' come?

2 My help comes ' from the ' Lord, ◆
   the ' maker of ' heaven and ' earth.

3 He will not suffer your ' foot to ' stumble; ◆
   he who watches ' over you ' will not ' sleep.

4 Behold, he who keeps watch ' over ' Israel ◆
   shall ' neither ' slumber nor ' sleep.

5 The Lord himself ' watches ' over you; ◆
   the Lord is your shade ' at your ' right ' hand,

6 So that the sun shall not ' strike you by ' day, ◆
   nei'ther the ' moon by ' night.

7 The Lord shall keep you ' from all ' evil; ◆
   it is ' he who shall ' keep your ' soul.

8 The Lord shall keep watch over your going out
       and your ' coming ' in, ◆
   from this time ' forth for ' ever'more.

   Glory to the Father and ' to the ' Son
   and ' to the ' Holy ' Spirit;
   as it was in the be'ginning is ' now
   and shall be for ' ever. ' A'men.

Optional Refrain

My help ' comes from the ' Lord, ◆
the ' maker of ' heaven and ' earth.

Chant: Jonathan Battishill

Psalm 121

1 I lift up my ' eyes to the ' hills, ✦
from where is my ' help to ' come?

2 My help ' comes from the ' Lord, ✦
the maker of ' heaven and ' earth.

3 He will not suffer your ' foot to ' stumble; ✦
he who watches over you ' will not ' sleep.

4 Behold, he who keeps ' watch over ' Israel ✦
shall neither ' slumber nor ' sleep.

5 The Lord himself ' watches ' over you; ✦
the Lord is your ' shade at your ' right hand,

6 So that the sun shall not ' strike you by ' day, ✦
neither the ' moon by ' night.

7 The Lord shall keep you ' from all ' evil; ✦
it is he who shall ' keep your ' soul.

8 The Lord shall keep watch over your going out
and your ' coming ' in, ✦
from this time forth for ' ever'more.

Glory to the Father ' and to the ' Son
and to the ' Holy ' Spirit;
as it was in the be'ginning is ' now
and shall be for ' ever. A'men.

Optional Refrain

Chant: Robert Fielding © Robert Fielding
Music: Peter Moger © 2000 Peter Moger

Psalm 130

1 Out of the depths have I cried to you, O Lord;
    Lord, ' hear my voice; ♦
let your ears consider well the voice of my sup'plication.

2 If you, Lord, were to mark what is ' done amiss, ♦
O Lord, ' who could stand?

3 But there is forgiveness ' with you, ♦
so that ' you shall be feared.

4 I wait for the Lord; my soul ' waits for him; ♦
in his word ' is my hope.

5 My soul waits for the Lord,
    more than the night watch for the ' morning, ♦
more than the night watch for ' the morning.

6 O Israel, wait ' for the Lord, ♦
for with the Lord there ' is mercy;

7 With him is plenteous re'demption ♦
and he shall redeem Israel ' from all their sins.

Glory to the Father and ' to the Son
and to the Ho'ly Spirit;
as it was in the beginning ' is now
and shall be for ev'er. Amen.

Optional Refrain

Out of the depths have I cried to you, O Lord.

Music: adapted from traditional chant, tone 3
© 2000 The Royal School of Church Music

Psalm 130

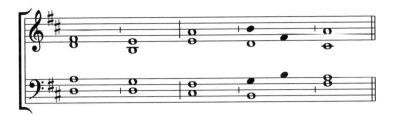

1 Out of the depths have I cried to you, O Lord;
     Lord, hear my ' voice; ♦
  let your ears consider well the voice of my ' suppli'cation.

2 If you, Lord, were to mark what is done a'miss, ♦
  O Lord, ' who could ' stand?

3 But there is forgiveness with ' you, ♦
  so that ' you shall be ' feared.

4 I wait for the Lord; my soul ' waits for him; ♦
  in his ' word is my ' hope.

5 My soul waits for the Lord,
     more than the night watch for the ' morning, ♦
  more than the night watch ' for the ' morning.

6 O Israel, wait for the ' Lord, ♦
  for with the ' Lord · there is ' mercy;

7 With him is plenteous re'demption ♦
  and he shall redeem Israel from ' all their ' sins.

  Glory to the Father and to the ' Son
  and to the ' Holy ' Spirit;
  as it was in the beginning is ' now
  and shall be for ' ever. A'men.

Optional Refrain

Out of the ' depths ♦
have I cried to ' you, ' O Lord

Chant: John Harper
© 2000 The Royal School of Church Music

Psalm 146

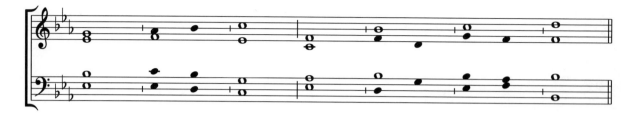

1 Alleluia.
    Praise the Lord, O my soul:
       while I live will I ' praise the ' Lord; ♦
  as long as I have any being,
       I will sing ' praises ' to my ' God.

2 Put not your trust in princes,
       nor in any ' human ' power, ♦
  for there ' is no ' help in ' them.

3 When their breath goes forth, they re'turn · to the ' earth; ♦
  on that day ' all their ' thoughts ' perish.

4 Happy are those who have the God of Jacob ' for their ' help, ♦
  whose hope is ' in the ' Lord their ' God;

5 Who made heaven and earth,
       the sea and ' all that is ' in them; ♦
  who ' keeps his ' promise for ' ever;

6 Who gives justice to those that ' suffer ' wrong ♦
  and ' bread to ' those who ' hunger.

7 The Lord looses ' those that are ' bound; ♦
  the Lord opens the ' eyes ' of the ' blind;

8 The Lord lifts up those who are ' bowed ' down; ♦
  the ' Lord ' loves the ' righteous;

9 The Lord watches over the stranger in the land;
       he upholds the ' orphan and ' widow; ♦
  but the way of the wicked ' he turns ' upside ' down.

10 The Lord shall ' reign for ' ever, ♦
  your God, O Zion, throughout all generations.
       ' Alle'lu'ia.

  Glory to the Father and ' to the ' Son
  and ' to the ' Holy ' Spirit;
  as it was in the be'ginning is ' now
  and shall be for ' ever. ' A'men.

Optional Refrain

Praise the Lord, ' O my ' soul: ♦
while I ' live · will I ' praise the ' Lord.

Chant: Peter Hurford
© Peter Hurford

Psalm 146

1 Alleluia.
   Praise the Lord, O my soul:
      while I live will I ' praise the ' Lord; ♦
   as long as I have any being,
      I will sing praises ' to my ' God.

2 Put not your trust in princes,
      nor in any ' human ' power, ♦
   for there is no ' help in ' them.

3 When their breath goes forth, they re'turn to the ' earth; ♦
   on that day all their ' thoughts ' perish.

4 Happy are those who have the God of Jacob ' for their ' help, ♦
   whose hope is in the ' Lord their ' God;

5 Who made heaven and earth,
      the sea and ' all that is ' in them; ♦
   who keeps his ' promise for ' ever;

6 Who gives justice to those that ' suffer ' wrong ♦
   and bread to ' those who ' hunger.

7 The Lord looses ' those that are ' bound; ♦
   the Lord opens the ' eyes of the ' blind;

8 The Lord lifts up those who are ' bowed ' down; ♦
   the Lord ' loves the ' righteous;

9 The Lord watches over the stranger in the land;
      he upholds the ' orphan and ' widow; ♦
   but the way of the wicked he turns ' upside ' down.

10 The Lord shall ' reign for ' ever, ♦
   your God, O Zion, throughout all generations.
      ' Alle'luia.

   Glory to the Father ' and to the ' Son
   and to the ' Holy ' Spirit;
   as it was in the be'ginning is ' now
   and shall be for ' ever. A'men.

Optional Refrain

Chant: Christopher Tambling   © Christopher Tambling
Music: Peter Moger   © 2000 Peter Moger

Psalm 150

1 Alleluia.
　　O praise God in his ' holiness; ♦
praise him in the firmament ' of his power.

2 Praise him for his ' mighty acts; ♦
praise him according to his excel'lent greatness.

3 Praise him with the blast of the ' trumpet; ♦
praise him upon ' the harp and lyre.

4 Praise him with timbrel and ' dances; ♦
praise him upon ' the strings and pipe.

5 Praise him with ringing ' cymbals; ♦
praise him upon the clash'ing cymbals.

6 Let everything ' that has breath ♦
praise the Lord.
　　Al'leluia.

Glory to the Father and ' to the Son
and to the Ho'ly Spirit;
as it was in the beginning ' is now
and shall be for ev'er. Amen.

Optional Refrain

Al – le – lu – ia:　Praise God in his ho-li-ness.

Music: adapted from traditional chant, tone 3
© 2000 The Royal School of Church Music

Psalm 150

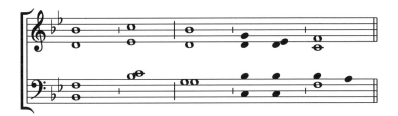

1 Alleluia.
   O praise God in his ' holiness; ♦
   praise him in the firmament ' of his ' power.

2 Praise him for his mighty ' acts; ♦
   praise him according to his ' excellent ' greatness.

3 Praise him with the blast of the ' trumpet; ♦
   praise him upon the ' harp and ' lyre.

4 Praise him with timbrel and ' dances; ♦
   praise him upon the ' strings and ' pipe.

5 Praise him with ringing ' cymbals; ♦
   praise him upon the ' clashing ' cymbals.

6 Let everything that has ' breath ♦
   praise the Lord.
      ' Alle'luia.

Glory to the Father and to the ' Son
and to the ' Holy ' Spirit;
as it was in the beginning is ' now
and shall be for ' ever. A'men.

Optional Refrain

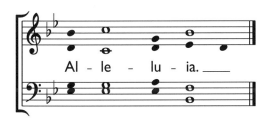

Al – le – lu – ia. ____

Chant: Norman Warren
© Norman Warren

A Song of David

1 Blessed are you, God of Israel, for ever and ' ever, ♦
  for yours is the greatness, the power,
      the glory, the splendour ' and the majesty.

2 Everything in heaven and on earth ' is yours; ♦
  yours is the kingdom, O Lord,
      and you are exalted as head ' over all.

3 Riches and honour ' come from you ♦
  and you rule ' over all.

4 In your hand are power ' and might; ♦
  yours it is to give power and ' strength to all.

5 And now we give you thanks, ' our God, ♦
  and praise your ' glorious name.

6 For all things ' come from you, ♦
  and of your own ' have we given you.

  Glory to the Father and to ' the Son
  and to the ' Holy Spirit;
  as it was in the beginning ' is now
  and shall be for ev'er. Amen.

1 Chronicles 29.10b-13,14b

Optional Refrain

Splen-dour and ma-jes-ty are yours, O God; you are ex-alt-ed as head o-ver all.

Music: adapted from traditional chant, tone 1
© 2000 The Royal School of Church Music

A Song of David

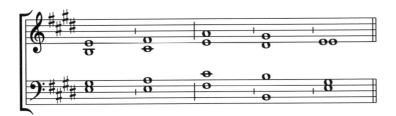

1. Blessed are you, God of Israel, for ever and ' ever, ♦
   for yours is the greatness, the power,
     the glory, the splendour ' and the ' majesty.

2. Everything in heaven and on earth is ' yours; ♦
   yours is the kingdom, O Lord,
     and you are exalted as ' head over ' all.

3. Riches and honour come from ' you ♦
   and you ' rule over ' all.

4. In your hand are power and ' might; ♦
   yours it is to give power and ' strength to ' all.

5. And now we give you thanks, our ' God, ♦
   and praise your ' glorious ' name.

6. For all things come from ' you, ♦
   and of your ' own · have we ' given you.

   Glory to the Father and to the ' Son
   and to the ' Holy ' Spirit;
   as it was in the beginning is ' now
   and shall be for ' ever. A'men.

I Chronicles 29.10b-13,14b

Optional Refrain

Splendour and majesty are yours, O ' God; ♦
you are exalted as ' head over ' all.

Chant: John Harper
© 2000 The Royal School of Church Music

A Song of the Lamb

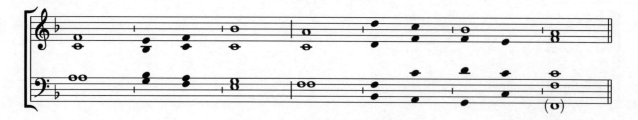

1 Salvation and glory and power be'long to our ' God, ♦
   whose ' judgements are ' true and ' just.

2 Praise our God, all ' you his ' servants, ♦
   all who ' fear him, both ' small and ' great.

3 The Lord our God, the Al'mighty, ' reigns: ♦
   let us rejoice and ex'ult and ' give him the ' glory.

4 For the marriage of the ' Lamb has ' come ♦
   and his ' bride has ' made herself ' ready.

5 Blessed are those who ' are in'vited ♦
   to the wedding ' banquet ' of the ' Lamb.

   To the One who sits on the throne and ' to the ' Lamb ♦
   be blessing and honour and glory and might,
        for ever and ' ever. ' A'men.

Revelation 19.1b,5b,6b,7,9b

Optional Refrain

Let us re'joice · and ex'ult ♦
and give ' glory ' to our ' God.

Chant: Jonathan Battishill

A Song of the Lamb

1 Salvation and glory and power be'long to our ' God, ♦
  whose judgements are ' true and ' just.

2 Praise our God, all ' you his ' servants, ♦
  all who fear him, both ' small and ' great.

3 The Lord our God, the Al'mighty, ' reigns: ♦
  let us rejoice and exult and ' give him the ' glory.

4 For the marriage of the ' Lamb has ' come ♦
  and his bride has ' made herself ' ready.

5 Blessed are those ' who are in'vited ♦
  to the wedding banquet ' of the ' Lamb.

  To the One who sits on the throne ' and to the ' Lamb ♦
  be blessing and honour and glory and might,
    for ever and ' ever. A'men.

Revelation 19.1b,5b,6b,7,9b

alternative chant

Optional Refrain

Let us re – joice   and ex – ult: and give glo – ry   to our God.

Chant: Christopher Tambling   © Christopher Tambling
Alternative chant: Norman Warren   © Norman Warren
Music: Peter Moger   © 2000 Peter Moger

Psalm Songs

Advent

Verse

joiced when I heard them say: _____ "Let us go to the house of God." _____ And _

now our feet are stand-ing _____ in your gates, O Je-ru-sa-lem.

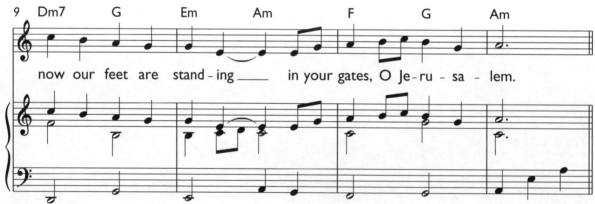

2 Like a temple of unity is the city Jerusalem.
   It is there all tribes will gather, all the tribes of the house of God.

3 It is faithful to Israel's law, there to praise the name of God.
   All the judgement seats of David were set down in Jerusalem.

4 For the peace of all nations pray: for God's peace within your homes.
   May God's lasting peace surround us; may it dwell in Jerusalem.

5 For the love of my friends and kin I will bless you with signs of peace.
   For the love of God's own people I will labour and pray for you.

Refrain

* optional descant and alto

The original accompaniment is available in Psalm Songs 1 (Cassell, 1998), or from OCP Publications.

Words & music: Bernadette Farrell, keyboard arrangement by Esther Jones
© 1992 Bernadette Farrell. Published by OCP Publications, 5536 NE Hassalo, Portland, OR 97213, USA.

Verse

I Sing a new song of joy to the Lord, Who has done such mar‑vel‑lous things; His strength he re‑veals with his arm, __ By his hand the vict'‑ry is won. __

Refrain

Sing new songs to the Lord, __ for his love is ev‑er‑last‑ing. __

Sing new songs to the Lord, __ who is come to save the world.
*[who has con‑quered sin and death.]

2 The Lord has made known his salvation; in the sight of all of his peoples.
His mercy he shows unto Israel, and his righteousness to the nations.

3 Sound praise to the Lord, all the earth; every voice now break into song:
with strings and the sound of the trumpet to the Lord give praise without end.

4 Let the sea and the land now ring out, let the streams and hills clap their hands;
He comes down to earth bringing justice and his saving help to the world.

5 To the Father, the Son and the Spirit, to the Three in One give the glory,
who was and who is and who shall be throughout all the ages to come.

* Use this text in Eastertide

Words: John Harper
© 2000 The Royal School of Church Music
Music: John Bell, from *Enemy of Apathy* (Wild Goose Publications 1988)
© 1988 WGRG, Iona Community, 840 Govan Road, Glasgow G51 3UU, Scotland

Lent

2 No-one whoever trusts in you shall find their hope is put to shame.
   Shame comes to those who turn away, who spurn the goodness of the living God.

3 Make known your paths to me, O Lord; show me the ways which I should take.
   Teach me and lead me, faithful God; you are my saviour and my hope is in you.

4 Remember, Lord, your tender care, your never failing, constant love.
   Forgive my sins, my youth's offence; in love and kindness remember me, Lord.

Words & music: John Bell
from *I lift my soul to you, O God* (Wild Goose Publications 1993)
© 1993 WGRG, Iona Community, 840 Govan Road, Glasgow G51 3UU, Scotland

Ostinato chorale

Verses

2 The Lord is com-pas-sion and love, slow to an-ger and
rich in mer-cy. God does not treat us ac-cord-ing to our
sins nor re-pay us ac-cord-ing to our faults.

3 As a Fa-ther has com-pas-sion on his chil-dren the Lord has
pi-ty on those who fear him; ___ for he knows of what we are
made, he re-mem-bers that we are dust.

Words of verse: The Grail (England)
Words of refrain & music: Jacques Berthier

I Clap your hands all you na – tions, A – men.＿ Hal – le – lu – jah!

Shout for joy all you peo – ple; A – men.＿ Hal – le – lu – jah!

Ho – ly is the Most High; A – men. Hal – le – lu – jah!

Migh – ty ov – er the earth. A – men. Hal – le – lu – jah!

2 God subdues every nation, *Amen. Hallelujah.*
   God is king of all creatures; *Amen. Hallelujah.*
   God has given this land *Amen. Hallelujah.*
   To the people he loves. *Amen. Hallelujah.*

3 To the shouting in triumph,
   To the blasting of trumpets,
   God has gone up,   ♩♩♩
   God ascends over all.

4 Praise the Lord with your singing,
   Sing God psalms for ever.
   God is monarch of all,
   Sovereign over the earth.

5 Those on earth who are mighty
   Still belong to our Maker,
   God exalted on high,
   God forever our Lord.

Words & music: John Bell
from *Psalms of Patience, Protest and Praise* (Wild Goose Publications 1993)
© 1993 WGRG, Iona Community, 840 Govan Road, Glasgow G51 3UU, Scotland

Words & music: Bernadette Farrell

2 You know my resting and my rising. You discern my purpose from afar.
And with love everlasting you besiege me: in ev'ry moment of life or death you are.

3 Before a word is on my tongue, Lord, you have known its meaning through and through.
You are with me beyond my understanding: God of my present, my past and future, too.

VERSE 4 *(a cappella, guitars tacent)*:

4 Al - though your _ Spi - rit is up - on _ me, still I search _ for shel - ter from your light. _ There is no - where on earth I can es - cape you: _ e - ven the dark - ness is ra - diant in your sight.

5 For you created me and shaped me, gave me life within my mother's womb.
For the wonder of who I am, I praise you: safe in your hands, all creation is made new.

An SATB version is available in Psalm Songs 3 *(Cassell, 1998) or from OCP Publications.*

Lord, be my help, be the rock where I hide, be my tower of strength each

day. _____ O _ Lord, be my hope, be the One whom I trust, be the

Sa - viour who guides my way.   O _ way.   way.

Verse

1 It is you, O Lord, who will res-cue me, who will hear my voice when I
2 It is you, O Lord, who will com-fort me, who will shel-ter me with _
3 All my life you've walked close _ by my side, a help and joy from _

call. _____ It is you, O Lord, who will free me from sin, and _
care. _____ It is you, O Lord, who will show me the truth and _
birth. _____ My _ lips shall speak of your migh - ty deeds, and your

hold me _____ when I fall. _____ O _
lis - ten _____ to my prayer. _____
won - ders _____ on the earth. _____

Words & music: David Ogden, keyboard arrangement by Esther Jones
© 1996 David Ogden

The original accompaniment is available in Psalm Songs 3 *(Cassell, 1998).*

Refrain

2 Such is God's great power and wisdom
None can calculate or tell;
Keen is God to ground the wicked
And with humble folk to dwell.

3 God, with clouds, the sky has curtained,
Thus ensuring rain shall fall;
Earth, responding, grows to order
Food for creatures great and small.

4 God's discernment never favours
Strength or speed to lift or move;
God delights in those who fear him,
Trusting in his steadfast love.

Words & music: John Bell
from *Psalms of Patience, Protest and Praise* (Wild Goose Publications 1993)
© 1993 WGRG, Iona Community, 840 Govan Road, Glasgow G51 3UU, Scotland

Appendix

Canticles pointed for use with Anglican Chant

Canticles pointed for use with Anglican Chant

Benedicite – a Song of Creation

1 Bless the Lord all you ' works of the ' Lord: ♦
 sing his ' praise · and ex'alt him for ' ever.

2 Bless the ' Lord you ' heavens: ♦
 sing his ' praise · and ex'alt him for ' ever.

3 Bless the Lord you ' angels · of the ' Lord: ♦
 bless the ' Lord all ' you his ' hosts;

 bless the Lord you waters a'bove the ' heavens: ♦
 sing his ' praise · and ex'alt him for ' ever.

4 Bless the Lord ' sun and ' moon: ♦
 bless the ' Lord you ' stars of ' heaven;

 bless the Lord all ' rain and ' dew: ♦
 sing his ' praise · and ex'alt him for ' ever.

5 Bless the Lord all ' winds that ' blow: ♦
 bless the ' Lord you ' fire and ' heat;

 bless the Lord scorching wind and ' bitter ' cold: ♦
 sing his ' praise · and ex'alt him for ' ever.

6 Bless the Lord dews and ' falling ' snows: ♦
 bless the ' Lord you ' nights and ' days;

 bless the Lord ' light and ' darkness: ♦
 sing his ' praise · and ex'alt him for ' ever.

7 Bless the Lord ' frost and ' cold: ♦
 bless the ' Lord you ' ice and ' snow;

 bless the Lord ' lightnings and ' clouds: ♦
 sing his ' praise · and ex'alt him for ' ever.

8 O let the earth ' bless the ' Lord: ♦
 bless the ' Lord you ' mountains and ' hills;

 bless the Lord all that ' grows in the ' ground: ♦
 sing his ' praise · and ex'alt him for ' ever.

9 Bless the ' Lord you ' springs: ♦
 bless the ' Lord you ' seas and ' rivers;

 bless the Lord you whales and all that ' swim in the ' waters: ♦
 sing his ' praise · and ex'alt him for ' ever.

10 Bless the Lord all ' birds of the ' air: ♦
 bless the ' Lord you ' beasts and ' cattle;

 bless the Lord all ' people on ' earth: ♦
 sing his ' praise · and ex'alt him for ' ever.

11 O people of God ' bless the ' Lord: ♦
 bless the ' Lord you ' priests of the ' Lord;

 bless the Lord you ' servants · of the ' Lord: ♦
 sing his ' praise · and ex'alt him for ' ever.

12 Bless the Lord all you of ' upright ' spirit: ♦
 bless the Lord you that are ' holy and ' humble in ' heart;

 bless the Father, the Son and the ' Holy ' Spirit: ♦
 sing his ' praise · and ex'alt him for ' ever.

Benedicite – a Song of Creation

shorter version

1 Bless the Lord all you ' works of the ' Lord: ♦
   sing his ' praise · and ex'alt him for ' ever.

2 Bless the ' Lord you ' heavens: ♦
   sing his ' praise · and ex'alt him for ' ever.

3 Bless the Lord you ' angels · of the ' Lord: ♦
   sing his ' praise · and ex'alt him for ' ever.

4 Bless the Lord all ' people on ' earth: ♦
   sing his ' praise · and ex'alt him for ' ever.

5 O people of God ' bless the ' Lord: ♦
   sing his ' praise · and ex'alt him for ' ever.

6 Bless the Lord you ' priests of the ' Lord: ♦
   sing his ' praise · and ex'alt him for ' ever.

7 Bless the Lord you ' servants · of the ' Lord: ♦
   sing his ' praise · and ex'alt him for ' ever.

8 Bless the Lord all you of ' upright ' spirit: ♦
   bless the Lord you that are ' holy and ' humble in ' heart;

‡   bless the Father, the Son and the ' Holy ' Spirit: ♦
   sing his ' praise · and ex'alt him for ' ever.

Venite – a Song of Triumph

Psalm 95

1 O come, let us ' sing to the ' Lord; ♦
   let us heartily rejoice in the ' rock of ' our sal'vation.

2 Let us come into his ' presence with ' thanksgiving ♦
   and be ' glad in ' him with ' psalms.

3 For the Lord is a ' great ' God ♦
   and a great ' king a'bove all ' gods.

4 In his hand are the ' depths of the ' earth ♦
   and the heights of the ' mountains are ' his ' also.

‡ 5 The sea is his, ' for he ' made it, ♦
   and his hands have ' moulded the ' dry ' land.

6 Come, let us worship ' and bow ' down ♦
   and kneel be'fore the ' Lord our ' Maker.

7 For ' he is our ' God; ♦
   we are the people of his pasture ' and the ' sheep of his ' hand.

The canticle may end here with 'Glory to the Father'

8 O that today you would listen ' to his ' voice: ♦
   'Harden not your hearts as at Meribah,
   on that day at ' Massah ' in the ' wilderness,

9 'When your forebears tested me, and put me ' to the ' proof, ♦
   though ' they had ' seen my ' works.

10 'Forty years long I detested that gene'ration and ' said, ♦
   "This people are wayward in their hearts;
      they ' do not ' know my ' ways."

11 'So I ' swore in my ' wrath, ♦
   "They shall not ' enter ' into my ' rest." '

   Glory to the Father and ' to the ' Son
   and ' to the ' Holy ' Spirit;
   as it was in the be'ginning is ' now
   and shall be for ' ever. ' A'men.

Jubilate – a Song of Joy

Psalm 100

1 O be joyful in the Lord, ' all the ' earth; ♦
serve the Lord with gladness
    and come before his ' presence ' with a ' song.

2 Know that the ' Lord is ' God; ♦
it is he that has made us and we are his;
    we are his people ' and the ' sheep of his ' pasture.

3 Enter his gates with thanksgiving
    and his ' courts with ' praise; ♦
give thanks to ' him and ' bless his ' name.

4 For the Lord is gracious; his steadfast love is ' ever'lasting, ♦
and his faithfulness endures from gene'ration to ' gene'ration.

Glory to the Father and ' to the ' Son
and ' to the ' Holy ' Spirit;
as it was in the be'ginning is ' now
and shall be for ' ever. ' A'men.

The Easter Anthems

1 Christ our passover has been ' sacrificed ' for us: ♦
so let us ' cele'brate the ' feast,

2 not with the old leaven of cor'ruption and ' wickedness: ♦
but with the unleavened ' bread of sin'cerity and ' truth.

3 Christ once raised from the dead ' dies no ' more: ♦
death has ' no more do'minion ' over him.

4 In dying he died to sin ' once for ' all: ♦
in ' living he ' lives to ' God.

5 See yourselves therefore as ' dead to ' sin: ♦
and alive to God in ' Jesus ' Christ our ' Lord.

6 Christ has been raised ' from the ' dead: ♦
the ' first fruits of ' those who ' sleep.

7 For as by ' man came ' death: ♦
by man has come also the resur'rection ' of the ' dead;

8 for as in ' Adam all ' die: ♦
even so in Christ shall ' all be ' made a'live.

Glory to the Father and ' to the ' Son
and ' to the ' Holy ' Spirit;
as it was in the be'ginning is ' now
and shall be for ' ever. ' A'men.

Benedictus – the Song of Zechariah

1 Blessed be the Lord the ' God of ' Israel, ♦
who has come to his ' people and ' set them ' free.

2 He has raised up for us a ' mighty ' Saviour, ♦
born of the ' house of his ' servant ' David.

3 Through his holy prophets God ' promised of ' old ♦
to save us from our enemies,
    from the ' hands of ' all that ' hate us,

4 To show mercy ' to our ' ancestors, ♦
and to re'member his ' holy ' covenant.

5 This was the oath God swore to our ' father ' Abraham: ♦
to set us ' free · from the ' hands of our ' enemies,

6 Free to worship him ' without ' fear, ♦
holy and righteous in his sight
    ' all the ' days of our ' life.

7 And you, child, shall be called the prophet of the ' Most ' High, ♦
for you will go before the ' Lord to pre'pare his ' way,

8 To give his people knowledge ' of sal'vation ♦
by the for'giveness of ' all their ' sins.

9 In the tender compassion ' of our ' God ♦
the dawn from on ' high shall ' break up'on us,

10 To shine on those who dwell in darkness and the ' shadow of ' death, ♦
and to guide our feet ' into the ' way of ' peace.

Glory to the Father and ' to the ' Son
and ' to the ' Holy ' Spirit;
as it was in the be'ginning is ' now
and shall be for ' ever. ' A'men.

Magnificat – the Song of Mary

1 My soul proclaims the greatness of the Lord,
    my spirit rejoices in ' God my ' Saviour; ♦
  he has looked with ' favour on his ' lowly ' servant.

2 From this day all generations will ' call me ' blessed; ♦
  the Almighty has done great things for me
    and ' holy ' is his ' name.

3 He has mercy on ' those who ' fear him, ♦
  from gene'ration to ' gene'ration.

4 He has shown strength ' with his ' arm ♦
  and has scattered the ' proud in ' their con'ceit,

5 Casting down the mighty ' from their ' thrones ♦
  and ' lifting ' up the ' lowly.

6 He has filled the hungry with ' good ' things ♦
  and sent the ' rich a'way ' empty.

7 He has come to the aid of his ' servant ' Israel, ♦
  to re'member his ' promise of ' mercy,

8 The promise ' made to our ' ancestors, ♦
  to Abraham ' and his ' children for ' ever.

Glory to the Father and ' to the ' Son
and ' to the ' Holy ' Spirit;
as it was in the be'ginning is ' now
and shall be for ' ever. ' A'men.

Nunc dimittis – the Song of Simeon

1 Now, Lord, you let your servant ' go in ' peace: ♦
  your ' word has ' been ful'filled.

2 My own eyes have ' seen the sal'vation ♦
  which you have prepared in the ' sight of ' every ' people;

3 A light to reveal you ' to the ' nations ♦
  and the glory ' of your ' people ' Israel.

Glory to the Father and ' to the ' Son
and ' to the ' Holy ' Spirit;
as it was in the be'ginning is ' now
and shall be for ' ever. ' A'men.

Te Deum laudamus

We praise you, O God,
    we acclaim you ' as the ' Lord; ♦
all creation worships you,
    the ' Father ' ever'lasting.

To you all angels, all the ' powers of ' heaven, ♦
the cherubim and seraphim, ' sing in ' endless ' praise:

Holy, holy, holy Lord, God of ' power and ' might, ♦
heaven and ' earth are ' full of your ' glory.

The glorious company of a'postles ' praise you. ♦
The noble ' fellowship of ' prophets ' praise you.

The white-robed army of ' martyrs ' praise you. ♦
Throughout the world the ' holy ' Church ac'claims you:

‡   Father, of majesty unbounded,
    your true and only Son, worthy ' of all ' praise, ♦
the Holy Spirit, ' advo'cate and ' guide.

You, Christ, are the ' King of ' glory, ♦
the e'ternal ' Son of the ' Father.

When you took our flesh to ' set us ' free ♦
you humbly ' chose the ' Virgin's ' womb.

You overcame the ' sting of ' death ♦
and opened the kingdom of ' heaven to ' all be'lievers.

You are seated at God's right ' hand in ' glory. ♦
We believe that you will ' come and ' be our ' judge.

Come then, Lord, and ' help your ' people, ♦
bought with the ' price of ' your own ' blood,

and bring us ' with your ' saints ♦
to ' glory ' ever'lasting.

The canticle may end here.

Save your people, Lord, and ' bless your in'heritance. ♦
Govern and up'hold them ' now and ' always.

Day by ' day we ' bless you. ♦
We ' praise your ' name for ' ever.

Keep us today, Lord, ' from all ' sin. ♦
Have mercy ' on us, ' Lord, have ' mercy.

Lord, show us your ' love and ' mercy, ♦
for we have ' put our ' trust in ' you.

‡   In you, Lord, ' is our ' hope: ♦
let us ' never be ' put to ' shame.

¶ Copyright, Reproduction and Acknowledgements

Both the Archbishops' Council of the Church of England and the Royal School of Church of Music recognise that many churches will wish to make their own service booklets.

Text copyright

Clear directions are given regarding copyright in the editions of *Common Worship*.

Further information on text copyright can be found on the Church of England web site
> www.cofe.anglican.org/commonworship/downloads/litcopy.rtf
> and also in
> *A Brief Guide to Liturgical Copyright* (Church House Publishing, 2000).

Music copyright and reproduction

If you or your church own at least one copy of *Music for Common Worship 1*, most of the items in this volume may be copied for local use without further permission, provided that you include the full copyright acknowledgements on the page on which the specific piece of music appears in your service book or leaflet. That service book or leaflet may not be offered for sale.

Some items are not covered by this arrangement, and separate permission will have to be obtained from the copyright holder before you make any copies. These items are identified by red type after the piece, and listed below. In some cases a CCL or Calamus licence will cover these items, but that will need to be checked before the music is reproduced.

Copyright details and acknowledgements

We gratefully acknowledge permission to reproduce copyright material in this publication. Every effort has been made to trace and contact copyright holders. If there are any inadvertent errors or omissions, we apologise to those concerned, and undertake to correct them in all future editions.

Unless otherwise stated, the texts are from *Common Worship* and the material is reproduced by permission of the copyright owners, The Archbishops' Council. Those who control the copyright in the words and music of other works are identified at the foot of each item. Please note that in many cases the RSCM does not own or control the copyright used in this publication.

Permission to reproduce works in connection with the following copyright holders must be sought directly (and not via the RSCM). In some cases, the text and/or music may be covered by an appropriate CCL or Calamus licence. Contact details for these licensing schemes are as follows:

CCL tel: +44 (0)1323 417711 fax: +44 (0)1323 417722
e-mail: sales@ccli.co.uk web: www.ccli.com

Calamus tel: +44 (0)1638 716579 fax: +44 (0)1638 510390
e-mail: decanimusic@msn.com web: www.decanimusic.co.uk

Ateliers et Presses de Taizé, 71250 Taizé-Community, France   Calamus
Curwen & Sons Limited, J, 8/9 Frith Street, London W1V 5TZ
Dudley-Smith, The Rt Revd Timothy, 9 Ashlands, Ford, Salisbury SP4 6DY   CCL
The Grail c/o Lesley Toll, 23 Carlisle Road. London NW6 6TL
Jubilee Hymns, Southwick House, 4 Thorne Park Road, Chelston, Torquay TQ2 6RX   CCL
    including John Barnard, Michael Baughen, Christopher Idle, and Mrs B Perry
Maraire, Abraham, United Methodist Church Service, Mutambara, CPS Box 61, Cashel, Zimbabwe
OCP Publications, 5536 NE Hassalo, Portland OR 97213 USA   Calamus
Studio SM, 34 Rue Michel-Ange, F 75016 Paris, France
WGRG, Iona Community, 840 Govan Road, Glasgow G51 3UU Scotland

The following copyright owners have granted permission for worshipping communities to reproduce the materials under their ownership or control in locally produced service sheets and booklets (not for sale), provided that such editions conform with the copyright conditions laid down in *A Brief Guide to Liturgical Copyright* (Church House Publishing, third edition).

Archbishops' Council of the Church of England, Copyright and Contracts Administrator,
     Church House, Great Smith Street, London SW1P 3NZ
Appleton, Gordon, see The Royal School of Church Music
Broomhill Church of Scotland, c/o William W Marshall, Clerk to the Deacon's Court,
     74 Marlborough Avenue, Broomhill, Glasgow G11 7BH
Cambridge University Press, The Edinburgh Building, Shaftesbury Road, Cambridge CB2 9RU
Chapman, Geoffrey, Cassell plc, Wellington House, 125 The Strand, London WC2R 0BB
Church Publishing Incorporated, 445 Fifth Avenue, New York NY 10016 USA
The Communities' Consultative Council, c/o The Revd. Father Aidan Mayoss CR,
     St Michael's Priory, 14 Burleigh Street, London WC2E 7PZ
Dienes, Katherine, 12 The Close, Norwich, Norfolk NR1 4DH
Duba, Arlo D., 111 Lake South Terrace, Hot Springs, Arkansas 7193 USA
ELLC, c/o Archbishops' Council of the Church of England, Church House, Great Smith Street, London SW1P 3NZ
GIA Publications, Inc., 7404 S. Mason Avenue, Chicago, Illinois 60638 USA
Harper, John, see The Royal School of Church Music
Hone, Timothy, 27 Blueburn Drive, Killingworth, Newcastle upon Tyne NE12 0GA
Hurford, Peter, Broom House, St Bernard's Road, St Albans, Hertfordshire AL3 5RA
LeCroy, Anne, 1105 Cherokee Street, Johnson City, TN 37601 USA
McCrimmon Publishing Company Limited, 10-12 High Street, Great Wakering, Southend-on-Sea, Essex SS3 0EQ
Moger, The Revd Peter, The Vicarage, 59 Post Street, Godmanchester, Cambs. PE29 2AQ
Mount St Bernard Abbey, Coalville, Leicestershire LE67 5UL
Murray, the late Dom Gregory, c/o Dom Charles Fitzgerald-Lombard, Downside Abbey, Bath BA3 4RH
Music from Glastonbury, Walnut Tree House, Middle Street, Ashcott, Somerset TA7 9QB
Ogden, David, Clifton Cathedral House, Clifton Park, Bristol BS8 3BX
Ollis, Peter, Pine Heights, Old Neighbouring, Chalford, Stroud, Gloucs. GL6 8AA
Oxford University Press, Great Clarendon Street, Oxford OX2 6DP
Panel of Monastic Musicians, c/o SCM-Canterbury Press Ltd, St Mary's Works, St Mary's Plain, Norwich NR3 3BH
Reindorf, Dinah, P.O. Box 13060, Accra, Ghana, West Africa
The Royal School of Church Music, Cleveland Lodge, Westhumble, Dorking, Surrey RH5 6BW
Sarum College Press, 19 The Close, Salisbury, Wiltshire SP1 2EE
Smith, Alan, 22 Downscroft, Burgess Hill, West Sussex RH15 0UF
Stubbings, Paul, St Martin-in-the-Fields, Trafalgar Square, London WC2N 4JJ
Tambling, Christopher, Downside Abbey, Stratton-on-the-Fosse, Bath BA3 4RJ
Walker, Robin, see under Music from Glastonbury
Warren, The Ven. Norman, 1 Sandling Way, St Mary's Island, Chatham, Kent ME4 3AZ
Warren, Raymond, 9 Cabote Rise, Portishead, Bristol BS20 6NX
Watson, Father Charles, Prinknash Abbey, Cranham, Gloucester GL4 8EX
Weinberger Ltd, Joseph, 12-14 Mortimer Street, London W1N 7RD
Wilson, Alan, 66 Crombie Road, Sidcup, Kent DA14 8AU

Table of Psalms and Canticles by Season and Service

All the settings use the complete modern text, except where otherwise stated.

*An asterisk * indicates an additional version in the appendix pointed for Anglican Chant.*

Advent
Psalm 80
Psalm 122
Psalm 122   song text
Psalm 126
Song of the Wilderness
Song of the Spirit

Christmas
Psalm 96
Psalm 97
Psalm 98   song text
Psalm 147 (13-21)
Song of the Messiah
Song of Redemption

Epiphany
Psalm 19 (1-6)
Psalm 72 (1-8, 11-15)
Song of the New Jerusalem
Song of Praise

Lent and Passiontide
Psalm 22 (1-11, 23-31)
Psalm 25 (1-10)
Psalm 25   song text

Psalm 51 (1-13)
Psalm 103   song text
Psalm 116 (10-17)
Song of Humility
Song of Christ the Servant

Easter and Ascension
Psalm 23
Psalm 47   song text
Psalm 67
Psalm 93
Psalm 98
Psalm 98   song text
(see Christmas section above)
Psalm 118 (14-29)
Song of Moses and Miriam
Song of Faith

Pentecost
Psalm 104 (26-36, 37b)
Psalm 139   song text
Song of Ezekiel
Song of God's Children

Ordinary Time
Psalm 1
Psalm 34 (1-10)
Psalm 71   song text
Psalm 85 (8-13)
Psalm 119 (1-8)
Psalm 121
Psalm 130
Psalm 146
Psalm 147   song text
Psalm 150
Song of David
Song of the Lamb

Morning Prayer

Benedicite	Song of Creation (two settings) *	short version
Benedicite	Song of Creation *	full text
Benedicite	Song of Creation	metrical text
Venite	Psalm 95 (two settings) *	
Venite	Psalm 95	short version
Venite	Psalm 95	metrical text
Jubilate	Psalm 100 (two settings) *	
Jubilate	Psalm 100	metrical text
Easter Anthems (two settings) *		
Benedictus	Song of Zechariah (three settings) *	
Benedictus	Song of Zechariah	traditional text
Benedictus	Song of Zechariah	metrical text

Evening Prayer

Phos hilaron	Song of the Light (three settings) *	
Psalm 141	verses from (four settings) *	
Psalm 104	verses from *	
Magnificat	Song of Mary (four settings) *	
Magnificat	Song of Mary	traditional text
Magnificat	Song of Mary	metrical text

Night Prayer

Before the ending of the day		
Psalm 4		
Psalm 91		
Psalm 134		
Nunc dimittis	Song of Simeon (four settings) *	
Nunc dimittis	Song of Simeon	traditional text
Nunc dimittis	Song of Simeon	metrical text

Hymn of Praise

Te Deum	(two settings) *	
Te Deum		traditional text
Te Deum		metrical text

Index of Psalms and Canticles

Index of Contents

COCKADOODLEDOO

FOR MY
BEAUTIFUL
DAUGHTER
RUBY AAMOR

THE WHOLE

CHICKEN

A COOKBOOK BY
CARL CLARKE

PHOTOGRAPHY BY
ROBERT BILLINGTON

Hardie Grant

BOOKS

6

THE BEGINNING

'You can either be a hairdresser or a chef.'

These were the first words that my mum uttered when I declared that I wanted to leave school and get a job. 'Why?' I asked. 'Because people will always need feeding, and will always need to get their hair cut.' Very wise at a time when jobs were non-existent and the problematic, poorly paid Youth Training Schemes (a government initiative for young people in the UK to be trained 'on the job') were prevalent. 'A hairdresser? F@&k that!' I said.

I come from an inner-city area of Birmingham, UK, where being a hairdresser at that time would have raised an eyebrow or two in my family, something to be dismissed and never mentioned in public again. In those days, rule number one was to learn to look after yourself, and then if you were lucky, everything else followed. Well, sort of…

My point is, by definition, I am very much an accidental chef. I did not sit on my grandmother's knee peeling broad (fava) beans looking at bubbling pots on the stove. I became a chef out of a necessity; to have a job, to earn money, and hopefully keep a roof over my head in the years to come. In fact, I didn't even have a pronounced interest in food, apart from what I knowing what I liked and what I didn't like. Little did I know at that time what the Universe had in store for me, or how colourful the journey of my career would turn out to be, so far.

My first kitchen job, unsurprisingly perhaps, came about by accident, too. After leaving school at sixteen, a friend and I decided enough was enough in Birmingham. We wanted to run away, find a new life, have a good time, get a job, whatever it took. We borrowed £200 ($250) from his brother, which back then was a lot of money, left a note on the table and headed off on the train from Birmingham New Street Station to catch a ferry to a small island off the coast of France called Jersey. I had heard that alcohol and cigarettes were cheap and the nightlife was great, what else did we need? Well, it didn't get off to a very good start. Possibly because we bought a bottle of vodka on the ferry, and while I was sleeping it off, my friend went and spent the rest of the money in the on-board casino.

When we disembarked on this unfamiliar island with terrible hangovers, we had a total of £1.50 ($2) left, no jobs and nowhere to live.

In the distance, I saw this great big colonial-style building; it was The Grand Hotel – which is still there to this day – and my mum's words came back to me. Leaving my friend outside, I marched into the noisy, busy kitchen to ask for a job. I was directed to the office of the very grand Austrian Executive chef, who was decked out in full regalia – a very tall hat, sparkling chef whites and wooden clogs. Whatever I said somehow worked: he gave me a job for £90 ($115) a week, which was tax free a good wage at the time, and sounded even better when a pint was just 14p (30 cents) and cigarettes were 23p (45 cents). That night, we got some chips and slept rough, and the next morning I set off for work. I managed to get an advance on my first pay packet, and the following afternoon we found a shared room in a house, which I smuggled sandwiches to after my shifts to feed my friend until he found a job. I spent the next six months peeling and turning potatoes into seven-sided barrel shapes, getting shouted at a lot, learning quite a bit, and obviously having the best time of my life.

However, in between leaving school and running away to Jersey, I'd explored a few other ways of escaping – including joining the Armed Forces. I was sent away because I was underweight, and told to eat more steak and mashed potatoes before coming back. Eventually I got to sit the test, but of course this became a hazy memory once I'd managed to skip town. Then one day when I called my mum from Jersey, she said that I'd received a draft letter saying that I'd been 'called up' for basic training … it was another way of saying 'a six-week journey to hell and back' … so to hell and back I went.

I spent the next six years as a cook in the Armed Forces, cyclically travelling around the world and getting into some very sticky situations, then trying to find a way out of them. When I look back, the experience gave me two things that I will be eternally grateful for: firstly, opening my eyes to different cultures, which is an opportunity I never would have had at that time otherwise, and secondly, the valuable lesson of discipline, which I passionately fought against up until then. Of course, it also gave me basic cooking skills, but at that point I still really had no interest whatsoever in food, outside of it being my job. I was more interested in going out drinking, getting into fights, and generally trying to survive.

Around 1989, the rave scene started to kick off in the UK. I remember going to my first illegal rave – I suppose they all were, then – and walking down a hill, hearing the dulcet bass line in the distance. Then out of nowhere, I saw 10,000 people with their hands in the air facing someone (who was the now-legendary DJ Sasha) looking like he was a god, playing records on turntables. I thought 'This is it!' A few too many happy pills later, electronic music had completely changed the course of my life.

I bought a pair of turntables and started to teach myself to DJ, getting random gigs here and there, scratching around trying to make a name for myself on the rave scene. After I moved to London in 1994, I was by chance given an opportunity to DJ every Thursday and Friday at the infamous Turnmills nightclub – the only 24-hour nightclub in the UK – and the rest is history. By that point I'd completed a degree and stopped cooking, and Turnmills became my home, my family, my life. I spent the next ten years DJing around the world; I basically got paid very well to party, but like all good things, this eventually came to an end. The gigs dried up, I stopped making music, and the moment was over. I was flat broke with a new baby, and pretty much lost as to what to do in the real world. There was only one other thing I kind of knew I could do, and that was cooking – but little did I know that everything I thought I knew about that actually amounted to fuck all.

MARCO

I figured if I was going to get back into the kitchen, then I needed to work for the best. There weren't many chefs with high-end restaurants to choose from in those days in London – there was Nico, Gordon Ramsay and Pierre Koffmann, to name a few – and funnily enough Chef Pierre became a good friend in years to come when he walked into our little chicken shop in East London. I'd read about this bad-tempered chef called Marco Pierre White who ran his kitchens military-style, and was of course an absolute genius. I loved his look in those iconic photos from his book *White Heat* by the photographer Bob Carlos Clarke – he was more rock 'n' roller than chef, cigarette in hand looking beaten up in a butcher's apron like he'd just done a five-year tour with Ozzy Osbourne. That was it – that's who I wanted to be. Or so I thought at the time. Off I went with a scrappy set of blunt knives to the back door of the Belvedere in Holland Park to ask if they had any jobs. I remember getting told to f@%k off more than twice, but I persevered, and finally the head chef conceded. I spent the next period of my life intensely learning how to cook 'the Marco way'. I'd gone from a glamorous life of being at all the

best parties and getting paid more money than I could spend in a week, to getting minimum wage and working 18–20 hour-long gruelling days. I was shell-shocked, to say the least, but ploughed through until eventually I could take no more, and on New Year's Day, I just didn't bother turning up for work. As a chef, when you do this, you know you're not going back, or more perhaps more to the point, would never dare to go back. Yes, I learned how to cook at the Belvedere, but I also learned that it takes equal parts skill and personal sacrifice to get to the top of your game at that level. The next day I went into the bank, took out what little money I had and bought a ticket to Savannah, Georgia, on the promise of a job from an American friend who said it was a cool place.

GLOBE TROTTING (THE LOST YEARS)

Once I landed in the US, the travelling didn't stop. For the next few years I took what I had learned from the Belvedere to various kitchens around the world. Starting in the kitchens of a private plantation in Savannah, I then went on to be the opening Executive Chef of the first-ever Harvey Nichols Restaurant outside of the UK, and spent two incredible years living in Istanbul. After that, I worked as temporary head chef of U2's The Clarence in Dublin, when it was Ireland's hottest restaurant, bar and nightclub all rolled into one; I admit that I enjoyed all three elements of that a little too much sometimes. Eventually, though, I returned to the UK, interspersing restaurant consultancy jobs with *stages* in the kitchens of chefs I admired, such as Simon Rogan, constantly trying to learn and develop my skills. But in truth, I was becoming bored of the bourgeois restaurant scene, and wanted to do something that went against everything I'd experienced thus far. So of course, fate introduced me to another path when I met my now business partner and brother-in-arms David Wolanski.

TEARING UP THE RULE BOOK

The well-covered story goes 'David and I first met in a field' … and it's true, we did. It was at Latitude Festival in 2010, at the very first full sit-down à la carte restaurant at a festival, which was owned by the incredibly creative Jonathan Downey of Milk and Honey, Street Feast and much more. David was brought in to help with the operations and organise the front of house, and I was drafted into the kitchen. Let's just say it was a baptism of fire, with me ending up on one side of the pass and David on the other for a few very hectic days with little to no sleep. We fed over seven thousand people in four days, and got to know each other at lightning speed.

We headed back to London together, swapping old raver stories, and hit upon this idea of taking what we had just experienced at the festival to create an immersive pop up called Disco Bistrothat would have a kind of modern-day dinner dance vibe, with incredible food, drinks and DJs. It took a few iterations in our heads to get it right, but we eventually set out on an incredible journey of curating immersive pops up in and around East London in some exciting spaces, part legal, part not, but I guess that was the fun.

Our first-ever pop up was called RockLobsta – a three-day lobster roll bar in a mate's clothes shop in Shoreditch with a punk attitude and the obligatory banging tunes. We didn't really know what we were doing at the time, let alone how to deal with what was to come; we served more than one thousand people in those three days, and we quickly learned some valuable lessons for the future. More pop ups swiftly followed: God Save The Clam; The English Launderette; a roller disco for the summer in King's Cross selling the incredible Roller Disco Burger and next-level cocktails, the list goes on. After all the incarnations, I ended up doing a six-month residency in the dining room above an old boozer near St Paul's Cathedral that harked back to our beginnings, given the suitably cyclical name of DiscoBistro. It was at this point that things started to change in a big way for me. I borrowed some tables, chairs and glasses, blagged some artwork on loan from various artists, and then cobbled together some kitchen equipment. I roped in a couple of talented young chef friends, Pat and Glyn, created a Twitter account, and then off we went. It was a surreal experience in many ways, not least because my dear friend, the late, great Howard Marks, opened the restaurant on Bonfire Night by reciting a poem about Guy Fawkes, who happened to have used the basement below the very pub we were standing in to prepare for the Gunpowder Plot. But that's another story entirely.

Ultimately, this is where I learned just to cook food I loved to eat. This is where I learned to start to look at food from a more scientific and geeky level. I began asking questions about how and why flavours worked, sometimes finding the answers and sometimes not, but always learning. And it was at this point, too, that I started to go deep into the rabbit hole of perfect fried chicken. With the help of Pat and Glyn, I put a fried chicken sandwich and chicken wings on the menu, which seemed to go down very well with all our customers. Once again, fate was leading me in another direction without my knowledge, and before I knew it, I was driving around East London on the back of David's scooter, trying to get some inspiration for what to do next, when we hit upon the idea of opening a chicken shop like no other.

CHICK 'N' SOURS

We set off walking up and down a pretty run-down row of shops and cafes in East London, which used to be called 'The Waste', putting letters through doors and asking if they would consider leasing their property to us. Then one day out of the blue we got a call from a Mr. Ali, a Turkish gent who owned an old cafe that he was willing to let us lease, and so we cobbled together what little money we could from family and friends and set to work with our dear friend Camilla to build our first-ever chicken shop. It was described recently by some as 'a classy fried chicken shop with an Asian twist'. We couldn't have put it better ourselves.

We wanted to build a restaurant that was more than just about the food. A place where people would feel like they were in our home with super friendly hospitality, incredible sour cocktails and next-level fried chicken. So with me in the kitchen, David out front, and our mate Sam behind the bar, we cranked up the tunes, turned down the lights, opened the doors and set out on a journey which can only be described as something beyond our wildest dreams. Let's just say that five years later, it's still there, and has become something of a London icon, now with two sister restaurants, and an incredible following of loyal customers who we love dearly. In fact, we often think it's more their restaurant than ours.

CHIK'N

And so, inevitably, there was a second chapter to the fried chicken story. Chik'n is what we call fast food, not rushed food. It felt like a natural follow on from Chick 'n' Sours, because we wanted to bring the same quality and ethos to a wider audience in a modern, fast-food environment with social responsibilities. A fried chicken brand that is not only better for you, but also better for our planet. It has the personality of Chick 'n' Sours at a much faster pace. David and I have a simple mantra 'We just want to be known as the guys who make the best fried chicken sandwich in the world'. Are we there yet? Probably not, but one thing is for sure we will never give up trying.

And so that leads me to this book. I wanted to write The Whole Chicken for the very same reason; to bring some light and life to an ingredient I have come to be very passionate about, with twists and takes that are designed to make you think differently, taste differently, and eat differently, wherever you are in the world. I firmly recommend that you approach my recipes with my random musings (see opposite) in mind. Not only will it help you to navigate your likes and dislikes, it will also encourage you to take your own path; in my experience, it's the only way to food heaven.

None of these recipes are authentic, but they were created by me through my lens, with love and respect for their origin.

This is happy food that is meant to make you smile (if it's not, then something's wrong).

This is not a cheffy book. Some are, of course, inspired by the food on my menus, but I have simplified the recipes to create a book for all to use and share with their friends and community. I've added difficulty indicators, to help you gauge what you are getting yourself in for.

Just accept that some things you will just have to weigh for the best results, so don't be lazy.

Swap out any ingredient you like, or even better, if you don't have it then just don't use it. Just don't let a small thing like that make you give up altogether.

If you think you can do better, then just do it. You never know, you may just be right.

Turn up the tunes when you cook these recipes – you'll find playlist recommendations on page 208.

I really hope these recipes bring you joy, but if they don't, then please pass this book onto someone else that may enjoy it more, and find something else to do that brings you happiness, because life is too short.

Finally, buy the best chickens you can afford. Just make sure they have been treated with kindness, and have led a full wholesome life. We can't all afford organic chickens but that's ok.

Be happy.

CARL CLARKE

BUTCHERY

12 Breaking down the chicken provides a clever way to cook all the separate parts of the chicken with the same heat distribution, thus resulting in a more even cook.

What it also allows is for you to use different parts of the chicken for various dishes that require different cooking methods. A salad may require grilling (broiling) of the breasts, whereas a braised dish will require the drumsticks and thighs to cook slowly for a much longer time. It's also handy for using all the pieces for a one-dish traybake, as you can just serve in the tray straight from the oven and let people help themselves. Don't be put off by the steps below, as it reads harder than it actually is, and once you've done it a few times you will be able to do it blindfolded, and very quickly.

B U T C H E R Y

① Place a damp cloth underneath your cutting board to stop the board sliding around. You will need a very sharp, long chef's knife for this.

② Place your knife between the wing and the breast and wiggle it around until you find the joint. Slice through the skin of the wing and then cut through the joint.

③ Take hold of the drumstick end of the leg and pull outwards to create some space between the body of the chicken. Make a shallow cut through the skin between the leg and the body. Gently pull the leg outwards to expose the thigh joint and cut through the joint to separate the leg from the body.

④ Find the crease where the thigh and the drumstick meet, cut through the skin and the joint. Repeat with the other leg.

⑤ Cut along both sides of the breastbone, separating the breast meat from the bone.

⑥ Using your chef's knife, place your non-dominant hand on the tip end of your knife and cut through the breastbone. (Keep the carcass for stock.)

⑦ Cut across the skin of each breast and through the bone to cut the breast into two equal parts. Repeat for the other breast leaving you with four breast pieces.

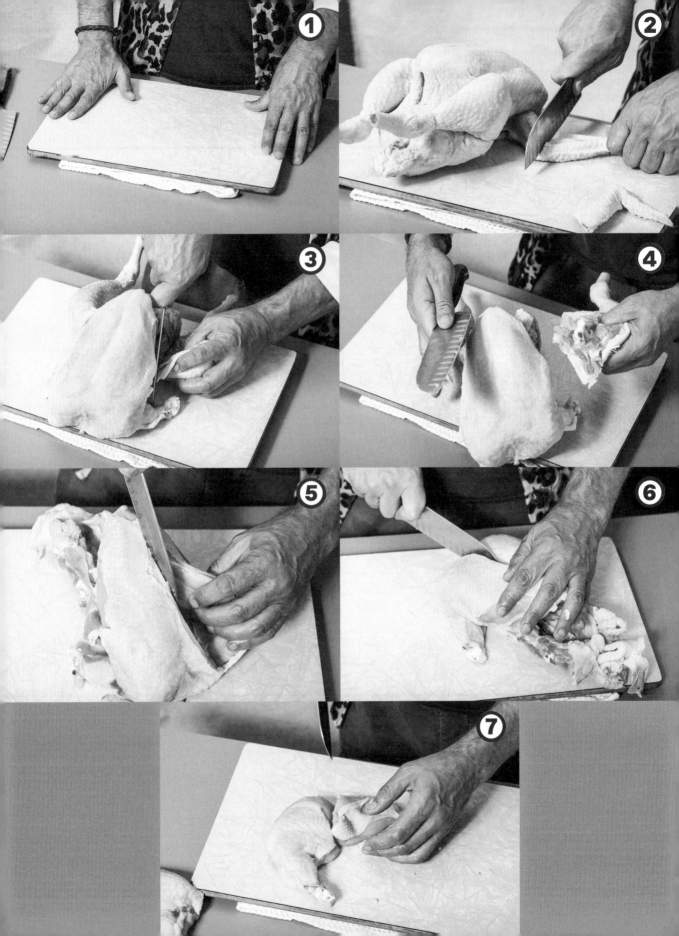

CHOP

CHOP

HOW TO SPATCHCOCK A CHICKEN

16 The term 'spatchcocking' first started to appear in 18th-century Irish cookbooks, and it is said that the word 'spatchcock' is an abbreviation of 'dispatch the cock', which means to kill the chicken.

However, nowadays to spatchcock a chicken means to remove the backbone and flatten the chicken out, to allow it to cook quickly by barbecuing, roasting or grilling (broiling). It's a really good technique when you are marinating whole chickens and super easy to cut into portions once it's cooked. I also find that it's the best way to get the crispiest skin on a chicken when roasting.

It is a very simple technique and easily achieved with little or no butchery skills if you follow these steps:

BUTCHERY

① Place the chicken on a cutting board with a damp cloth underneath to stop the board from sliding around. Remove the neck and giblets from the cavity and pat the chicken dry using paper towels.

② Turn the chicken upside down so the breasts are on the cutting board and, using a heavy pair of kitchen scissors, cut along one side of the backbone, then along the other side. Remove the backbone.

③ Rotate the chicken a half turn so the neck end is uppermost. Using a heavy kitchen knife, make a notch along each side of the breastbone as this will help flatten it out and help when carving later.

④ Turn the chicken back over so the breasts are now facing upwards again and push the breastbone downward to help flatten it.

⑤ Using the palm of your hand, push hard on the breastbone to flatten out the chicken.

⑥ Tuck the wingtips behind the breasts as this will prevent them burning while the chicken is cooking.

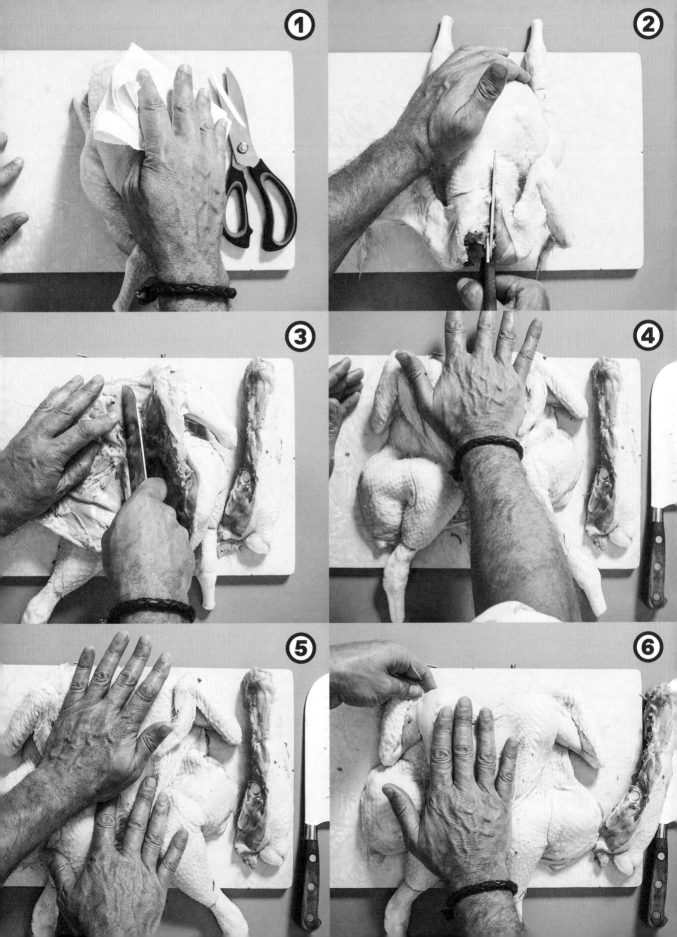

CRACK!

A COUPLE OF WAYS TO COOK
CRISPY CHICKEN SKIN

20 Crispy chicken is right up there with pork crackling and crispy duck skin as one of the greatest things the Universe has ever given us, right? Here are a couple of different methods that give you two really different types of texture once the skin is crisped up. The Chicken Scratchings have a slightly more fatty mouthfeel, much like that of good pork scratchings, and the Chicken Crispies are more akin to delicate crisps (chips), which is ideal for small snacks or adding crunch to salads or stir-fries. One of my favourite ways to serve the Chicken Crispies are as a snack is as a bite-sized cracker with sour cream and pineapple bacon jam. This is a pretty much 'find your own way' kind of technique and it may take you a few attempts to get it right, but that's OK. Don't be put off, as it's about progression not perfection, and the end results are really worth it.

BUTCHERY

CHICKEN CRISPIES

① Preheat the oven to 180°C (350°F/gas 4).

② Lay your cutting board on a damp kitchen cloth to stop the board from sliding around.

③ Lay the piece of chicken skin around 10 cm (4 in) long, skin-side down, on your cutting board. Using a sharp chef's knife, begin to scrape the excess fat off the skin, being careful not to tear the skin in the process. Once done, set aside and continue the same process with all the other skin until finished.

④ Line a flat baking tray (pan) with baking parchment, then lay the pieces of chicken skin on the tray, flattening them out so there are no creases. Leave a small gap in between each piece as they will shrink slightly during the cooking process. Season with Maldon sea salt. Once one layer is finished, lay another sheet of baking parchment on top and repeat until you have a couple of layers, then top with a final sheet of baking parchment.

⑤ Place another flat baking tray on top of the chicken skin and press down. This will keep the chicken skin flat and will allow it to crisp up evenly through cooking. Roast in the oven for about 50 minutes, checking the skin occasionally, until golden brown. Remove from the oven and carefully place the pieces of chicken skin on a wire rack to cool. It may not be crispy, but it will crisp up as it cools in the air. If the skin overcooks and becomes too dark, it will become bitter and not very nice, so keep a close eye on it.

CHICKEN SCRATCHINGS

① Heat a scant tablespoon of rapeseed (canola) oil in the base of a large, cold, heavy pot and add the chicken skin.

② Turn the heat onto the lowest possible setting and allow the oil to heat slowly. This will take some time, possibly 2 hours if done correctly, but once you get the hang of it you can speed things up.

③ Stir the chicken skin occasionally to stop it sticking to the base of the pot.

④ The chicken skin will release its own fat during the cooking process and, when ready, the rendered chicken skin will float to the top of the oil.

⑤ Remove the chicken skin carefully with a slotted spoon or tongs and leave to cool slightly on a wire rack or something that will let the air circulate around it.

⑥ Preheat the oven to 160°C (325°F/gas 3). Place the skin on a wire rack on a tray and roast for 25–30 minutes, until golden brown. It may not be too crispy at this point, but it will crisp up completely as it cools to room temperature. Serve immediately.

FAT-

HOW TO MAKE SCHMALTZ

Schmaltz is basically rendered, clarified chicken fat and its origins are rooted in the Ashkenazi Jewish community. It is considered an integral part of their cuisine and has been used by them for centuries in dishes such as chicken soup, latkes, chopped liver and matzah balls. It's also used with the addition of sweated onions as a delicious spread.

Nowadays, this technique has been adopted by chefs including myself to add a depth of flavour to dishes such as a chicken pie or cornbread. If you really want to push the boat out and can gather enough, then it probably makes the best fried chicken ever. Fatty chicken skin from around the legs and undercavity is best for this technique.

① Place the fatty chicken skin in a cold, heavy pot with a little rapeseed (canola) oil at the bottom.

② Turn the heat onto the lowest possible setting and cook the chicken skin, stirring occasionally, until the skin has rendered all its fat; this will take around 60–90 minutes.

③ Use a very fine-mesh sieve (strainer) – ideally lined with muslin (cheesecloth) as well – strain the rendered chicken fat into a sterilised glass container. You can also use a coffee filter. Keep in the refrigerator for up to a month and use as you wish – you can use the leftover chicken skin to make Chicken Scratchings (page 21).

BUTCHERY

-TA-TA-TA-TA-TA-TA-TA

24

Chicken, especially the breasts, can dry out very quickly during cooking. The brining method is an incredibly simple and effective way of preventing this from happening. How many dry turkeys have you had in your time? What is brining I hear you ask? Well, brining is as simple as placing meat in a solution of water and salt. This is the most basic level; the skill is in getting the ratio of salt to water right, and in judging the amount of time that the meat can stay in the brine before becoming too salty. The salt brine not only tenderises the meat, but it also seasons it at the same time as well as keeping it from drying out in the cooking process.

For a basic brine, I like to use a 6 per cent salt to water solution, so that's 60 g (2 oz/scant ¼ cup) table salt to 1 litre (34 fl oz/4 cups) water.

Simply put the salt into a large saucepan with the water. Bring to the boil, dissolving the salt, then remove from the heat and leave to cool completely in the refrigerator before brining the meat. You can also add other aromatics to the brine if you like, such as peppercorns, allspice or whatever you fancy. Sugar is also sometimes used for a sweeter flavour.

You need to brine for at least 1 hour for boneless chicken and up to 24 hours for bone-in chicken. There's a bit of trying different timings out for yourself with brining, to see what works for you. What is important is that you rinse the meat under plenty of cold running water after the brine and pat dry with paper towels to dry completely before cooking, especially if you want crispy skin. I have added brining into the recipes that I think most benefit from it, but it's optional – if you do have time, do it every time you cook chicken. If you don't, just go ahead as you are, but it's worth trying to see the difference.

FULL
WHO
WIN

SPATCHCOCK CHICKEN
WITH FIVE SPICE, HONEY AND SOY

SERVES 2–4, DEPENDING ON HOW HUNGRY YOU ARE

1.5 kg (3 lb 5 oz) whole chicken, skin on and spatchcocked (page 16)

200 g (7 oz/generous 1 cup) steamed white or brown jasmine rice (optional)

FOR THE MARINADE

4 tablespoons (a good squeeze or two) runny honey

2 tablespoons groundnut (peanut) oil

6 fat garlic cloves, very finely chopped

knob of fresh ginger root, peeled and very finely chopped (to make about 4 teaspoons)

3 heaped teaspoons Chinese five-spice powder

1 tablespoon dark soy sauce

4 tablespoons light soy sauce

2 tablespoons hoisin sauce

1 tablespoon mirin (Japanese rice wine)

This is a simple recipe, but one of the most delicious in this book. The marinade creates a beautiful burnished glaze that chars around the edges as you would get when cooking on a barbecue. This is one of those dishes you can marinate the night before and just cook in the oven when you get in from work, then 40 minutes later it's ready. Once you've made it, I guarantee you will make it time and time again. It's great served with Smacked Cucumbers with Sesame and Seaweed (page 190) and maybe some rice on the side.

Mix all the marinade ingredients together in a large shallow bowl. Using a sharp knife, make a few slashes in the chicken skin, then add the chicken to the marinade and mix to coat well. Cover with cling film (plastic wrap) and marinate in the refrigerator for at least 1 hour, preferably overnight, turning the chicken in the marinade occasionally.

Remove the chicken from the refrigerator at least 15 minutes before you are ready to cook.

Preheat the oven to 200°C (400°F/gas 6).

You can either pop the chicken onto a shallow baking tray (pan) or cook on a roasting rack over a roasting tray. Drizzle the chicken with the remaining marinade, then roast for 40–45 minutes, basting every 15 minutes or so with the marinade until the chicken is completely cooked through. Serve with steamed rice, if you like.

EASY PEASY

WHOLE

TRACK ONE

PEKING CHICKEN WITH PANCAKES, CUCUMBER AND SPRING ONIONS

SERVES 4

30

ALMOST
BREEZY

W
H
O
L
E

1.5–2 kg (3 lb 5 oz–4 lb 8 oz)
whole chicken

½ teaspoon Chinese five-spice
powder

2 tablespoons maple syrup or honey

FOR THE MARINADE

60 ml (2 fl oz/¼ cup) light soy sauce
or soy sauce

2 tablespoons dark soy sauce or
soy sauce

1 tablespoon caster (superfine) sugar

5–6 slices fresh ginger root
(about ½ thumb)

1 teaspoon Chinese five-spice powder

TO SERVE

200 g (7 oz/generous 1 cup) steamed
white or brown jasmine rice

12 pancakes

½ cucumber, sliced into batons

4 spring onions (scallions),
finely sliced lengthways

store-bought hoisin sauce

Peking duck when it's done well is one of my favourite things to eat in the world. It's a technical dish that includes a bicycle pump to get it right, so I have skipped that bit. Traditionally, the crispy skin would be served first with icing (confectioners') sugar, which sounds strange but really works. I wanted to include this recipe because when I eat duck with pancakes it always feels special to me. It feels like a treat, an occasion that's only visited once in a while. It took me a few attempts to get the glaze right and the skin crispy. The trick is to leave the chicken uncovered in the refrigerator overnight after brining to dry the skin out as much as possible before roasting it. The other trick is to continually baste the chicken every 20 minutes or so throughout the cooking process to get a beautiful shiny glaze.

Brine the chicken for 1 hour according to the brine instructions on page 24 (optional).

Lightly dust the inside of the chicken with the five-spice powder.

Mix all the marinade ingredients together in a large shallow dish. Add the chicken and, using your hands, massage the chicken a few times with the marinade until it is well coated. Cover with cling film (plastic wrap) and marinate in the refrigerator for at least 4 hours, or preferably overnight.

Remove the chicken from the refrigerator 30 minutes before cooking. Take the ginger out of the marinade and place it into the cavity of the chicken. Pour the leftover marinade into a small saucepan. Cook for 5–10 minutes over a medium-low heat, then add the maple syrup and remove from the heat. Set aside for basting the chicken at the end of roasting.

Meawhile, preheat the oven to 180°C (350°F/gas 4). Set up a baking tray (pan) with an adjustable roasting rack or a regular grilling (broiling) rack and set the chicken on it. If you don't have a rack, crumple up pieces of kitchen foil into balls and set the chicken on them, or cut onions into large pieces and set the chicken on top. If you are using an ovenproof digital probe thermometer, insert it into the thickest part of the chicken, usually into the thigh without touching the bone, then roast for 1 hour 20 minutes–2 hours, basting the chicken with the oil drippings from the chicken every 20 minutes or so, for 1 hour. If you don't get any oil drippings, use 1–2 tablespoons oil instead. For the last 30 minutes, start basting the chicken every 10–15 minutes with the reserved basting sauce. Be sure to close the oven door every time you baste the chicken, otherwise the oven temperature will drop too much. Once the internal temperature of the chicken reaches 74°C (165°F), remove the chicken from the oven. If you don't have a thermometer, slice the skin between the thigh and body cavity, you should be able to pull the thigh easily from the body and the chicken meat near the joint should be white. If the chicken is not cooked, return it to the oven until it is cooked through.

Leave the chicken to rest for 15 minutes before carving. Serve the chicken as a main dish over steamed rice with pancakes, cucumber, spring onions and hoisin sauce. Enjoy!

FIRECRACKER CHICKEN

SERVES 4

35 g (1 oz/½ cup) gochugaru or Korean chilli (hot pepper) flakes

2–3 tablespoons gochujang (Korean red chilli paste)

1 tablespoon soy sauce

3 tablespoons vegetable or corn oil

½ teaspoon ground black pepper

115 g (4 oz/⅓ cup) honey

6 large garlic cloves, very finely chopped

2 teaspoons very finely chopped fresh ginger root

1.5–2 kg (3 lb 5 oz–4 lb 8 oz) whole chicken, jointed (page 12)

225 g (8 oz/1 cup) sliced rice cakes (optional)

500 g (1 lb 2 oz) stringy mozzarella cheese, cut into small pieces (optional)

1 spring onion (scallion), chopped

This recipe is inspired by my love of Korean food. Korean food is very different from other Asian countries and has many influences from America. The base ingredients for a lot of Korean recipes is gochujang, which is a spicy fermented red pepper paste made by putting it into clay pots left out in the hot sun to ferment. It has a vibrant red colour and a funky, spicy umami flavour, which is quite different to anything else I've tasted. The Koreans also have a love for street food and this recipe, although not authentic, has an American/Korean vibe to it with the use of stringy mozzarella. It's a bit filthy by nature and a little sweet and spicy. This is pretty straight forward, especially if you skip the rice cakes, and all you probably need with this is a green salad with a sharp dressing and you're good to go.

Preheat the oven to 180°C (350°F/gas 4).

Mix the chilli flakes, chilli paste, soy sauce, 2 tablespoons of the oil, the black pepper, honey, garlic and ginger together in a bowl until combined into a sweet and spicy paste. Add the chicken and mix well with clean hands.

Heat the remaining oil in a casserole or ovenproof frying pan with a lid over a medium heat. Add the sliced rice cakes (if using) and fry for a few minutes, turning them over with a spatula once or twice until both sides are crispy and light golden brown.

Remove the rice cakes from the pan and add the chicken and marinade. Cook over a medium heat for 3–4 minutes, until browning a little. Uncover, stir and turn over the chicken with a wooden spoon. Add the rice cakes to the top of the chicken (if using).

Cover and roast for 30–40 minutes, until all the chicken pieces are cooked through.

If you are using cheese, preheat the grill (broiler). Arrange the cheese over the top, then grill for a few minutes until the cheese is melted and bubbly.

Sprinkle the chopped spring onion over the top and serve hot.

EASY PEASY

W H O L E

T R A C K   O N E

TIP

You can find sliced rice cakes either online or in specialist Asian grocery stores.

BALINESE BBQ CHICKEN

SERVES 2–4

1.8–2.8 kg (4–6 lb 3 oz) chicken, jointed (page 12)

lettuce cups or sticky rice, to serve

FOR THE MARINADE

1 teaspoon shrimp paste

6 small Asian red shallots, roughly chopped

1 lemongrass stalk, pale part finely chopped

6 garlic cloves, roughly chopped

1 large mild red chilli, roughly chopped

2 cm (¾ in) piece of fresh ginger root, peeled and roughly chopped

2 tablespoons fish sauce

2 tablespoons kecap manis (Indonesian sweet soy sauce) (optional)

1 teaspoon sea salt

1 teaspoon ground coriander seeds

1 teaspoon ground turmeric

1 teaspoon soft brown sugar

400 ml (14 fl oz) tin coconut milk

FOR THE SPICE PASTE

115 g (4 oz) shallot, sliced

65 g (2¼ oz) garlic, sliced

30 g (1 oz) piece of galangal, peeled and sliced

10 g (¼ oz/1 tablespoon) cashew nuts

60 g (2¼ oz) piece of fresh turmeric, peeled and sliced

2 bird's eye chillies, finely sliced

2½ tablespoons coconut palm sugar, chopped

1 lemongrass stalk, bruised

1 Kaffir lime leaf

125 ml (4¼ fl oz/½ cup) water

1 teaspoon salt

2 tablespoons coconut or rapeseed (canola) oil

FOR THE SAMBAL BELACAN

1 tablespoon belacan shrimp paste

1 mild red chilli, thinly sliced

1½ teaspoons coconut palm sugar

2 tablespoons lime juice

FOR THE PICKLED PINEAPPLE

1 tablespoon salt, plus extra for rubbing

1 medium pineapple, peeled

2 tablespoons muscovado sugar

100 ml (3½ fl oz/scant ½ cup) water, boiled and cooled

1 tablespoon finely chopped green or red chilli

1 teaspoon tamarind pulp

120 ml (4 fl oz/½ cup) cider or rice wine vinegar

WORTH THE EFFORT

W H O L E

T R A C K   O N E

When I asked a few friends to collaborate on a recipe with me,
I knew I had ask my good friend and brilliant chef Jack Stein.
I first met Jack on a kind of Blair Witch Project-style deer hunting
trip in Cornwall a few years ago … but the less said about that,
the better. We've been good mates ever since, and Jack has been
a constant inspiration to me in all the time I've known him. Along
with his brother (who's also my good friend) Charlie, they head
up the food and wine side of the business. Over the years, I have
become close friends with the whole Stein family who are not only
the kindest, most hospitable and down-to-earth restaurateurs,
but also people, in our industry today. The Seafood restaurant in
Padstow is still my death-row meal and will always remain so till
the end. Jack is a surfer and loves Bali, so it only made sense to
develop a recipe from there. We've tried to capture all the flavours
of Indonesia, and hope you enjoy cooking this recipe as much as
we enjoyed creating it.

To make the marinade, wrap the shrimp paste in a piece of kitchen
foil and roast in the oven for 15–20 minutes until fragrant. Transfer
to a blender or food processor with the remaining marinade
ingredients and blend until smooth. It doesn't need to be super
smooth. Place the chicken pieces on a tray or in a large bowl, add
the marinade and turn the chicken in it until covered. Refrigerate
for at least 6 hours, but preferably 24 hours.

At the same time, make the pickled pineapple. Rub salt all over
the whole pineapple, then leave for 1 hour at room temperature.

Rinse it well under cold running water to remove the salt, then
cut the pineapple into quarters and mix them with chopped chilli,
sugar and 1 tablespoon of salt. Pack the pineapple mixture into a
sterilised Kilner jar and allow to cool before closing the lid. Bring
the water, tamarind pulp and vinegar to a simmer in a saucepan,
then pour the mixture over the pineapple. This can be eaten the
next day or it will keep for at least 3 months in the refrigerator.

Once the chicken has marinated, remove from the refrigerator
and strain off all the liquid and discard, then leave the chicken to
come to room temperature.

Preheat the oven to 180°C (350°F/gas 4).

Meanwhile, to make the spice paste, place all the ingredients,
except the oil, in a food processor and blend to a smooth paste.
Mix the oil through the paste and set aside.

Arrange the chicken pieces in a deep roasting tray and rub
the spice paste very generously all over the chicken. Roast for
30–40 minutes, until cooked through. There should be some
charred edges around the sides of the skin.

Meanwhile, to make the sambal, heat a wok or saucepan over
a low heat, add the shrimp paste and roast for 2–3 minutes until
fragrant. Remove and add either to a mortar and pestle or food
processor with the chilli, sugar and lime juice and pound or blend
until fine. Set aside.

To serve, place the roasted chicken pieces on a large serving
plate, then serve with the sambal, pickled pineapple and either
lettuce cups or sticky rice.

SOY & MOLASSES POACHED CHICKEN

SERVES 6 (OR 4 IF YOU'D LIKE LEFTOVERS!)

1.8–2.8 kg (4–6 lb 3 oz) chicken

4–5 thick slices of fresh ginger root, peeled and lightly bashed

3–4 spring onions (scallions), cut into 5 cm (2 in) segments

4 garlic cloves, peeled and lightly bashed

250 ml (8½ fl oz/1 cup) dark soy sauce

125 ml (4 fl oz/½ cup) dark molasses

1 tablespoon Shaoxing wine

125 ml (4 fl oz/½ cup) light soy sauce

½ teaspoon ground white pepper

1 litre (34 fl oz/4 cups) water or good-quality chicken stock

1 cinnamon stick

2 star anise

FOR THE GINGER AND SPRING ONION DIPPING SAUCE

1 bunch of spring onions (scallions), thinly sliced

3 cm (1¼ in) piece of fresh root ginger, peeled and grated

5 tablespoons rapeseed (canola) oil

1½ teaspoons light soy sauce

2 teaspoons Shaoxing rice wine

½ teaspoon Maldon sea salt

FOR THE EXPLOSIVE CHILLI DIPPING SAUCE

4 tablespoons store-bought peanut chilli oil (I love the Laoganma brand)

1 tablespoon rapeseed (canola) oil

2 tablespoons crispy shallots (available at most supermarkets in the Asian aisle)

½ teaspoon ground Sichuan pepper

TO SERVE

400 g (14 oz/2 generous cups) cooked sushi rice

2 heads crispy baby gem lettuce

This recipe is a showstopper and very easy to prepare. I love making this at home at the weekends or on Saturday night for a nostalgic Chinese takeaway. It looks great when it comes to the table and is a fun dish to share with friends.

This recipe just keeps giving, and is one you can get at least two extra treats from. Place some leftover chicken between two slices of white bread, add lettuce and Japanese Kewpie mayonnaise and you have a tasty Monday snack, or cook some fat stir-fry noodles in some of the leftover stock, add greens of your choice and serve with chilli oil for a comforting Sunday-night treat. You can also freeze the leftover stock and use as a master stock for any future food experiments (page 44 for inspiration).

Here, I'm serving the chicken with two of my favourite dipping sauces – a bright fresh spring onion (scallion) and ginger dip and a spicy explosive chilli dip that we serve at my restaurants. I want the chicken to be the star of the show so I have kept everything else light and have served it in lettuce cups with sushi rice, so everyone can build their own dish. You can prepare this a day in advance and just reheat the chicken in the stock before serving, leaving you more time to have fun with your friends!

For the poached chicken, place all the ingredients, except the chicken, in a large pot big enough to hold the whole chicken and bring to the boil over a high heat. Carefully place the bird in the boiling stock, breast-side down, cover with a lid, reduce the heat to medium and simmer for 30–45 minutes until the bird is cooked through. The stock should be rolling very gently so be careful not to boil too furiously as the bird will become tough and dry out.

To check if the chicken is cooked, either use a temperature probe and insert into the fat part of the thigh close to the bone where the temperature should read 70–75°C (158–167°F) or insert a spike into the same part of the chicken and see if the juices run clear. If they are still a little pink, leave to simmer for another few minutes and check again.

Turn off the heat and leave the chicken in the pot with the lid on for at least 3 hours, but 6 is better. When you are ready to serve, simply heat very gently, then remove the chicken from the stock and place on a large serving plate.

For the ginger and spring onion dipping sauce, place all the ingredients in a bowl and mix together. This can be made a day or two in advance and gets better with age. If making on the day, leave to stand for at least 2–3 hours for maximum flavour vibes.

For the chilli dipping sauce, mix all the ingredients together in a bowl and set aside. This will keep for up to two weeks in the refrigerator.

To serve, put the cooked sushi rice in a large serving bowl. Tear the lettuce leaves apart, being careful to keep them whole so they can hold some of the rice and chicken. Place the dipping sauce in small bowls, then arrange everything on the table with the chicken. Dive in, making lettuce cups with some of the chicken and rice and dipping into a sauce.

W
H
O
L
E

T
R
A
C
K

O
N
E

BREASTS

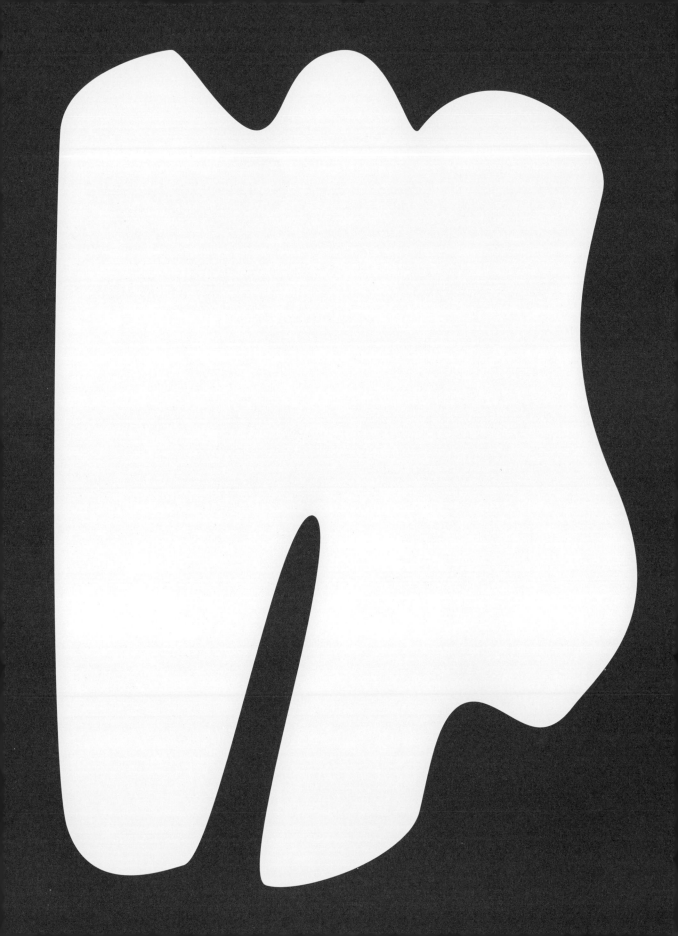

SOY AND MAPLE-GLAZED CHICKEN BREAST

SERVES 4

4 chicken breasts, skin on

120 g (4 oz/scant ½ cup) pure maple syrup

80 ml (2½ fl oz/⅓ cup) light soy sauce

1 tablespoon rice wine vinegar

2 tablespoons rapeseed (canola) oil

Maldon sea salt and freshly ground black pepper

TO SERVE

1 quantity of Spicy Pineapple and Mango Pickles (page 173)

1 quantity of Smacked Cucumbers with Sesame and Seaweed (page 190)

This is by far the most simple recipe in this book and a really quick delicious afterwork type of dish, provided you remember to marinate it the day before. Chicken breasts are easy to dry out when cooking, and there's nothing worse than a dry chicken breast. This is where the brine really starts to work its magic. There is little or no fat on the breast, so we are cooking pure muscle that needs a technique to keep it as moist as possible while cooking. To get the skin crisp it's also important to dry the skin back out after brining, by leaving it uncovered in the refrigerator for a while to allow the cold air to circulate around it. Dry skin means crispy skin, wet skin means flabby skin. The chicken in this recipe is salty and sweet at the same time and goes well with the cold spicy Smacked Cucumbers with Sesame and Seaweed (page 190) or the Spicy Pineapple and Mango Pickles (page 173).

Brine the chicken for 1 hour according to the brine instructions on page 24 (optional).

If brining, remove the chicken from the brine and pat dry with paper towels. Place the chicken in a shallow bowl and chill in the refrigerator for 1 hour to dry out the skin. Otherwise, pat your chicken dry with paper towels and leave to dry uncovered in the refrigerator for 30 minutes.

In another large shallow bowl, mix the maple syrup, soy sauce and rice wine vinegar together until combined. Season the chicken with salt and pepper, add to the maple syrup mixture, cover with cling film (plastic wrap) and marinate in the refrigerator for 3 hours, but preferably for 24 hours.

Preheat the oven to 180°C (350°F/gas 4).

Heat the oil in a large ovenproof frying pan (skillet) or baking tray (pan), if you don't have one big enough not to overcrowd the pan. Place the chicken, skin-side down, in the pan and cook gently over a medium heat for 5 minutes, or until the skin starts to turn golden brown. Turn the chicken over and place in the hot oven for 10–12 minutes, turning occasionally so the marinade doesn't burn. When cooked, remove and leave to rest for 5 minutes.

Serve the chicken with mango pickle and smacked cucumbers.

TEMPURA CHICKEN TENDERS
WITH BLUEBERRY HOISIN

SERVES 2 AS A MAIN, 4 AS A SNACK

40

ALMOST
BREEZY

B
R
E
A
S
T
S

1.5 litres (50 fl oz/6½ cups) rapeseed (canola) oil

12 chicken strips (tenders) (inner fillets from the breast)

FOR THE TEMPURA BATTER

1 large egg

200 ml (7 fl oz/scant 1 cup) very cold fizzy water

120 g (4 oz/scant 1 cup) plain (all-purpose) flour

120 g (4 oz/scant 1 cup) cornflour (cornstarch)

½ teaspoon salt

FOR THE BLUEBERRY HOISIN

20 g (¾ oz) fresh ginger root, very finely chopped

250 ml (8½ fl oz/1 cup) pineapple juice

450 g (1 lb/scant 3 cups) fresh blueberries

375 ml (12½ fl oz/1½ cups) hoisin sauce

100 g (3½/¼ cup) honey

60 ml (2 fl oz/¼ cup) white wine vinegar

40 g (1½ oz/3¼ tablespoons) caster (superfine) sugar

10 g (¼ oz) Sriracha (hot chilli sauce)

55 g (2 oz) butter

The 'tenders' are the inner fillets from the breasts and the most tender part of the chicken. They are very delicate and so require a delicate way of cooking to stop them from drying out. Tempura is perfect for this as it cooks quickly and, of course, anything deep-fried is better, right? This dish is a kind of Japan-meets-China-meets-Carl recipe and as with most things I tend to create, makes sense most of the time, but honestly, not always. I first made this version of hoisin for an all-day Chick 'n' Sours takeover of Brad Carter's Michelin-starred restaurant in my hometown of Birmingham. It was right at the end of the raspberry season and I served it with a Chengdu chilli bomb as a snack. Blueberries are a great alternative as they are around all year long and add a fruity sweetness to the funky flavours of the hoisin. This sauce works well with just about anything fried, especially fried cheese.

To make the batter, using chopsticks, mix the egg and water together in a bowl, then add the flours and salt. Do not overmix, it's fine to have lumps. Cover with cling film (plastic wrap) and chill in the refrigerator until ready for cooking. Be sure to keep the batter very cold through all the stages.

To make the blueberry hoisin, place all the ingredients in a saucepan and simmer over a low heat for about 30 minutes, until it coats the back of a spoon, then whizz with a hand-held blender until smooth. Transfer to a bowl, cover and chill in the refrigerator until ready to serve.

Heat the oil in a large deep saucepan until the temperature of the oil reaches 180–190°C (350–375°F), or until a cube of bread dropped in sizzles in 30 seconds. Coat a chicken strip in the batter, shaking off any excess and fry the chicken for 4–5 minutes until crispy and golden, dipping and frying each piece as you go, tempura-style. While the chicken is frying, carefully drip some of the batter on top of the chicken with chopsticks to create a little texture. Once cooked, remove from the oil, drain on a wire rack and serve with the cold blueberry hoisin.

T
R
A
C
K

T
W
O

MY FRIEND ROMY'S
BUTTER CHICKEN RECIPE

SERVES 4

1 kg (2 lb 4 oz) boneless chicken breast, diced

naan, to serve (page 102; optional)

FOR THE MARINADE

50 g (2 oz/3 tablespoons) plain Greek yoghurt

2 teaspoons finely grated fresh ginger root

2 teaspoons finely grated garlic

1 teaspoon garam masala

1 teaspoon Masala Seasoning (page 195)

1 teaspoon ground cumin

1 teaspoon ground coriander

1 teaspoon red Kashmiri chilli powder

1 teaspoon salt

FOR THE SAUCE

6 tablespoons cashew nuts

6 teaspoons ghee or butter

2 teaspoons finely grated fresh ginger root

2 teaspoons finely grated garlic

6 teaspoons tomato purée (paste)

3 teaspoons dried fenugreek leaves

1 teaspoon garam masala

1 teaspoon Masala Seasoning (page 195)

½ teaspoon ground turmeric

1 teaspoon Kashmiri chilli powder

2 teaspoons salt

500 ml (17 fl oz/2 cups) single (light) cream

400 ml (13 fl oz/generous 1½ cups) water

FOR THE RICE (OPTIONAL)

200 g (7 oz/1 cup) basmati rice

1 tablespoon butter or oil

1 tablespoon cumin seeds

300 ml (10 fl oz/1¼ cups) hot water

When I was asked to write this book I wanted to include a few recipes from my chef friends, people I respect for their genuine love and passion for our industry and the food they serve in their restaurants and beyond into their communities every day. Romy is a British Indian chef who was appointed an MBE on the Queen's 90th birthday and formerly chef-owner of Romy's Kitchen in Thornbury, Gloucestershire, where her cooking was very unique and natural: she combines spices and flavours that she grew up with in India with ingredients from the UK that she was introduced to when she moved here. The restaurant is now sadly closed, but Romy continues to cook incredible food at various pop-ups and also writes cookbooks, her last one notably being vegan. She is one of the loveliest, sincerest and hardworking people I know in our business. Here is her butter chicken recipe, which is the best I have ever had, and I have eaten a few in my time. It's rich, comforting and luxurious. For me, it's the perfect Sunday night dish served with some naan bread or a few chapati on the side.

Mix all the marinade ingredients together in a bowl until combined. Add the chicken, stir to coat the chicken in the marinade, then cover with cling film (plastic wrap) and marinate in the refrigerator for at least 2 hours, or preferably overnight.

When ready to cook, preheat the oven to 200°C (400°F/gas 6) or a grill (broiler) to medium-high.

Place the marinated chicken on a baking tray (pan) and bake or grill (broil) for 10–12 minutes until the chicken is tender and cooked through (depending on the oven it might take less time to cook).

To make the sauce, grind the cashew nuts in a blender to a fine powder.

Heat the ghee in a large saucepan with a lid over a medium heat. Add the ginger and garlic and cook for 1–2 minutes until they turn light brown. Add the tomato purée and cook for 3–4 minutes until it turns dry and the oil separates. Add the fenugreek leaves, the remaining spices, salt, cream, ground cashews and water, stir and mix well, then cook for 5 minutes. Add the cooked chicken, mix well and cook over a low heat for 10–20 minutes. Remove the pan from the heat, cover with a lid and leave to rest for 30 minutes before serving, or use the time to make the rice.

If serving the rice with the chicken, soak the rice in a bowl of water for 30 minutes, then drain and set aside. Heat the butter or oil in a large saucepan with a lid over a medium heat. Add the cumin seeds and soaked rice and fry for 2 minutes. Add the hot water, mix well and cover with a lid. After about 5 minutes, when the water has evaporated, remove the pan from the heat, cover with paper towels and put the lid on. Leave for 5 minutes to rest before serving with the butter chicken. And naan, if you like.

WORTH THE EFFORT

B R E A S T S

T R A C K   T W O

MASTERSTOCK CHICKEN BREAST
WITH PRESERVED LEMON AND CHILLI SLAW

SERVES 4

44

WORTH THE
EFFORT

B
R
E
A
S
T
S

4 boneless chicken breasts, skin on

3 tablespoons rapeseed (canola) oil

FOR THE CHINESE STOCK

1.5 litres (51 fl oz/6 cups) chicken stock (broth)

115 ml (4 fl oz/½ cup) light soy sauce

250 ml (8½ fl oz/1 cup) Shaoxing rice wine

125 g (4¼ oz/½ cup plus 2 tablespoons) coconut palm sugar

3 garlic cloves

1 cinnamon stick

2 cloves

3 star anise

1 teaspoon cumin seeds, toasted

1 teaspoon Sichuan peppercorns

½ teaspoon coriander seeds

½ teaspoon fennel seeds

FOR THE GREEN SLAW

100 g (3½ oz) mooli (daikon), julienned

100 g (3½ oz) green kale, julienned

100 g (3½ oz) pak choi (bok choi), julienned

2 shiso, mint or coriander leaves, julienned

FOR THE DRESSING

6 whole long green chillies, deseeded

1 whole preserved lemon, pips removed

1 tablespoon rapeseed (canola) oil

150 g (5 oz/⅔ cup) Japanese Kewpie mayonnaise

2 tablespoons plain yoghurt

sea salt and freshly ground black pepper

I first cooked this recipe on *Saturday Kitchen* when it was game season and used partridge instead of chicken. Partridge is a very lean bird, so I adopted the old-school French method of *poche grille*, which was a method I learned while cooking at Marco Pierre White's Belvedere restaurant back in the day. It was a cooking technique used to keep the breast as moist as possible during cooking and also to add flavour from the crock it was first poached in, before finishing off in a hot pan to crisp up the skin. For this recipe, I have used both a brine to begin with and then a Chinese masterstock. It's called masterstock because the Chinese use it again and again, as it becomes more flavourful as time goes on. Legend has it that there are a some that are over 100 years old that are still used. To use again though you must always bring the masterstock back to the boil and skim off any scum that forms on the surface before returning it to the refrigerator. My tip is to make a batch and then freeze it after use, using again and re-freezing as you go. I have served this dish with a fresh green chilli slaw, which cuts through all the spices in the recipe perfectly and adds freshness.

Brine the chicken for 1 hour according to the brine instructions on page 24 (optional, but you should make the effort for this one).

To make the Chinese stock, place all the ingredients in a large saucepan and simmer gently over a low heat for 30 minutes. Add the chicken and gently poach for 10–12 minutes. Remove the chicken from the stock and set aside (the chicken won't be fully cooked at this point).

To make the green slaw, mix all the vegetables together in a bowl and set aside.

To make the dressing, purée the chillies, preserved lemon, oil and salt together in a blender until smooth. Add the mayonnaise and yoghurt, then season and mix well. Mix just enough into the green slaw vegetables to bind but don't make it too wet.

Heat the oil in a sauté pan or frying pan (skillet) over a medium low heat. Add the chicken breasts and cook, skin-side down, for 8 minutes until golden brown, turning at the last minute. Remove from the heat and serve the chicken with the green slaw on the side.

SLICED CHICKEN BREAST
WITH NOODLES AND BLACK BEAN SAUCE

SERVES 4–6

400 g (14 oz) udon noodles

3 tablespoons rapeseed (canola) oil

3 large boneless chicken breasts, diced into 1 cm (½ in) pieces

FOR THE BLACK BEAN SAUCE

15 g (½ oz) grated fresh ginger root

2 large garlic cloves

2 teaspoons light soy sauce

2 teaspoons dark soy sauce

1 tablespoon fermented black beans or black bean paste

65 ml (2¼ fl oz/¼ cup) mirin or rice wine vinegar

50 g (2 oz/3 tablespoons) oyster sauce

50 g (2 oz/¼ cup) caster (superfine) sugar

50 ml (1¾ fl oz/3 tablespoons) chicken stock (broth)

2 tablespoons Shaoxing rice wine

2 teaspoons sesame oil

50 ml (1¾ fl oz/3 tablespoons) water

1 teaspoon cornflour (cornstarch)

TO GARNISH

100 g (3½ oz) spring onions (scallions), sliced

50 g (2 oz) red chilies, sliced (optional)

½ cucumber, sliced into batons

Udon noodles are the most eaten noodles in Japan. They are usually served in a hot soup broth-type of dish or eaten cold with dipping sauces. The difference between hot and cold udon is the different textures, with the cold having more chew. Cold udon also gives you the option of having something refreshing in summer compared to a hot steaming broth in winter. Although this recipe bears no relation to Japanese-style udon, for me the thick chewy texture of the noodles works really well with this dish. Chinese black beans are made by salting and fermenting soybeans resulting in a funky, slightly bitter and sweet taste and are used in a variety of Chinese dishes. They are great served with some steamed or wok-fried garlic and Chinese greens, such as pak choi (bok choi) on the side.

To make the black bean sauce, blend the ginger, garlic and soy sauces in a blender until smooth. Add the black beans and purée until the beans are broken down but you can still see specks of bean in the mix. Tip the mixture into a saucepan with all the remaining ingredients, except the water and cornflour, and simmer over a low heat for 10 minutes. Place the cornflour in a small bowl, add the water and whisk well to combine, then whisk into the sauce.

Cook the noodles according to the packet instructions and set aside.

Heat a little rapeseed oil in a wok or deep frying pan (skillet) over a medium heat. Add the chicken and fry for 2 minutes. Add the sauce and cook for another 5 minutes until the chicken is cooked through (do not reduce the sauce too much), then remove the pan from the heat.

Place the warm noodles into deep noodle bowls and spoon the chicken and black bean sauce on top. Garnish with finely sliced spring onions, sliced red chillies (if using) and cucumber batons.

B
R
E
A
S
T
S

T
R
A
C
K

T
W
O

NOTE

You can buy fermented black beans or black bean paste in large supermarkets or specialist Asian grocery stores.

RE-IMAGINED CHICKEN KIEV

SERVES 4

46

ALMOST
BREEZY

**B
R
E
A
S
T
S**

4 large boneless chicken breasts, skin on

2 eggs

200 g (7 oz/1 ¾ cups) plain (all-purpose) flour

200 g (7 oz/3⅓ cups) panko breadcrumbs

1 litre (34 fl oz/4 cups) rapeseed (canola) oil

FOR THE GARLIC BUTTER

1 teaspoon shrimp paste, roasted

1 bird's eye chilli, deseeded (optional)

1 garlic clove

1 large banana shallot, finely diced

1 teaspoon coconut palm sugar

2 tablespoons lime juice

250 g (9 oz) good-quality unsalted butter

2 tablespoons chopped coriander (cilantro)

TO SERVE

crunchy green salad

fries

I love chicken Kiev, an absolute classic dish, which is a beautiful thing when done right. It's simple in its components but you need to have some skills to keep the garlic butter inside while it's cooking. The best moment is when you slice into one and the molten garlic butter sprays out in all directions. The trick is to seal the chicken breasts well after stuffing them with the flavoured butter, then put the breasts back in the refrigerator to chill right down and to keep the butter nice and cold before cooking. I wanted to have some fun in this book and put my own spin on a couple of classic dishes. Not that there's anything wrong with the original recipe, it's just the way my mind works when looking at food. My imagination runs wlld and a million 'what ifs' pop into my head. Here, I've given it a kind of Thai twist, adding shrimp paste, palm sugar, lime juice and chillies to the butter for some heat. If the butter is soft it will escape during the cooking process and there's nothing worse than an empty Kiev! This dish is great served with a green salad dressed with lemon oil or – as I like it – with fries.

To make the garlic butter, blend all the ingredients, except the coriander, together in a food processor until smooth, then mix in the chopped coriander. Set aside.

Using a sharp knife, make an incision in the side of the chicken breasts without going all the way through to the other side. Divide the garlic butter into 4 portions and pack each portion into the chicken pockets. Pull the flesh over the butter to seal and chill in the refrigerator for at least 1 hour to set.

Preheat the oven to 180°C (350°F/gas 4).

Beat the eggs in a bowl, then place the flour in a second bowl and add the panko breadcrumbs to a third bowl. Dip each chicken breast first into the flour, shaking off excess, then dip into the egg and finally dip into the breadcrumbs until the chicken is evenly coated on both sides. Return to the refrigerator to set for 30 minutes.

Heat the oil in a wok or deep saucepan to 160°C (325°F), or until a cube of bread dropped in sizzles in 30 seconds. Deep-fry the chicken in pairs for 3–4 minutes on each side, or until golden brown. Remove and place the chicken Kievs on a baking tray (pan) and bake for 8–10 minutes until cooked through.

Serve with a crunchy green salad or fries.

**T
R
A
C
K

T
W
O**

JAPANESE MEATBALLS
WITH STICKY BASTING SAUCE

SERVES 4

10 shiso (perilla) leaves (optional)

500 g (1 lb 2 oz/2½ cups) minced (ground) chicken breast (ask your butcher to do this for you)

1 tablespoon sesame oil

1 tablespoon miso paste (red if possible)

4 spring onions (scallions), thinly sliced

Maldon sea salt

shichimi togarashi, to taste

FOR THE STICKY TARE GLAZE

125 ml (4¼ fl oz/½ cup) dark soy sauce

125 ml (4¼ fl oz/½ cup) mirin

60 ml (2 fl oz/¼ cup) sake

60 ml (2 fl oz/¼ cup) water

15 g (½ oz/4 teaspoons) muscovado (soft brown) sugar

1 spring onion (scallion), green part only, finely sliced

**B
R
E
A
S
T
S**

These Japanese meatballs are usually served in teppanyaki restaurants and cooked over special Japanese charcoal called binchotan, which burns very slow and very hot, but you can get just as tasty results at home by cooking them under your grill (broiler) or in a ridged cast-iron frying pan (skillet), if you prefer. I'm using shiso (perilla) leaves here, which you should be able to find in Asian grocery stores. They have a unique pungent flavour with a hint of basil, anise and cinnamon. They work so well with this recipe but if you can't find them don't worry, make the meatballs anyway as they will still be delicious. During cooking, the meatballs are basted with a sticky tare sauce leaving them with a delicious salty, sweet sticky glaze. They are great to serve as snacks with drinks or at the beginning of a feast as a sharing plate with a group of friends.

Soak 4 x 12 cm (5 in) bamboo skewers in a bowl of hot water for 30 minutes to prevent them burning while cooking.

Meanwhile, to make the glaze, bring the soy sauce, mirin, sake, water, sugar and the spring onion to the boil in a small saucepan over a high heat. Reduce the heat to low and simmer, uncovered, for 30 minutes until the liquid has reduced by half. The sauce will be thick and glossy. Leave to cool to room temperature before using.

Preheat the grill (broiler) to medium-high.

Pile and roll up the shiso leaves (if using) on a cutting board, then cut into thin julienne slices.

Place the chicken in a large bowl, add the sesame oil and miso and mix well. Add the spring onions and shiso leaves and combine well with a silicone spatula. Using clean hands, knead the mixture 30 times clockwise. Work the chicken really well with your hands until it becomes an almost fine paste. Divide the mixture into small 50 g (2 oz) balls, then thread onto the end of the soaked skewers to form a kind of round patty. Lightly season with salt. Grill (broil) the skewers for about 4 minutes on each side, then start to baste with the sauce for the last 2–3 minutes of cooking. You can also use a frying pan (skillet) to cook the skewers if you prefer. When cooked, season with shichimi togarashi, to taste.

NOTE

You can find shiso or perilla leaves either online or in specialist Asian grocery stores. Shichimi togarashi is a Japanese spice mix and can be found in large supermarkets, in specialist Asian grocery stores or online.

**T
R
A
C
K

T
W
O**

BLACKENED CHICKEN SANDWICH WITH POTATO CHIPS AND BREAD AND BUTTER PICKLES

SERVES 2 GENEROUSLY

2 large boneless chicken breasts

2 large ciabatta rolls or 4 small individual rolls, halved

12–18 Bread and Butter Pickles (page 173 or use shop-bought dill pickles or gherkins)

few large leaves of butter lettuce

FOR THE BLACKENED SEASONING

½ teaspoon ground black pepper

½ teaspoon Sichuan peppercorns

½ teaspoon ground cardamom

1 tablespoon coriander seeds

4 tablespoons black mustard seeds

1 teaspoon cumin seeds

1 teaspoon whole allspice

1 tablespoon ground kombu, made from 1 sheet of kombu (optional)

3 tablespoons onion powder

6 tablespoons cayenne pepper (this is very hot so reduce as required)

60 g (2 oz/½ cup) smoked sweet paprika

20 g (¾ oz) tomato soup packet mix (optional)

FOR THE MISO MAYO

200 ml (7 fl oz/scant 1 cup) mayonnaise

2 tablespoons white miso paste

FOR THE BLACKENED POTATO CHIPS (OPTIONAL)

2 baking potatoes, peeled

1.5 litres (50 fl oz/6½ cups) rapeseed (canola) oil, for frying

sea salt

I wanted to include this recipe as it's based on my childhood memories of crisp (potato chip) sandwiches. Crisp sandwiches are a thing of beauty in their most basic form of cheap white sliced bread, butter and whatever your favourite crisps are, but here I have taken that idea a step further and pimped this crisp sandwich out to the max. This is basically a chicken and crisp sandwich with a Cajun twist using blackened seasoning and with some Japanese thrown in using miso mayo. This is not by any means an authentic Cajun mix, as I have used Sichuan pepper for a floral numbing flavour and kombu seaweed for umami. The tomato soup powder is a good shortcut and a great way of adding an addictive MSG flavour to the whole dish. You can make whole large ciabatta sandwiches and cut them into portions to share or just make up smaller individuals ones for yourself, whichever you fancy really. Once you have prepped the Cajun blackened seasoning, you will have lots leftover to use on a host of other things, such as Cajun fries and chicken wings.

Preheat the grill (broiler) to medium high or the oven to 180°C (375°F/gas 4).

To make the blackened seasoning, mix all the ingredients together in a bowl until combined. Store in an airtight container.

To make the miso mayo, mix the ingredients together in a bowl until combined. Set aside.

Place 4 tablespoons of the blackened seasoning on a plate, lay the chicken breasts on top and rub the seasoning in until both sides are completely coated. Grill (broil) or bake for 8 minutes on each side, until cooked through.

For the blackened potato chips, you can use shop-bought ready salted crisps tossed with the seasoning, but this is the real deal. Slice the potatoes on a mandoline or as thinly as possible with a sharp knife, then rinse under cold running water for 15 minutes, or until all the starch has been removed and the potato water is clear. Heat the oil in a large deep saucepan until the temperature of the oil reaches 180–190°C (350–375°F), or until a cube of bread dropped in sizzles in 30 seconds, and fry the potato chips for 2–3 minutes, or until golden brown and crispy. Remove and season well with salt and the blackened seasoning.

Toast each side of the ciabatta and smear with the miso mayo. Arrange the sliced chicken and the pickles on top of the mayo on one side of the ciabatta, then add the lettuce and potato chips. Put together, slice in half and secure with fancy cocktail sticks (toothpicks).

XIAN-STYLE FAJITAS

SERVES 4–6

**B
R
E
A
S
T
S**

4 large boneless chicken breasts, sliced into strips

2 tablespoons rapeseed (canola) oil

12 flour or corn tortillas, warmed

FOR THE XIAN FAJITA SEASONING

3 tablespoons cumin seeds

3 tablespoons coriander seeds

1 teaspoon dried chilli flakes

4 teaspoons Demerara sugar

¼ teaspoon MSG (optional)

¼ teaspoon salt

FOR THE PAN DEGLAZE

2 tablespoons rapeseed (canola) oil

1 garlic clove, finely chopped

thumb-sized piece of fresh ginger root, peeled and finely chopped

2 tablespoons light soy sauce

1½ tablespoons oyster sauce

1½ tablespoons rice wine vinegar

2 teaspoons sesame oil

1 tablespoon sesame seeds

FOR THE SOY PICKLED PEPPERS

3 tablespoons rapeseed (canola) oil

2 large red (bell) peppers, thinly sliced

2 tablespoons caster (superfine) sugar

2 tablespoons light soy sauce

1½ tablespoons dark soy sauce

100 ml (3½ fl oz/scant ½ cup) rice wine vinegar

TO SERVE

250 ml (8½ fl oz/1 cup) sour cream or labneh

1 quantity of Explosive Chilli Dipping Sauce (page 35)

2 tablespoons sesame seeds

1 bunch spring onions, finely sliced

When I was thinking about this dish, I was wondering how to put a Chinese twist on everyone's secret favourite dish – fajitas. Even the ones out of the packet were a real treat when I was a child and I remember getting excited on the rare occasion we had them. Cumin is not an ingredient usually associated with Chinese cooking, but was in fact brought north with Arabic traders travelling the Silk Route and it became a staple in Xian food. We serve this spice mix on our chicken strips (tenders) at my restaurant Chick 'n' Sours and they are a favourite on the menu. This is a big family or group of friends sharing dish where everyone can just get stuck in and build their own. I hope this brings back fond memories of fajitas in days gone by.

To make the seasoning, roast all the whole spices and dried chilli in a dry frying pan (skillet) over a medium heat for 2–3 minutes. Transfer to a mortar and pestle with the rest of the seasoning ingredients and pound to a powder.

For the sauce, heat the rapeseed oil in a frying pan over a medium heat and quickly fry the garlic and ginger, then add the soy sauce, oyster sauce and vinegar and bring to a simmer. As soon as it is simmering at the edges, add the sesame oil and seeds, then remove the pan from the heat.

To make the pickled peppers, heat the oil in a large saucepan over a medium heat until very hot. Add the peppers and fry for 3–4 minutes until they are charred at the edges but still have some crunch. Add the sugar and toss around until the peppers are coated in the sugar. Add all the remaining ingredients and coat the peppers in the sauce. Remove the pan from the heat and set aside.

To finish, heat the rapeseed oil in a frying pan over a medium heat. Add the chicken strips and fry for 4–5 minutes until they are almost cooked. Pour in the sauce and stir scraping up any crispy bits on the base of the pan. Cook for a minute or so, until the chicken is glazed but don't overcook or over reduce. Remove the pan from the heat and set aside.

Heat the tortillas in a dry frying pan for 2 minutes, then set aside and keep warm.

To serve, pile some chicken in the centre of a warm tortilla, top with the pickled peppers, sour cream, chilli sauce, sesame seeds and spring onions and liberally sprinkle with Xian seasoning.

COCONUT POACHED CHICKEN

SERVES 4

2 tablespoons coconut oil

2 tablespoons rapeseed (canola) oil

15 curry leaves

1 white onion, grated

20 g (¾ oz) piece of fresh ginger root, peeled and grated

3 garlic cloves, crushed

1 tablespoon ground turmeric

1 tablespoon ground cumin

2 teaspoons ground coriander

2 teaspoons smoked paprika (pimenton)

3 cardamom pods

1 cinnamon quill

2 cloves

4 boneless chicken breasts

250 ml (8½ fl oz/1 cup) chicken stock (broth)

400 ml (13 fl oz/generous 1½ cups) coconut milk

3 red bird's eye chillies, split in half

2 tablespoons cashews, crushed

salt

TO SERVE

small handful of curry leaves, fried

2 spring onions (scallions), sliced

handful of toasted coconut shavings

handful of roasted cashews, crushed

I first went to Sri Lanka a few years ago and fell in love with the island from the moment I arrived. Ever since, I have been going for a month every year to reconnect with one of the most beautiful places in the world. Sri Lanka is a special place, not only for its food but also its people, diverse cultures and natural beauty. It is a small island, but the food is varied from the different cultures that populate the island, which is made up of Buddhists, Tamil and a small Muslim community. Each culture has their own style of cooking with varying degrees of heat, ingredients and flavour. I have travelled all over the island from Jaffna in the north to the central highland tea fields of Nuwara Eliya, which has a much cooler climate than the rest of the island, but I spend most of my time in the south with its beautiful beaches on the Indian Ocean. Fish is mostly eaten on the south coast and made into fragrant curries using curry leaves, spices and fresh coconut milk and served with a variety of vegetable curries, such as cashew nut curry and my favourite pineapple curry, along with sambals and mini poppadoms. Here, I have taken the flavours of Sri Lanka and created a light fragrant creamy curry using chicken, turmeric and coconut milk, which will transport you to the jewel of the Indian Ocean.

Heat the coconut oil and rapeseed oil in a large saucepan over a medium heat. Add the curry leaves and fry briefly for 2 minutes. Add the onions and fry for another 5 minutes, until dark brown. Add the ginger and garlic and cook for another 5 minutes, then add all the spices and chicken and stir until the chicken is coated. Add the stock, coconut milk and chillies, then poach the chicken gently for about 20 minutes, or until the chicken is cooked through. Add the cashews for the last 10 minutes of cooking, then season with salt to taste.

Remove the chicken from the curry and cut into slices. Pour the sauce into a warmed bowl and serve the chicken with the sauce with fried curry leaves, spring onions, toasted coconut and roasted cashews.

EASY
PEASY

B
R
E
A
S
T
S

T
R
A
C
K

T
W
O

CHICKEN STRIPS WITH QUESO FONDUE

SERVES 4

4 boneless chicken breasts, each cut into 4 equal strips

6 eggs

400 g (14 oz/2½ cups) plain (all-purpose) flour

300 g (10½ oz/4½ cups) panko breadcrumbs

100 g (3½ oz) strong Cheddar, cubed

100 g (3½ oz) Red Leicester, cubed

5 American cheese slices

1 tablespoon cornflour (cornstarch)

8 g (¼ oz) butter

2 large garlic cloves, very finely chopped

½ small white onion, very finely chopped

2 tomatoes, deseeded and finely diced

375 g (13 oz/1¾ cups) evaporated milk

5 jalapeño chillies from a jar, deseeded and finely diced

¼ teaspoon onion powder

¼ teaspoon ground cumin

2–3 tablespoons full-fat (whole) milk or water, more if needed

2 tablespoons rapeseed (canola) oil, for frying

salt, to taste

Who doesn't love chicken strips? The great thing is that you can have a lot of fun coating them in a million different things, from crushed Doritos to Scampi Fries. I've used Japanese breadcrumbs in this recipe as they are freeze-dried and keep things incredibly crunchy after cooking, but feel free to go your own way instead. Queso is a very Tex-Mex thing and if you go into any restaurant from Houston to San Antonio in Texas, you will find a good queso on nearly every menu. It's a gooey, rich cheese sauce made slightly sweet with the use of condensed milk, which also gives it its unique texture. It's a great sharing snack for a group of friends and each place will have their own version with different toppings served with freshly fried tortilla chips. I've stayed on the Tex-Mex theme with mine, but used good English cheeses and a few American cheese slices to give it the stringy cheese effect. It's topped with guacamole, diced tomatoes and jalapeños or chopped gherkins (dill pickles) to cut through the cheese. This is the perfect way to eat piles of chicken strips sat around with friends.

Brine the chicken for 1 hour according to the brine instructions on page 24 (optional).

Beat the eggs in a bowl, add the flour to a second bowl and add the panko breadcrumbs to a third bowl. Dip the chicken strips first into the flour, shaking off excess, then dip into the egg and finally dip into the breadcrumbs until coated on all sides. Place in the refrigerator to set.

Place all the cheeses and cornflour in a bowl and toss to coat.

Melt the butter in a large saucepan or small pot over a medium heat. Add the garlic and onion and cook slowly for 3 minutes, or until the onion is translucent but not browned. Add the diced tomatoes, evaporated milk and cheese mixture. Stir, then add the chillies, onion powder and cumin. Stir for 3–4 minutes until the cheese melts and it becomes a silky sauce. Add salt to taste, then stir in the milk or water to adjust the consistency. The dip thickens when it cools, and liquid can be added later to adjust to taste. Remove the pan from the heat and season again, to taste. Serve warm or at room temperature. It will be soft and scoopable even when it cools.

For the chicken, heat the oil in a large frying pan (skillet) over a medium heat. Add the chicken, in batches if necessary, and fry for 3–4 minutes, or until golden brown.

Serve the chicken with the dip and dip away. If there are any leftovers, eat with corn chips.

55

WORTH THE EFFORT

B R E A S T S

T R A C K

T W O

CHICKEN, HOTDOG AND KIMCHI FRIED RICE

SERVES 4

56

EASY
PEASY

150 g (5 oz) dry cured streaky bacon, cut into 1 cm (½ in) lardons (small cubes)

1 large boneless chicken breast, cut into 2 cm (¾ in) dice

½ tablespoon vegetable oil (optional)

100 g (3½ oz) onions, sliced into thin strips

500 g (1 lb 2 oz/scant 2½ cups) cooked rice (175 g/6 oz/¾ cup uncooked)

75 g (2½ oz) shop-bought kimchi

100 g (3½ oz) smoked frankfurters

2 eggs

2 American cheese slices

toasted nori seaweed strips, to garnish

FOR THE SAUCE

2 tablespoons gochujang (Korean red chilli paste)

3 tablespoons sesame oil

2 tablespoons ketchup

1 tablespoon light soy sauce

1 teaspoon MSG (optional)

1 teaspoon caster (superfine) sugar

1 tablespoon vegetable oil

This is a really fun recipe that I love and make time and time again. It's got that American-Korean fusion going on as I have used smoked hotdog frankfurters. It's basically breakfast fried rice with sausage, bacon and eggs and I love to make this for brunch on the weekend. The sauce is sticky, spicy and sweet and, yes, it does have MSG in it. If you prefer not to use MSG then just leave it out and it will still be as delicious. The secret to good fried rice is all in the preparation of the rice itself. One trick I have learned over the years is to cook the rice the night before, drain it really well, then freeze it overnight. By doing this it separates out all the individual grains of rice, giving you a lighter, fluffier fried rice as opposed to a heavy stodgy fried rice. Make sure the wok or pan is really hot before adding the rice and let the rice sit at the bottom of the pan without moving it around for a few minutes, so you get nice crunchy bits. I finish it with American cheese slices, which melt into a gooey cheesy wonder when placed on top of the hot rice. The kimchi adds a beautiful freshness with its funky acidity that works a treat.

To make the sauce, mix all the ingredients together in a bowl until combined. Set aside.

Next, fry the bacon lardons in a large frying pan (skillet) or wok over a medium high heat for 3–4 minutes until golden brown and crispy but not burned. Remove the bacon from the pan, add the chicken and cook for 4–5 minutes until cooked through. Remove from the pan, then add a little more oil, if needed, and fry the onions over a high heat for 2–3 minutes until slightly charred and golden brown. Add the rice to the very hot pan, mix with the onions and spread it out over the base. Do not move for 1–2 minutes so it becomes crispy on the bottom. Stir in the crispy bacon, chicken, kimchi and frankfurters and cook for another 1–2 minutes. Add the sauce and toss to combine.

In a very hot separate large pan, fry the eggs over a high heat for 2–3 minutes until crispy on the bottom but still have soft yolks.

Pile the rice onto plates and arrange the cheese slices on top, then place the fried eggs on top of the cheese and garnish with strips of toasted nori seaweed.

BREASTS

DORITOS-COATED SCHNITZEL WITH FRIED EGGS AND ANCHOVIES

SERVES 1

58

EASY
PEASY

80 g (3 oz) tangy cheese-flavoured Doritos

20 g (¾ oz/⅓ cup) panko breadcrumbs

20 g (¾ oz/2¼ tablespoons) plain (all-pupose) flour

1 egg

1 large boneless chicken breast, butterflied and batted out with a mallet until it is about 2 mm (⅟₁₆ in) thick

2 tablespoons rapeseed (canola) oil

knob of butter

1 large egg

2 good-quality salted anchovies, rinsed

1 tablespoon chopped chives

squeeze of lemon juice

This recipe is a take on the classic Austrian dish Schnitzel Holstein, which is a flattened veal escalope (scallop) that's coated in breadcrumbs, fried in butter and served with a fried egg on top and a couple of anchovies. Here, I have swapped the veal for a flattened chicken escalope, which is then coated in tangy cheese Doritos. The crushed Doritos pack an incredible crunch and give the chicken a cheesy back note to the flavour. Doritos are great for coating just about anything from fried cheese to chicken strips (tenders), so just choose whatever flavour you like best. Don't be put off by the flattening out of the chicken breast, as it is a simple technique that takes no time at all and allows the chicken to cook quickly so the Doritos aren't burned before the chicken is cooked through. If you don't fancy flattening the chicken, then you can always ask your butcher to do it for you. The anchovies give a salty note to the dish and work so well with the soft egg yolk. This dish is simple and quick to prepare – you can get the chicken flattened out and coated a few hours before frying and then just store in the refrigerator until ready to cook.

Blitz the Doritos in a food processor until crushed, then mix with the panko breadcrumbs. Transfer to a bowl, then place the flour in a second bowl and beat the egg in a third bowl.

Dip the chicken first into the flour, shaking off excess, then dip into the egg and finally dip into the Doritos mixture until the chicken is evenly coated on both sides. Place in the refrigerator to set for around 30 minutes.

Heat the oil in a frying pan (skillet) over medium heat, add the chicken and gently fry on both sides for 3–4 minutes until cooked through and golden brown. At the last minute, add a knob of butter and cook until the butter turns slightly brown. Remove the pan from the heat.

In a separate pan, fry the egg as you like.

Place the schnitzel on a warmed serving plate, place the fried egg on top and arrange the anchovies on top of the egg. Add the chives and lemon juice to the brown butter and pour over the eggs and chicken. Serve.

B
R
E
A
S
T
S

T
R
A
C
K

T
W
O

A RE-IMAGINED CLUB SANDWICH

SERVES 1

60

EASY PEASY

2 eggs

2 spring onions (scallions), sliced

2 tablespoons rapeseed (canola) oil

1 teaspoon sesame oil

1 poached or pre-cooked chicken breast, diced

1 tablespoon sour cream mixed with ½ tablespoon Sriracha sauce

1 tablespoon chopped chives

salt and freshly ground black pepper

3 slices of thick-sliced brioche

1 tablespoon mayonnaise mixed with ½ teaspoon gochujang

1 large tomato, sliced

3 American cheese slices

3 leaves of butter lettuce

1 quantity of Pink Pickled Onions (page 175)

6 slices of streaky (lean) bacon, cooked

B R E A S T S

A club sandwich is my poolside go-to on holiday every time. There's something decadent about the triple-layered toasted sandwich full of different flavours and textures that just feels luxurious and a treat. However, it's a difficult sandwich to get right for many reasons. The timing of putting it together is crucial as the toasted bread needs to remain crisp and not soggy when you eat it. I have added an Asian twist to my club using gochujang and Sriracha (hot chilli sauce). I have also replaced the traditional hard boiled egg with an omelette that's sliced beforehand, making the assembly much quicker. Traditionally made with sliced white bread, I prefer to use a buttery thickly sliced brioche to add some luxury. This is a great sandwich for breakfast, a snack or even dinner with chips (fries).

To make the omelette, whisk the eggs together in a bowl. Add the sliced spring onions, then add a little of the rapeseed and all of the sesame oil. Heat the remaining rapeseed oil in a small frying pan, pour in the omelette mixture and cook for 2 minutes on each side, until firm. Roll and leave to chill in the refrigerator until cool, then cut into thick slices and set aside.

To make the chicken salad, mix the diced chicken with the Sriracha sour cream in a bowl, then add the chives, season and set aside.

Toast the brioche, then spread liberally with the mayonnaise. Arrange the tomatoes in a single layer on top, then arrange the cheese slices on top of the tomatoes. Lay the sliced omelette on top of the tomatoes, then the lettuce. Add another piece of brioche, then arrange the diced chicken salad mix on top, then lay the pickled onions on and arrange the bacon on top of the onions. Finally, add another layer of lettuce on top of the bacon, spread with more mayonnaise and top with another brioche slice. Cut the sandwich into quarters and secure with fancy cocktail sticks (toothpicks).

T R A C K   T W O

GREEN MANGO AND CHICKEN SALAD
WITH AVOCADO AND CRISPY SKIN (SOM TAM)

SERVES 4

EASY PEASY

1 packet plain instant noodles

2 tablespoons dried shrimp, rinsed

3 tablespoons roasted peanuts

2 garlic cloves

2–6 bird's eye chillies, depending on degree of bravery

25 French beans, cut into 1 cm (½ in) lengths

20 cherry tomatoes, halved

2 green mangoes

3 tablespoons lime juice

1 tablespoon tamarind water (to make your own, soak tamarind pulp in warm water for 15 minutes, drain, then pass through a sieve. You can use store-bought tamarind sauce, but fresh is SO much better)

2 tablespoons fish sauce

3 tablespoons coconut palm sugar

3 large cooked boneless skinless chicken breasts, sliced

pinch of coarse salt

handful of coriander leaves, to serve

handful of mint, to serve

B R E A S T S

Som tam is a dish you will find all across Thailand, and there are many different variations depending on which part of the country you are from. Some will have coconut palm sugar, some won't, some will use fish sauce while others will use these tiny little salted crabs instead. This dish comprises green beans, green papaya, tomatoes and other variations with an incredibly spicy, sweet and sour dressing that lends itself to lots of other Thai salads or just as a dipping sauce for grilled (broiled) chicken or cold noodles. When I'm in Thailand, I often see dishes created with instant noodles. In fact, I once ate at a restaurant in Chiang Mai that was a pimped up instant noodle restaurant. Here, I have recreated one of the dishes I ate in Thailand that was made with giant prawns (shrimp), but I have used green mango for crunchiness instead of prawns. The instant noodles add a nice chewy texture to the salad and, of course, lots of fun.

Place the instant noodles in a heatproof bowl and pour in enough boiling water to cover. Leave to stand until cooked, then cool to refrigerator temperature.

Toast the shrimp in a dry frying pan (skillet) over a medium heat for 3 minutes until crisp. Remove from the pan and set aside, then add the peanuts to the pan and fry for 3 minutes until toasted. Set aside.

Transfer the shrimp, peanuts and garlic to a mortar and pestle and crush to a rough paste. Add the chillies to the mortar and just bruise them, then add the beans and tomatoes and roughly bruise them. Scoop out of the mortar and set aside with all the liquid in a large bowl.

Peel the green mangoes and cut into thin julienne. A mandoline is perfect for this, otherwise a very sharp knife will do. Add the strips in batches to the mortar and pestle and bruise, then add to the bowl with the tomatoes.

In a separate bowl, mix the lime juice, tamarind water, fish sauce and sugar together until the sugar has dissolved. Pour over the other salad ingredients, then add the sliced chicken and cold noodles and toss to combine, seasoning with salt to taste. Sprinkle over the toasted peanuts, coriander and mint, and serve.

T R A C K   T W O

LE
CU
NZ
II
MV

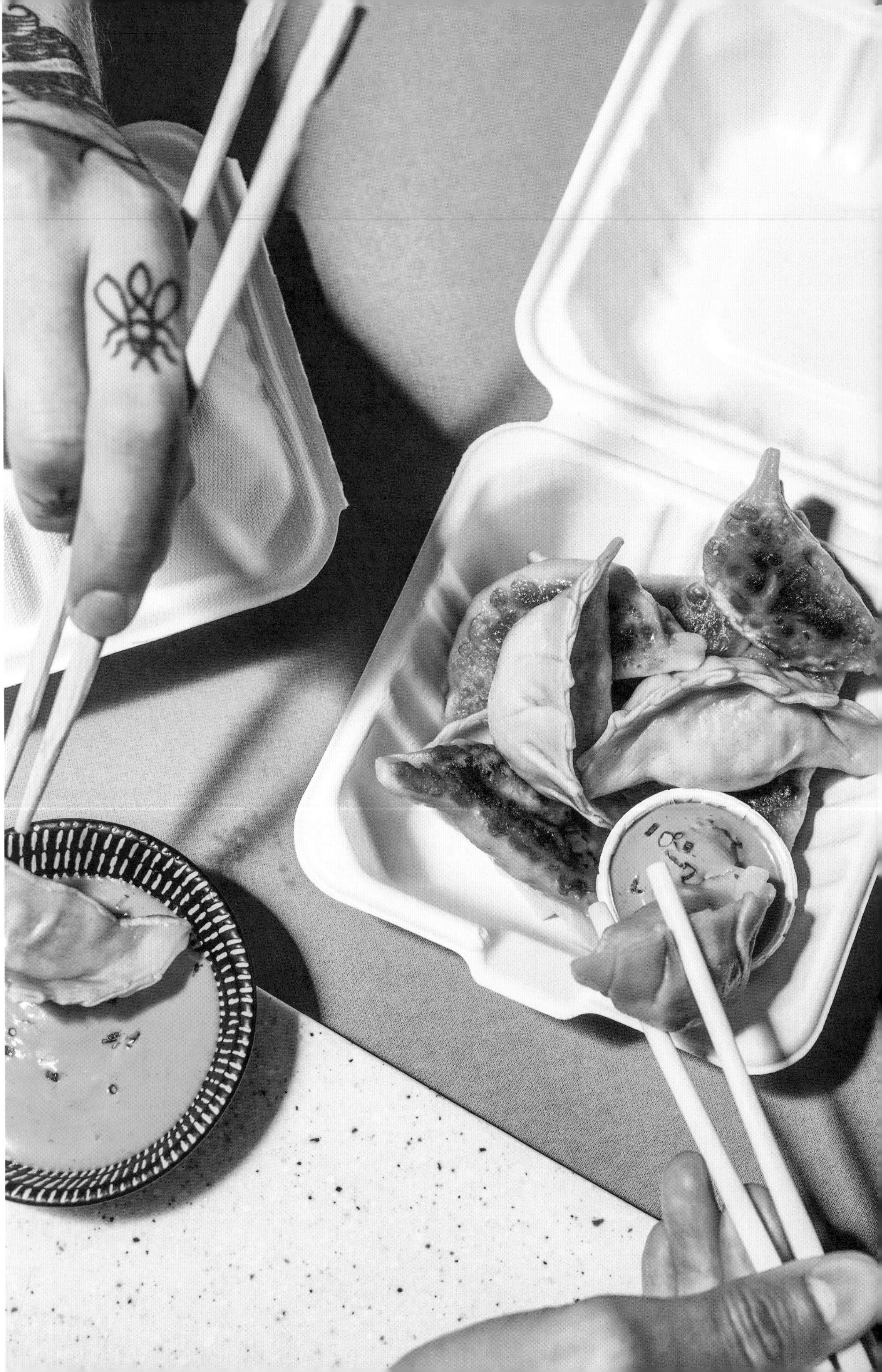

CHEESEBURGER DUMPLINGSWITH KIMCHI CHEESE AND BIG MAC-STYLE DIP

MAKES ABOUT 20–25

WORTH THE
EFFORT

M
I
N
C
E

T
R
A
C
K

T
H
R
E
E

1 tablespoon vegetable oil, for frying

FOR THE KIMCHI CHEESE

1 tablespoon grated garlic

¾ tablespoon grated ginger root

2 tablespoons fish sauce

1 teaspoon Korean chilli flakes

½ teaspoon caster (superfine) sugar

340 ml (11½ fl oz/1½ cups) milk

300 g (10 oz) Cheddar, roughly chopped

280 g (9¾ oz) American cheese slices, torn into pieces

FOR THE FILLING

250 g (9 oz) boneless chicken thighs

50 g (2 oz) bone marrow (optional)

1 tablespoon Maldon sea salt

1 tablespoon grated fresh ginger root

1 tablespoon finely chopped garlic

1 tablespoon sesame oil

100 g (3½ oz) shop-bought kimchi

FOR THE DOUGH (OPTIONAL)

125 g (4 oz/1 cup) plain (all-purpose) flour, plus extra for dusting

120 ml (4 fl oz/½ cup) cold water

FOR THE BIG MAC-STYLE DIP

100 g (3½ oz/scant ½ cup) prepared BBQ Sauce (page 104)

100 g (3½ oz/scant ¼ cup) mayonnaise, such as Japanese Kewpie

TIP

If you don't have time to make the dough, then buy frozen dumpling wrappers instead.

To me, a dumpling is just a vehicle that can be filled with anything, and you will find hundreds of variations of what a dumpling is according to various countries and cultures. I love dim sum and would dare to say that it's my favourite food. It's a great way to get together with friends and order your body weight in a variety of different dumplings all with different flavours and textures. In this recipe, I have taken the idea of recreating a cheeseburger but using chicken not beef and flavoured the cheese sauce with kimchi seasonings to give it a twist. The bone marrow is a game changer as it adds a juicy, fatty mouthfeel that all good burger patties have. Although the dumplings will be delicious without it, it really does make a difference and can be bought from your local butcher. The Big Mac-style dip really is the closest thing I have made to the real thing, so close your eyes, dip a dumpling in and think of Ronald. You'll know what I mean ...

To make the cheese, combine the garlic, ginger, fish sauce, chilli flakes and sugar in a bowl and blend with a stick blender until smooth. Pour the milk into a large saucepan, add the purée and gently bring to a simmer over a medium low heat. Add the cheeses and whisk until the cheese has melted into the milk. Blend with a stick blender for a few minutes until it is a smooth, shiny sauce. Pour the sauce into a deep-sided baking tray (pan) and leave to chill in the refrigerator overnight. This makes far more than you need, but you can use it for several recipes in this book.

To make the filling, blitz all the ingredients, except the kimchi, in a food processor so it retains a little of its texture. Transfer the mixture to a bowl, cover and chill in the refrigerator for at least 1 hour. Cut 100 g (3½ oz) of the set cheese into very small pieces and mix with the filling (you can keep the rest for another time).

To make the dough, place the flour in a large bowl and add the water all at once. Mix with your hands until it just comes together. Turn the dough out onto a lightly floured work surface and knead for 5 minutes, or until smooth. Leave to rest for 5 minutes.

To make the dip, whisk the BBQ sauce and mayonnaise together in a bowl until combined. Set aside.

Take a small knob, about 30 g (1 oz), of dough and smash it flat onto a lightly floured work surface, then use a floured rolling pin to roll it into a 7.5–10 cm (3–4 in) diameter round. Place a small scoop of the filling in the centre of the round and top with a pinch of the kimchi. Seal the edges with your fingertips, then place on a piece of baking parchment and repeat until all the dough, filling and kimchi have been used up.

Heat the vegetable oil in a large, wide saucepan with a lid over a medium-high heat. Place the dumplings in the pan in a circular formation, packing the pan so the dumplings are just touching one another. Cook for 1–2 minutes until the bottoms are lightly browned. Add a splash of water to the pan and cover immediately. Reduce the heat slightly and keep covered for 3–4 minutes until the meat is completely cooked. The dumplings are done when the skins look translucent and the bottoms are crisp. Serve immediately with the dipping sauce.

MY CHICKEN BOLOGNESE

SERVES 4

EASY PEASY

M I N C E

2 tablespoons dark soy sauce

3 tablespoons Toban Djan (Sichuan chilli bean sauce)

2 teaspoons gochujang (Korean red chilli paste)

2 teaspoons caster (superfine) sugar

200 ml (7 fl oz/¾ cup) water

2 tablespoons black vinegar

3 tablespoons Shaoxing rice wine

1 tablespoon ketchup

1½ tablespoons Sriracha sauce

150 ml (5 fl oz/scant ⅔ cup) rapeseed (canola) oil

200 g (7 oz) streaky bacon, finely diced or minced (ground)

500 g (1 lb 2 oz) minced (ground) chicken

2 medium onions, finely diced

2 garlic cloves, finely diced

1 teaspoon tapioca starch

½ teaspoon gochugaru or Korean chilli (hot pepper) flakes

1 teaspoon Sichuan peppercorns, ground

TO SERVE (OPTIONAL)

egg noodles or spaghetti, cooked according to packet instructions

shredded nori seaweed

pickles of your choice
(pages 170–177)

This is not in any way your normal Bolognese, but what it *is* is the tastiest ragout known to man with a Sichuan twist. We have used this in the past in my restaurant Chick 'n' Sours and created 'Mexinese' nachos with it – a kind of Mexican-Chinese mash-up of flavours and textures that people loved (page 71). Like any ragout, it takes some time to cook and shouldn't be rushed. In fact, it is best cooked the day before you are going to eat it and left to stand overnight to allow all the flavours to come together. The secret here is to cook the bacon bits nice and slow until they have fully rendered all their fat, leaving you crispy bacon bits and a base of bacon fat to start cooking the onions. If it's not cooked out enough it can make the finished ragout taste a little like hotdogs, which is not a bad thing, but it's better to cook the bacon until crispy. Instead of spaghetti, I have served the ragout with egg noodles. You can even grate Parmesan over the top if that's your thing or, for a filthier finish, top with two slices of American cheese, let them melt slightly and add some strips of nori seaweed and pickles of your choice on the side.

Mix the soy sauce, chilli bean sauce, chilli paste, sugar, water, vinegar, rice wine, ketchup and Sriracha together in a bowl until combined, then set aside.

Heat the oil in a saucepan over a medium heat, then add the bacon and gently cook for 3–4 minutes until golden and crisp. Add the chicken mince, onions and garlic and cook for another 5 minutes until the onions soften. Pour over the reserved sauce and bring to a gentle simmer over a low heat. Cook gently for 1½ hours until the liquid has reduced.

Sprinkle over the tapioca starch and stir to combine and thicken the sauce. Add the chilli flakes and Sichuan pepper, then stir well.

GOING GOING GONE

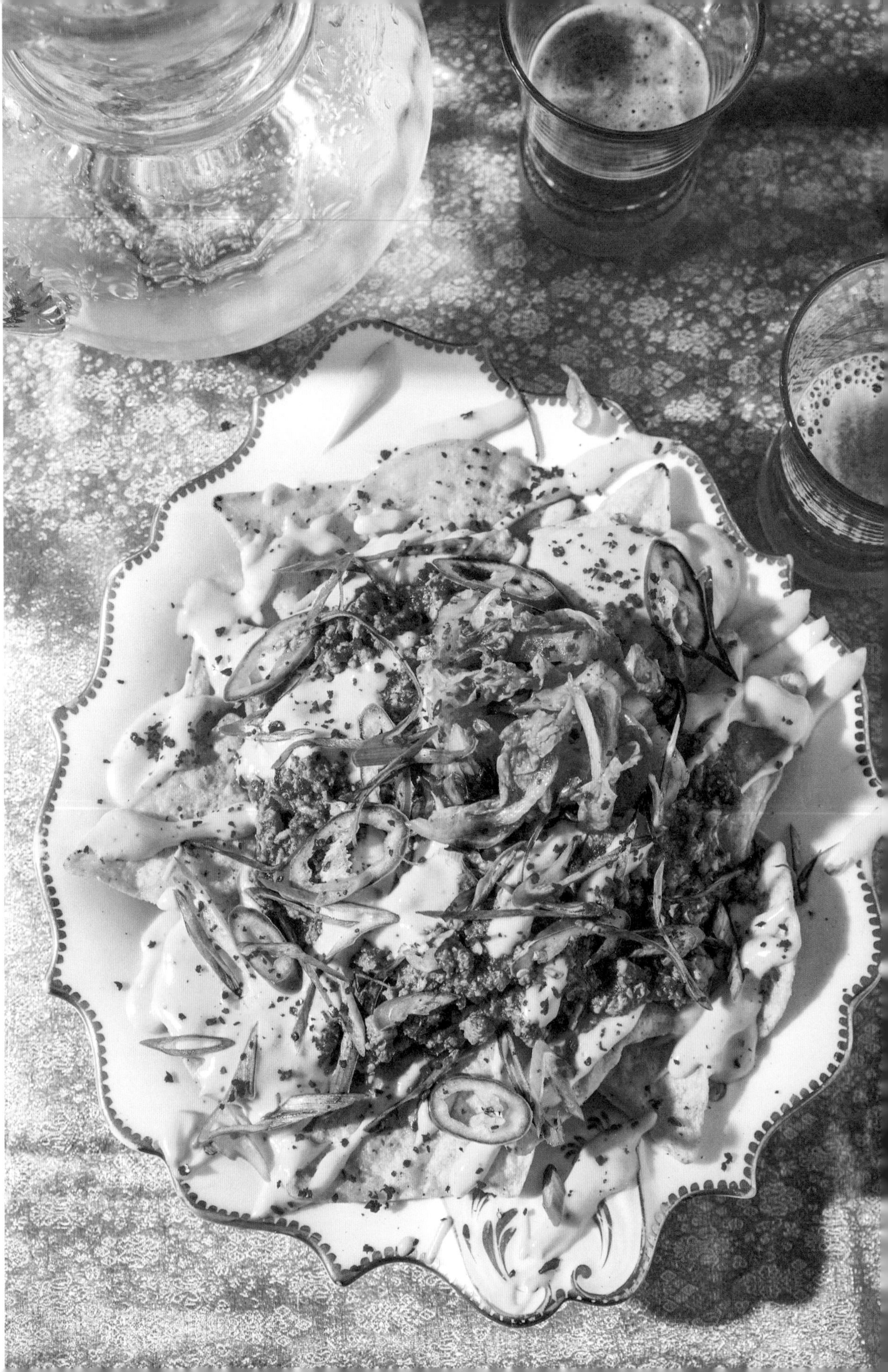

INCREDIBLE SUPERIOR NACHOS!

MAKES 1 LARGE PORTION

150 g (5 oz) My Chicken Bolognese (page 68)

75 g (2½ oz) Kimchi Cheese (page 67)

50 g (2 oz) plain corn all-natural tortilla chips

25 g (1 oz) shop-bought kimchi, chopped

2 spring onions (scallions), finely sliced

1 long green chilli, thinly sliced, or 2 fresh jalapeños

pinch of gochugaru or Korean chilli (hot pepper) flakes (optional)

The Chicken Bolognese recipe in this book (page 68) just keeps on giving and I have used it here to create these incredible nachos. We serve these in my restaurant Chick 'n' Sours, but we called them 'Mexinese' Nachos for obvious reasons. Once everything is made, these are very easy to assemble and you can freeze bits and pieces as you make other recipes until you have everything ready to go. These nachos are both spicy and cheesy, just as nachos should be, but in a different way. The kimchi gives them a nice funky freshness, but if that's not your thing then use some of the pink pickled onions you may have made previously (page 175). Freshly fried hot corn chips are best, but you can also use shop-bought tortilla chips – just warm them up in the oven before you assemble the nachos as they can get cold very quickly and add as little or as much chilli as you wish according to how spicy you like them. These nachos are great when you have friends or family round on just about any occasion.

Heat the Bolognese mix and cheese in separate saucepans for 5 minutes, or until heated through.

Layer some of the corn chips on a large plate and drizzle some of the cheese over the chips, being careful to leave some space on each chip so you can pick them up. Add some of the Bolognese mix, then continue until the cheese and Bolognese mix are used up. Liberally sprinkle with chopped kimchi, spring onions, fresh chilli and chilli flakes.

Serve immediately and as hot as possible.

EASY PEASY

M I N C E

T R A C K   T H R E E

ANTS CLIMBING A TREE NOODLES

SERVES 4

72

EASY PEASY

400 g (14 oz) dried mung bean vermicelli noodles

6 tablespoons rapeseed (canola) oil

4 tablespoons Sichuan chilli bean paste

2 teaspoons chilli powder

500 g (1 lb 2 oz/2½ cups) minced (ground) chicken

100 g (3½ oz/⅔ cup) fatty streaky bacon, finely chopped

4 teaspoons very finely chopped fresh ginger root

4 teaspoons Shaoxing rice wine

2 teaspoons light soy sauce

500 ml (17 fl oz/2 cups) hot water

4 teaspoons sugar

1 teaspoon ground white pepper

2 spring onions (scallions), chopped

4 garlic cloves, very finely chopped

1 fresh chilli, chopped (optional)

M I N C E

You will be glad to hear that this dish contains no ants whatsoever. It's a classic Sichuan noodle dish that traditionally uses glass noodles and minced (ground) pork, which I have swapped out for minced chicken. The glass noodles are meant to be representative of tree branches, spring onions (scallions) are the leaves and the minced pork is the ants, if that makes any sense to you at all. I have used some fatty streaky bacon here in addition to the minced chicken, as pork is a little fattier and chicken can dry out quite easily if overcooked. Like in the Bolognese recipe (page 68) it's best to caramelise the bacon for depth of flavour when cooking. Another thing to note is when cooking this noodle dish is that the glass noodles will soak up the sauce very quickly, so if you like more sauce then just add a little more water or chicken stock (broth). You can make this noodle dish in no time at all once all your ingredients are weighed out and prepped – a great after-work, filling, comforting noodle dish.

Soak the noodles in a bowl of warm water for 5 minutes (or in cold water for 10 minutes) until they are soft and pliable. Rinse under cold running water and drain. Set aside.

Heat the oil in a wok over a medium-high heat. Add the chilli paste and chilli powder and fry briefly, then stir in the minced chicken, bacon, ginger, rice wine and soy sauce and fry for 8–10 minutes until well combined and the chicken is a nice caramelised dark colour.

Pour the hot water into the wok, then add the sugar, white pepper and reserved noodles. When most of the water has been absorbed by the noodles, add the spring onions, garlic and fresh chilli (if using). Stir-fry for another 30 seconds, then serve warm.

T R A C K T H R E E

NEXT LEVEL BREVILLE (GRILLED SANDWICH)

MAKES 2

74

WORTH THE EFFORT

butter, for spreading

4 slices of thick sliced white bread, crusts on, or thick sliced brioche

150 g (5 oz) My Chicken Bolognese (page 68)

100 g (3½ oz) Kimchi Cheese, chilled and sliced (page 67)

2 tablespoons Pink Pickled Onions (page 175)

5 tablespoons Blueberry Hoisin (page 40), or shop-bought hoisin sauce

I love an old school Breville sandwich maker toastie. It evokes childhood memories of cheese and baked bean toasties, but everyone has their own favourite filling. I still make them every now and again and never get tired of them. With this recipe, I wanted to take the idea to another level and started to think about a messy, cheesy, Sloppy Joe-style sandwich. All the components appear in other dishes in this book, so you can freeze bits and pieces as you go along and pull them all together when you are ready to make this sandwich. The filling is very rich so works well with the sweet, tangy blueberry hoisin as a dip, but will work just as well with straight up hoisin sauce as well. You can batch-cook the pickled onions and use them on just about anything as they will just get better as time goes on, but if you don't have time to make them, then just chop up some shop-bought pickled onions and they will do the job just as well.

To assemble, butter the outside surface of the slices of bread and place them, buttered-side down, on a cutting board. Spread the Bologese mixture over one of the slices of bread followed by the chilled, sliced cheese. Top with pickled onions, then place the other slice of bread on top so that the buttered side is on the outside. Repeat with the remaining bread and ingredients to make another sandwich. Toast each in a sandwich maker for 3–4 minutes until golden brown and the cheese is melted and gooey, or alternatively, toast in a pan over a medium heat until crisp and golden. Serve with the cold blueberry hoisin as a dip.

M
I
N
C
E

T
R
A
C
K

T
H
R
E
E

DIM SUM-STYLE STUFFED PEPPERS

SERVES 4 AS A STARTER

2 medium (bell) peppers (any colour or type of pepper works)

1 tablespoon cornflour (cornstarch)

rapeseed (canola) oil, for frying

about 3 tablespoons water

FOR THE GARLIC BLACK BEAN SAUCE

1 tablespoon rapeseed (canola) oil

1 tablespoon fermented black beans

1½ tablespoons cornflour (cornstarch)

2 tablespoons cold water

2 garlic cloves, finely chopped

1½ tablespoons oyster sauce

1 tablespoon soy sauce

¼ teaspoon caster (superfine) sugar or honey

1 tablespoon Shaoxing rice wine

375 ml (12½ fl oz/1½ cups) water or stock (broth)

FOR THE FILLING

300 g (10½ oz/1½ cups) minced (ground) chicken (ideally thigh)

½ teaspoon sesame oil

1 teaspoon soy sauce

¼ teaspoon white pepper

1 salad (green) onion, finely chopped

1 tablespoon cornflour (cornstarch)

1 tablespoon rapeseed (canola) oil

There's an old classic stuffed peppers dish called Piedmontese peppers, which I once saw Keith Floyd make and have since made myself many times. The peppers are stuffed with blanched tomatoes, anchovies and olive oil and roasted very slowly in the oven until caramelised, super sweet, salty and delicious. I wanted to create a dish that people could share and enjoy as part of a feast or as an individual starter (appetiser), so I have taken the same idea and stuffed the peppers with a seasoned minced (ground) chicken mix and Chinese fermented black beans, which pack so much umami and flavour that they do the job of the anchovies well. It's a sticky, sweet, savoury sauce, which is also great served with straight up grilled (broiled) chicken or any noodle dish as a base sauce.

To make the sauce, gently rinse the fermented black beans under cold running water for a few seconds to reconstitute them and remove some of the salt. Once the beans are softer, use the side of a knife or fork to smash them flat, then set aside.

Mix the cornflour and water together in a small bowl until combined, then set aside.

Heat the oil in a small pot over a medium heat. Once the oil is hot and shimmering, add the garlic and black beans and cook for 1 minute, or until the garlic is soft. Add the remaining sauce ingredients, except the cornflour mixture, and mix together. Cook for 5 minutes until the sauce starts bubbling. Stir the cornflour mixture in case the flour has settled to the bottom of the bowl, then pour it into the sauce while stirring constantly. Keep stirring until thickened. Set aside.

To make the filling, mix all the ingredients in a bowl with clean hands. The smoother the paste the better. Set aside.

Turn one of the peppers upside down so that the bottom is facing up. You should see 4 bumps. Cut the pepper into quarters using the space between the bumps as a guideline, then remove the core, seeds and membranes. Cut the top and bottom tips off the pepper so it can lay flat against the frying pan (skillet), then repeat with the remaining peppers. Place a little cornflour in a small bowl and rub it on the inside of the pepper wedges, then stuff each pepper wedge with the filling. Try not to overstuff them, the deeper the pockets and the thicker the filling, the harder it will be to cook the filling all the way through. I like to stuff it no more than 2.5 cm (1 in) thick and have the filling slightly above the pepper by 1–2 mm.

Heat a little oil in a frying pan with a lid over a medium-low heat. Place the peppers in the pan, filling-side down, and cook for 3 minutes, or until the filling has browned, then carefully flip the peppers over onto the other side. Add the water to the pan and cover with a lid. Steam for 3–4 minutes until the water has evaporated. If you are using thinner peppers with less filling, you can skip the steaming step. Uncover and cook the peppers for another 3 minutes, or until the pepper skins brown.

Reheat the sauce over a gentle heat, then spoon some of the sauce over the top of the peppers and serve.

WORTH THE EFFORT

M I N C E

T R A C K   T H R E E

SUPER NOODLE LASAGNE
WITH BLACK GARLIC BREAD

SERVES 8

EASY
PEASY

4 packs instant noodles

500 g (1 lb 2 oz) My Chicken Bolognese (page 68)

400 g (14 oz) Kimchi Cheese (page 67)

100 g (3½ oz) kimchi

gochugaru or Korean chilli (hot pepper) flakes, for sprinkling (optional)

FOR THE BLACK GARLIC BREAD

1 teaspoon shrimp paste, roasted

1 bird's eye chilli, deseeded if you like

1 whole black or regular garlic head

1 large banana shallot, finely diced

1 teaspoon palm sugar

2 tablespoons lime juice

250 g (9 oz) pack good-quality unsalted butter

1 good-quality large baguette

I love a Saturday night lasagne, and for me at home no lasagne is complete without garlic bread. Here, I have used the base recipes from the book for the Bolognese (page 68) and Kimchi Cheese (page 67) so once you have made these all you need to do is to build the noodle lasagne. The noodles give it a fun twist instead of using the usual lasagne sheets and the layer of kimchi gives it a nice funky freshness. Of course, I was never going to make straight up garlic bread, so I have used black garlic, which you can find online and in most good delicatessens. Black garlic is fermented in a temperature-controlled environment, which takes the sharpness out of the garlic and gives it a sticky caramel-like flavour that blends beautifully with the other Thai ingredients I have used to make the butter for the garlic bread. If you can't find black garlic, then it's fine to just use normal garlic. This is a really fun and memorable dish and you may never eat a regular lasagne again!

Preheat the oven to 170°C (340°F/gas 4).

Cook the instant noodles according to the packet instructions, then leave to chill. Heat the Bolognese mix and cheese in separate saucepans for 5 minutes, until warm. Place the fresh kimchi in a bowl and squeeze out any excess liquid.

To assemble the lasagne, start with a layer of noodles on the bottom of a large baking dish, then add a layer of the Bolognese mix. Continue until all the noodles and Bolognese mix have been used up, making sure to leave some room at the top. Add a layer of kimchi and top with the cheese. Bake for 30–40 minutes until the cheese bubbles and goes brown in places.

Meanwhile, to make the black garlic bread, blend all the ingredients, except the baguette, in a food processor until smooth.

Cut the baguette into 1 cm (½ in) slices without cutting it all the way through. Stuff each pocket with as much garlic butter as you can possibly get in there. Wrap in kitchen foil and bake in the oven for 15–20 minutes until all the butter has melted through the bread and the baguette is golden and crispy.

Sprinkle chilli flakes on top of the lasagne for colour, if you like, and serve with the garlic bread.

MINCE

TRACK THREE

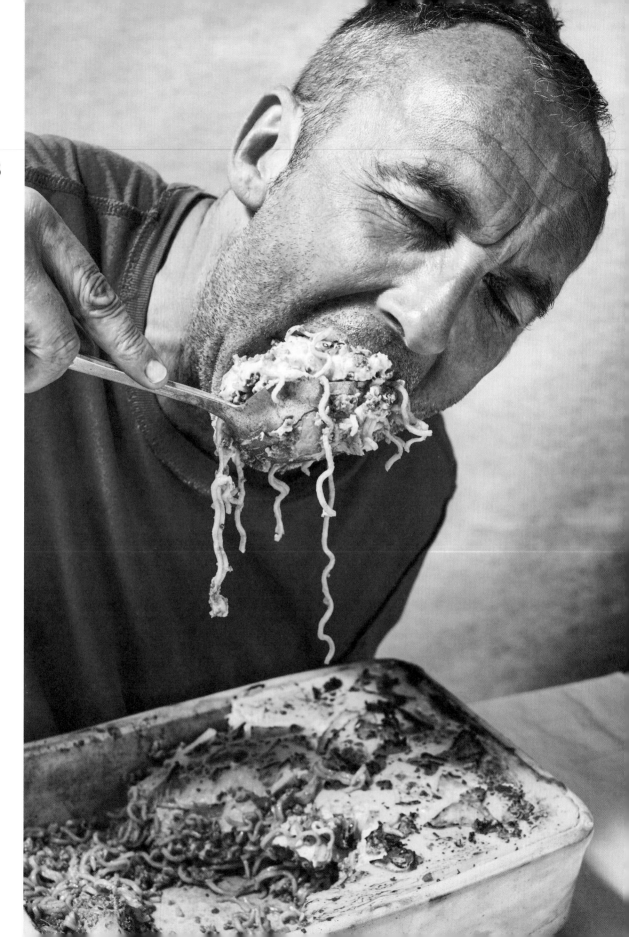

THIRTY-EIGHT

BANG BANG CHICKEN SALAD
WITH CRISPY NOODLES

SERVES 4

4 boneless chicken thighs, skin on

2 tablespoons rapeseed (canola) oil

2 baby gem lettuces,
leaves separated

4 celery stalks, peeled and thinly
sliced diagonally

handful of coriander (cilantro)
leaves, torn

2 green (bell) peppers, sliced into
thin strips

handful of tortilla chips

chopped shop-bought dry-roasted
peanuts, to garnish

FOR THE 'STRANGE FLAVOUR' SAUCE

6 tablespoons light soy sauce

2 tablespoons tahini

2 tablespoons good-quality crunchy
peanut butter

2 tablespoons Chinese black vinegar
(Chinkiang) or red wine vinegar

2 tablespoons sesame oil

4 teaspoons caster (superfine) sugar

½ teaspoon Maldon sea salt

6 tablespoons Chinese chilli oil

2 small spring onions (scallions),
thinly sliced

2 tablespoons finely chopped
fresh ginger root

2 large garlic cloves, finely chopped

1 teaspoon Sichuan peppercorns,
crushed to powder

EASY PEASY

Bang Bang chicken is traditionally a dish of cold chicken served with a spicy peanut and sesame sauce sold by street vendors in the Sichuan region of China. The chicken is tenderised and shredded by pounding it with a heavy wooden stick, hence the name, but you will be pleased to know that I have left that part out here! 'Strange flavour' sauce is also known as 'odd flavour' sauce and is so because it's the closest English translation to describe it. The sauce is actually not strange or odd at all, but is super delicious as it is creamy from the peanut butter and sesame paste and sweet, spicy and numbing from the Sichuan pepper. I have used it in this recipe to create a beautiful fresh crunchy salad. The contrast of cold salad, warm crispy chicken thighs and spicy peanut sesame oil is incredible. The nacho chips add a nice twist by adding another layer of crunch. Use any flavour of nachos you like. It is a really great and super-easy salad that can be made up for one or served in a large family-style bowl for everyone to help themselves.

Brine the chicken for 1 hour according to the brine instructions on page 24 (optional).

Meanwhile, to make the sauce, mix all the ingredients together in a bowl until combined. Set aside.

Heat the oil in a cold pan over the lowest possible heat, add the chicken and cook for 8–10 minutes, or until the skin is golden and crispy and the thighs are almost cooked through. Turn and then cook for a further 2 minutes. (You can also grill/broil the chicken under a medium heat, if you prefer.)

To build the salad, slice the chicken, then place in a large bowl along with the lettuce leaves, celery, torn coriander and green peppers. Spoon over the sauce and mix until everything is coated. Add the whole tortilla chips at the last minute and mix again. Divide the salad among 4 bowls and sprinkle with the roasted peanuts to garnish.

THIGHS

TRACK FOUR

SHOOT ME DOWN

CHICKEN 65

SERVES 2–4

4 large boneless chicken thighs,
skin on (optional)

1.5 litres (51 fl oz/6½ cups) rapeseed
(canola) oil, for deep-frying

FOR THE SPICE MIX

30 g (1 oz/½ cup) coriander seeds

1–2 tablespoons cumin seeds

1 teaspoon black peppercorns

1 teaspoon whole cloves

2 tablespoons ground ginger

1–2 teaspoons garlic powder

2 teaspoons ground nutmeg

2 tablespoons kasuri methi
(fenugreek leaves)

2 black cardamom pods

1 cinnamon stick

4–5 mace blades

2 tablespoons Kashmiri chilli powder

1 teaspoon ground turmeric

1 teaspoon amchoor powder
(dry mango powder)

¼ teaspoon red food colour (optional)

1 teaspoon caster (superfine) sugar

½ teaspoon salt

FOR THE GARLIC-GINGER PASTE

25 g (1 oz) garlic cloves, peeled

25 g (1 oz) piece of fresh ginger
root, peeled

FOR THE QUICK DIP

2 teaspoons shop-bought
mint sauce

4 tablespoons plain yoghurt

FOR THE WET BATTER

1 large egg

120 ml (4 fl oz/½ cup) full-fat
(whole) milk

FOR THE DRY FLOUR MIX

200 g (7 oz/1½ cups) rice flour

100 g (¾ cup) cornflour (cornstarch)

pinch of salt

pinch of coarse black pepper

TO GARNISH

1 tablespoon rapeseed (canola) oil

1 teaspoon black mustard seeds

1 teaspoon cumin seeds

20 fresh curry leaves

6 whole green chillies

12 garlic cloves, finely sliced

10 cm (4 in) piece of fresh ginger
root, peeled and julienned or very
finely sliced

4 spring onions (scallions),
roughly chopped

THIGHS

TRACK FOUR

Chicken 65 is a classic South Indian dish, invented in 1965 at the famous Buhari restaurant in Chennai. There are many theories to how it got its name. One theory is that the chicken was cut into 65 pieces and 65 ingredients were used to prepare the dish. Another theory is that the menu was written in Tamil, which the North Indian soldiers couldn't read, so they ordered dishes by numbers and it was number 65 on the menu. Over the years, the restaurant added Chicken 78, 82 and 90 to their menu. There *are* a lot of ingredients in this dish, but it's well worth the time and effort in doing it properly. This is one of those dishes that you will crave over and over again. It is great served as a snack with a group of friends or as part of an Indian feast with my cheat's mint yoghurt recipe using 2 teaspoons of shop-bought mint sauce mixed with 4 tablespoons of thick plain yoghurt.

Brine the chicken thighs according to the instructions on page 24 for 1 hour, then pat dry with paper towels (optional).

To make the spice mix, roast all the whole spices together in a dry frying pan (skillet) over a medium heat for 1–2 minutes. Leave to cool, then blend in a small food processor with the remaining ingredients. Store in an airtight jar for up to 3 months.

To make the garlic-ginger paste, blitz the garlic and ginger in a small food processor to a purée. Set aside.

To make the marinade, mix 4 tablespoons of the spice mix with 2 tablespoons of the garlic-ginger paste together in a small bowl. Set aside.

Cut the brined chicken thighs into 5 cm (2 in) pieces, place in a shallow bowl and rub the marinade all over. Cover with cling film (plastic wrap) and leave to marinate in the refrigerator for 24 hours.

When ready to cook, make the quick dip, mixing the ingredients together in a small bowl, then cover with cling film (plastic wrap) and leave in the refrigerator until ready to serve.

To make the wet batter, whisk the egg and milk together in a bowl until combined. Set aside.

For the dry flour mix, blend all the ingredients together in a medium bowl with a whisk.

Submerge the chicken pieces in the wet batter, then dip them into the flour mix until coated all over.

Heat the oil for deep-frying in a deep-fryer or a large, deep saucepan to 160°C (325°F), or until a cube of bread dropped in sizzles in 30 seconds. Deep-fry the chicken, in batches if necessary, for 7–8 minutes, or until cooked through. Remove and drain on paper towels.

Heat 1 tablespoon oil for the garnish in a frying pan (skillet) over a medium heat. Add the mustard seeds and cumin and fry for 30 seconds until they start to pop, then add all the remaining ingredients, except the spring onions, and fry for 1 minute. Set aside.

Pile the fried chicken up high on a warmed serving plate and season again liberally with the spice mix, then top with all the garnish ingredients and spring onions. Serve with the dip.

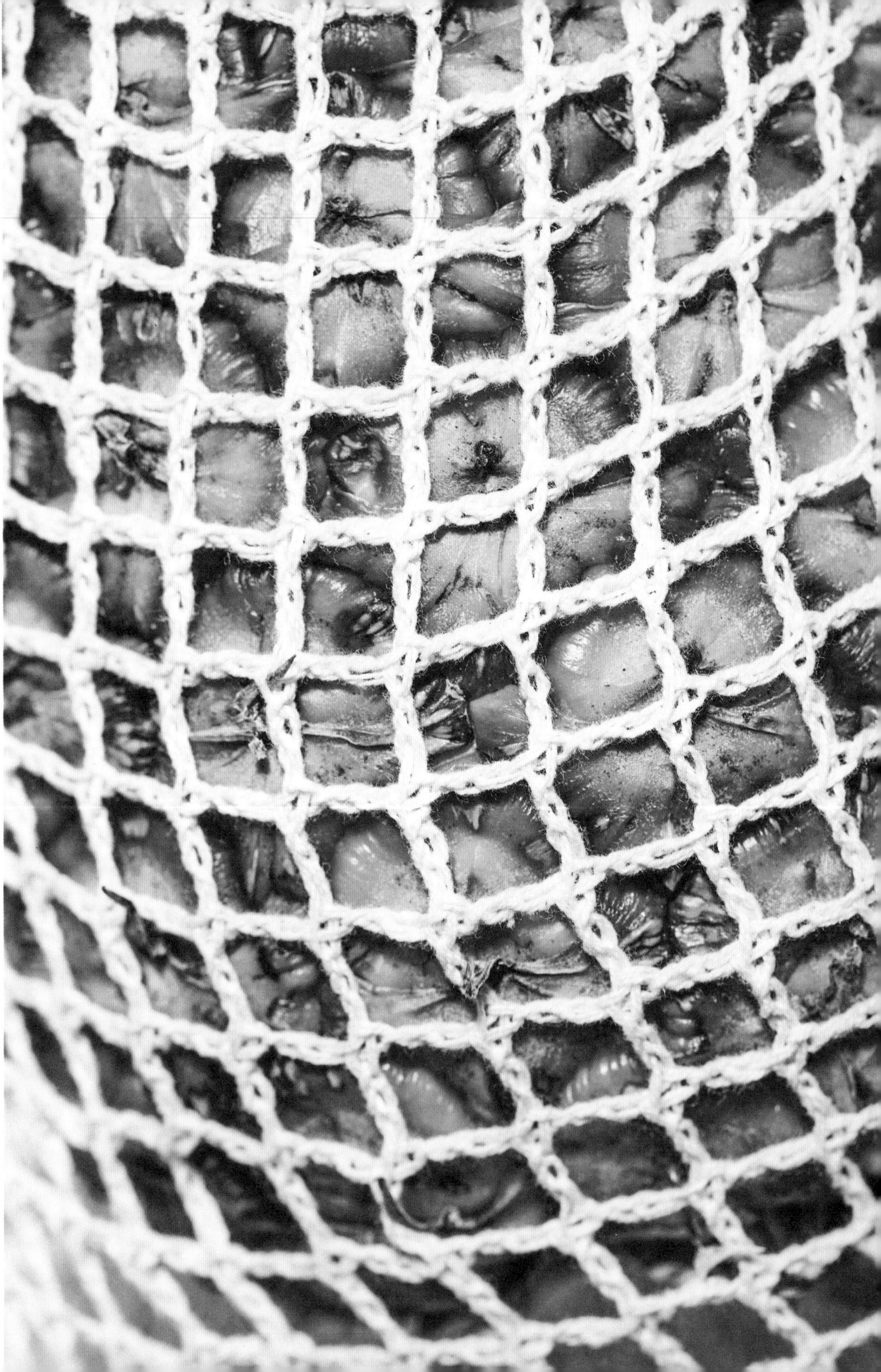

CHICKEN EL PASTOR
WITH TOMATILLO SALSA

SERVES 4

88

**WORTH THE
EFFORT**

T
H
I
G
H
S

4 boneless chicken thighs, skin on

8 corn tortillas

½ pineapple, peeled, cored and
cut into 5 mm (¼ in) dice

handful of coriander (cilantro),
chopped

½ red onion, very finely diced

lime wedges, to serve

FOR THE EL PASTOR MARINADE

½ teaspoon black peppercorns

1 cinnamon stick

3 cloves

1 tablespoon cumin seeds

4 dried guajillo chillies,
torn and deseeded

4 ancho or chipotle chillies,
torn and deseeded

4 garlic cloves, peeled

2 tablespoons achiote paste

100 ml (3½ fl oz/scant ½ cup)
pineapple juice

100 ml (3½ fl oz/scant ½ cup)
orange juice

½ onion, cut into small pieces

3 tablespoons cider vinegar

1 tablespoon dried oregano

FOR THE BURNT TOMATILLO SALSA

500 g (1 lb 2 oz) tomatillos,
fresh or tinned

1 onion, cut into 5 mm (¼ in) rings

8 garlic cloves

1 jalapeño chilli

rapeseed (canola) or olive oil,
for rubbing

handful of coriander (cilantro) stalks
and leaves, chopped

juice of 3 limes

1 teaspoon Maldon sea salt

NOTE

You should be able to find achiote
paste and tomatillos, when in season,
in specialist grocery stores or online.

Tacos Al Pastor were created in the 1930s in Mexico by Lebanese immigrants who introduced shawarma to the region, cooking roast lamb on a vertical spit and serving it on a flour tortilla or pitta bread. Over the years it became marinated pork and pineapple on a spit served in fresh corn tortillas and sold on street corners all over Mexico. All the speciality chillies used in this dish are easily available online, so don't be put off by them. Tomatillos come wrapped in their husk and are a beautiful shade of green. Burning them gives the salsa a nice back note, while the pineapple adds a nice fruity note at the end. If you can't find fresh, used tinned, making sure you drain them well and pat dry.

Brine the chicken according to the instructions on page 24 for 1 hour (optonal).

To make the marinade, heat a dry frying pan (skillet) over a medium heat. Add the peppercorns, cinnamon, cloves and cumin seeds and toast for 3 minutes, or until they start to become fragrant. Transfer to a mortar and pestle or spice grinder and grind to a powder. In the same pan, toast the chillies for 2 minutes, or until they start to smoke, then remove and soak them in a bowl of cold water for about 20 minutes to soften. Drain and place in a food processor with all the other ingredients and blend to a smooth paste.

Place the chicken in a bowl, add the marinade, then cover with cling film (plastic wrap) and leave to marinate in the refrigerator for 6 hours, but preferably overnight.

Meanwhile, to make the salsa, preheat the grill (broiler) to high. Rub the tomatillos, onions, garlic cloves and jalapeño with a little oil and char under the hot grill. Really char, don't just brown so you have burned edges. Remove the seeds from the jalapeño and pop the garlic cloves out of their skins. They should be a little soft by this point. Place in a food processor along with the charred onions, coriander stalks and lime juice and blend to a purée. Add a little oil if necessary. Roughly chop the tomatillos into small pieces and mix together with the purée and coriander leaves. Season with salt and more of the lime juice if needed. Set aside.

When ready to cook, heat a medium frying pan (skillet) over a medium high heat. Remove the chicken from the marinade and cook, skin-side down, in the hot pan for 8 minutes, or until the skin is crisp and golden. Turn at the last minute to finish cooking through. Alternatively, you can cook, skin-side up, under a medium-hot grill. Set aside.

To build the tacos, heat a dry frying pan over a medium heat. Sprinkle the tortillas with a little water and cook in the dry pan, in batches, for 30 seconds on each side. Place the warm tortillas in a tea towel to keep warm while cooking the rest.

Lay 2 tacos on individual warmed serving plates. Slice the chicken thighs and lay on the tacos, then spoon over some of the salsa. In a separate bowl, mix the pineapple, chopped coriander and red onion together, then spoon some on top. Serve the tacos warm with a lime wedge on the side.

CHICKEN LAKSA

SERVES 4

90

ALMOST
BREEZY

**T
H
I
G
H
S**

60 g (2 oz/1 cup) panko breadcrumbs

40 g (1½ oz/¼ cup) plain (all-purpose) flour

1 egg

4 large boneless chicken thighs, batted out to 2 mm (¹⁄₁₆ in) thick

400 ml (14 fl oz/1¾ cups) vegetable oil, for shallow-frying

150 g (5 oz) Hokkein noodles, cooked according to packet instructions

160 g (5½ oz/1 cup) roasted cashew nuts, crushed, to serve

FOR THE LAKSA PASTE

1 medium onion, roughly chopped

10 g (½ oz) shrimp paste

¼ teaspoon chilli (hot pepper) flakes

2 cm (1 in) piece of galangal, peeled and roughly chopped

6 garlic cloves, roughly chopped

5 lemongrass stalks, tough outer layers removed and roughly chopped

25 g (1 oz/scant ¼ cup) cashew nuts

generous pinch of ground coriander

generous pinch of ground cumin

generous pinch of ground turmeric

small pinch of sweet paprika

3 g (¼ teaspoon) salt

FOR THE SOUP

1 tablespoon vegetable oil

400 ml (13 fl oz/generous 1½ cups) water

800 ml (27 fl oz/3¼ cups) coconut milk

20 g (¾ oz/1 tablespoon) palm sugar

2 tablespoons fish sauce

5 Kaffir lime leaves

juice of 1 lime

FOR THE TOPPINGS

20 g (¾ oz) cucumber, cut into thick strips

15 g (½ oz) red onion, finely sliced

20 g (¾ oz/¼ cup) bean sprouts

Laksa is a spicy noodle soup popular in Malaysia. It is usually served with thick wheat noodles, although sometimes with vermicelli noodles. It is a filling, comforting dish that keeps you going back for more every time. It takes a little bit of time to prepare the spice paste, so I have simplified the recipe to make it easier, but the results are definitely worth it. The soup is made in two parts with the spice paste being made first, then the coconut milk and all the other seasonings are added. The secret is to cook the spice paste out over a low heat until it turns a dark brown colour and starts to let out oil. If it's not cooked out enough then the soup will lack depth of flavour and the spices may taste raw. The laksa is topped with cucumber, raw sliced red onion and beansprouts for freshness while the breadcrumbed crispy chicken thighs add a nice crunch. Take your time when making this recipe to get it right, but after a few goes you will get faster. You can also make a larger batch of the spice paste and keep some for the next time you cook this dish. It will easily keep for up to two weeks in the refrigerator or even longer in the freezer.

To make the paste, place all the ingredients in a blender and whizz to a smooth paste. Set aside.

To make the soup, heat the oil in a large saucepan over a medium heat. Add the laksa paste and sauté while stirring constantly for 10–15 minutes until caramelised and aromatic. Be careful not to burn the paste. Add the water, coconut milk, sugar, fish sauce and lime leaves, then bring to a simmer and gently cook for 5 minutes. Remove the pan from the heat.

Place the panko in a shallow bowl, then place the flour in a second bowl and beat the egg in a third bowl.

Dip the chicken first into the flour, shaking off excess, then dip into the egg and finally dip into the panko until the chicken is evenly coated on both sides.

Heat the oil for frying in a large frying pan (skillet) over a medium heat. Add the chicken and shallow-fry gently on each side for 4 minutes each side, until golden and cooked through. Remove from the pan and cut into slices.

To serve, heat the noodles. Bring the soup to a simmer until hot, then add the lime juice. Transfer to a warmed deep noodle bowls, add the sliced chicken and all the toppings, then sprinkle over the crushed cashews.

T
R
A
C
K

F
O
U
R

COFFEE-RUBBED 'RED EYE' CHICKEN THIGHS

SERVES 4

4 large bone-in chicken thighs, skin on

FOR THE COFFEE RUB

½ tablespoon good-quality ground coffee (medium ground)

½ tablespoon garlic powder (not garlic salt)

½ tablespoon onion powder

½ tablespoon paprika

¾ teaspoon ground cumin

½ teaspoon Madras Curry Powder (page 116)

½ tablespoon cayenne pepper (optional, if you like it spicy)

FOR THE HONEY BUTTER GLAZE

1½ tablespoons unsalted butter

1 tablespoon honey

½ teaspoon light soy sauce

FOR THE RED EYE MAYO

60 g (2 oz/¾ cup) coffee beans

340 ml (11½ fl oz/1⅓ cups) rapeseed (canola) oil

115 g (4 oz) garlic cloves, peeled

2 eggs

100 ml (3½ fl oz/scant ½ cup) espresso

1 tablespoon soft brown sugar

1 teaspoon salt

small pinch of cayenne pepper

Red eye gravy originates from the southern states of America and is usually associated with the country ham of that region where coffee is added to the dripping fats of the ham to create a gravy. In Louisiana, they make it with roast beef drippings and chicory, a coffee substitute. It sounds a little weird, I know, but I promise you it works, so don't let that put you off. The slightly salty, sweet honey butter works really well against all the spices in the red eye rub. Coffee is not the dominant flavour here and just adds a really interesting back note to the overall flavour of the dish. It's really easy and quick to make and you can use the leftover spice mix on any number of ingredients from sweet potato wedges to seasoning a straight up mayo for chips (fries).

Brine the chicken for 1 hour according to the brine instructions on page 24 (optional).

To make the coffee rub, combine all the ingredients together in a bowl and set aside.

To make the glaze, melt the butter in a small pot or in the microwave. If using a microwave, heat it at 15-second intervals so it doesn't splatter everywhere. Once the butter has melted or is soft, mix in the honey and soy sauce, then set aside.

Preheat the oven to 180°C (350°F/gas 4).

Remove the chicken thighs from the brine and pat dry with paper towels. Rub the coffee rub over the top and bottoms of the chicken thighs and place in an ovenproof roasting pan. Roast in the oven for about 40 minutes, then use a brush to dab the glaze over the chicken. If the butter has separated, use a fork to mix everything together until it is a paste again – it doesn't need to be smooth. Return the thighs to the oven for another 15 minutes, or until cooked through, continuing to glaze the thighs every 5 minutes or so. Once the thighs are cooked, remove from the oven and place on a wire rack set over a plate or tray and pour over the remaining glaze.

To make the mayo, blend the coffee beans with the rapeseed oil in a blender until smooth, then strain through a fine sieve (strainer). Some small granules will pass through, but this is OK. Pour the infused oil into a saucepan, add the garlic cloves, place over a low heat and gently confit the garlic until soft, about 15 minutes. Remove from the heat and leave to cool completely.

Place the egg in a small saucepan and cover with water by 2.5 cm (1 in). Bring to the boil over a medium heat and cook for 3 minutes, then drain and rinse under cold running water to cool. Once cold, peel the egg, then place it in a blender with the espresso, brown sugar, salt and cayenne pepper and purée until completely smooth. While still blending, slowly pour in the coffee oil and confit garlic to make an emulsion. Spoon into a serving bowl and serve a big dollop with the roasted chicken thighs.

BANGKOK TACOS WITH CHILLI JAM, THAI HERBS AND CRISPY SHIZZLE

SERVES 4

92

WORTH THE EFFORT

8 boneless chicken thighs, skin on

30 ml (1 fl oz/2 tablespoons) vegetable oil

1 bunch of Thai basil, torn

1 bunch of coriander (cilantro), torn

200 g (7 oz) queso fresco cheese or very mild feta

3 tablespoons shop-bought crispy shallots, for sprinkling

12 blue or white corn tortillas, to serve

FOR THE MARINADE

2 tablespoons Thai fish sauce

2 tablespoons Thai light soy sauce

½ teaspoon granulated sugar

¼ teaspoon ground black pepper

2 tablespoons water

FOR THE CHILLI JAM

about 200 ml (7 fl oz/scant 1 cup) rapeseed (canola) oil, for frying

60 g (2 oz) garlic cloves, very thinly sliced

80 g (3 oz) shallots, very thinly sliced

20 g (1 oz) dried shrimp

30 g (1¼ oz) dried red chillies, seeded

20 g (¾ oz) Thai shrimp paste

190 g (7 oz/1 cup) coconut palm sugar, chopped into small pieces

4 tablespoons tamarind pulp

4 tablespoons fish sauce

240 ml (8 fl oz/1 cup) water

120 ml (4 fl oz/½ cup) vegetable oil

THIGHS

I recently visited Chiang Mai in Thailand with my friend Dan who took me to a backstreet restaurant that specialised in *gai yang* or Thai roast chicken. It was incredible, the crispiest and juiciest chicken I have ever eaten, and it got me thinking about how I could use the traditional recipe to create something a little different. So I started thinking about tacos and how well the super crispy chicken would work in contrast with soft warm corn tortillas. The chilli jam takes a bit of work, but is worth it and you can always use it as a condiment on anything else you fancy, as it adds sweetness, a bit of a funky flavour and heat. The crispy shallots add a crunchy texture with the freshness of the herbs. Queso fresco is just fresh Mexican cheese, but difficult to find, so you can just use a mild feta if you like. It adds a nice note of acidity and creaminess to the final taco. Make sure you dampen your tortillas with a little water before reheating and keep them fresh by placing a damp tea (dish) towel over them to avoid them drying out.

Brine the chicken according to the instructions on page 24 (optional).

To make the marinade, stir all the ingredients together in a small bowl until the sugar is fully dissolved. Add the thighs and marinate uncovered in the refrigerator for about 2 hours to dry out the skin.

To make the chilli jam, heat the oil for frying in a deep-fryer or large, deep saucepan over a medium heat until it reaches 180°C (350°F), or until a cube of bread dropped in sizzles in 30 seconds. Fry the garlic and shallot slices separately for 1–2 minutes until light brown and crisp. Remove from the pan and set aside.

Do the same with the dried shrimp and set aside.

Toast the chillies in a dry frying pan (skillet) over a medium-low heat for 1 minute, or until crispy and not burnt.

Transfer the garlic, shallots, dried shrimp and chillies to a granite mortar or food processor and pound or grind into a fine paste, then place in a shallow, wide saucepan with the remaining jam ingredients and the vegetable oil. Cook over a medium heat, stirring occasionally, for 15 minutes, or until everything has dissolved and it becomes a fried paste. Remove the pan from the heat and leave the mixture to cool completely.

To cook the chicken thighs, add the oil to a cold frying pan and lay the chicken thighs, skin-side down, in the oil. Turn the heat to as low as possible and cook for 8–10 minutes, or until the thighs are almost cooked all the way through and the skin is super crispy. Turn and cook for a further 2–3 minutes, then set aside to cool a little.

To build the tacos, dampen the tortillas with a little water and heat through in a dry non-stick pan. Remove from the pan and cover with a clean tea towel to keep warm. Slice the chicken thighs and lay one on each of the tortillas. Put a dollop of chilli jam on top, then add the herbs. Crumble about 20 g (¾ oz) of cheese onto each taco, then sprinkle with the crispy shallots to serve.

SUPERIOR CHICKEN NOODLE STEW

SERVES 4–6

94

**ALMOST
BREEZY**

**T
H
I
G
H
S**

2 tablespoons rapeseed (canola) oil

8 bone-in chicken thighs, skin on

Maldon sea salt

steamed rice, to serve

FOR THE STEW

100 g (3½ oz) Spam, thinly sliced

2 large frankfurters, thinly sliced

100 g (3½ oz) smoked tofu (optional)

125 g (4 oz) oyster mushrooms, thinly sliced lengthways

125 g (4 oz) shiitake mushroom caps, thinly sliced

100 g (3½ oz) kimchi

2 litres (70 fl oz/8 cups) chicken stock (broth) (page 146)

1 packet instant ramen noodles

6 spring onions (scallions), thinly and sliced diagonally

4 American cheese slices

2 sheets of toasted nori seaweed, cut into thin strips (optional)

FOR THE SAUCE

2 tablespoons gochugaru or Korean chilli (hot pepper) flakes

2 tablespoons mirin

1 tablespoon soy sauce

1 tablespoon very finely chopped garlic

½ tablespoon caster (superfine) sugar

½ tablespoon gochujang (Korean red chilli paste)

a few sprinkles of freshly ground black pepper

The origins of this dish are from Korea and it originated shortly after the Korean War with the US when food was scarce and many Koreans were starving to death. People smuggled food out of the American army bases and then local Koreans added their own ingredients and spices to processed meats such as Spam and hotdogs. It was all thrown into a big pot with whatever leftovers were lying around to create a delicious filling meal. This dish was truly created out of necessity during a very difficult time. The crazy mix of East-meets-West flavours are complex yet balanced, but most of all it is super tasty. Here, I have added instant noodles for some texture and also used oyster mushrooms and shiitakes, but it works just as well with regular button mushrooms or, better still, meaty portobello mushrooms. If you don't like the idea of using Spam, then you can use just about anything else you like, but Spam does lend something unique to the finished dish because of its fat content. In fact, you can add just about any leftovers you fancy, and it will still be tasty. It's a one-pot wonder and a dish you can just plonk down on the table and let everybody help themselves. Give it a go and I promise it will be unforgettable.

Mix all the sauce ingredients together in a small bowl and set aside.

Season the skin side of the chicken thighs with a little salt. Heat the oil in a casserole dish (Dutch oven) over a low heat and cook the chicken thighs very slowly, skin-side down, for 8 minutes until the skin takes on a golden brown colour. Don't not turn over, and remove from the heat.

Assemble the main stew ingredients, except for the noodles, spring onions, cheese and nori, in a kind of overlapping circle in a shallow casserole dish. Add the sauce to the middle and pour the stock in the corner of the pot. Close the lid and bring to the boil over a medium-high heat, then reduce the heat and cook for about 8 minutes. Add the noodles and spring onions on top of the dish and boil, uncovered, for 2–3 minutes until the noodles are cooked.

Top with the American cheese and nori, then serve with steamed rice and any other sides you fancy.

**T
R
A
C
K

F
O
U
R**

VIET-CAJUN GUMBO

SERVES 4

1 tablespoon vegetable oil

4 skinless, boneless chicken thighs, each cut into 4 pieces

3 frankfurters, sliced

100 g (3½ oz) cooked wide flat rice noodles or rice cakes

FOR THE SPICED BUTTER SAUCE

60 g (2 oz) unsalted butter

1 lemongrass stalk, finely chopped

3 garlic cloves, finely chopped

½ teaspoon cayenne pepper

1 tablespoon lime juice

FOR THE CAJUN SPICE MIX

4 teaspoons garlic powder

2 teaspoons dried oregano

1 tablespoon paprika

½ teaspoon smoked paprika

1 teaspoon Maldon sea salt

2 teaspoons freshly ground black pepper

2 teaspoons cayenne pepper

2 teaspoons dried thyme

2 teaspoons onion powder

FOR THE COOKING STOCK

250 ml (8½ fl oz/1 cup) chicken stock (broth)

2 tablespoons Cajun spice mix

2 tablespoons fish sauce

2 lemongrass stalks, smashed

10 g (¼ oz/2½ teaspoons) palm sugar

5 garlic cloves, unpeeled and smashed

GARNISH

handful of chopped coriander (cilantro)

handful of torn Vietnamese mint

juice of 1 lime

3 spring onions (scallions), thinly sliced

I first got the idea for this dish after reading a fascinating article about how the children of Vietnamese migrants from years ago had opened restaurants in Houston, Texas and Louisiana, embracing the local Cajun culture by using crawfish and Cajun spices with their own Vietnamese flavours to fuse both cultures together. Since then a huge Viet-Cajun food scene has become a thing. I first developed my version of this dish using all kinds of fresh seafood for an appearance on *Saturday Kitchen*, but I have made a few changes to that recipe as it works really well with chicken. I have also used hotdog sausages instead of Cajun andouille sausages, which give a smoky flavour to the dish, and rice cakes or fat rice noodles for some texture. You can even throw in a few large prawns (shrimp) as well, if you like. It's well worth making your own Cajun spice mix as most sold in shops are not very good and can taste stale. You can see the Vietnamese influence in this recipe as I have used lemongrass, fish sauce and coconut palm sugar. The bubbling, slightly browned spiced butter is poured over the finished dish giving it a really nutty flavour, so you will need lots of good crusty bread to mop up all that buttery goodness.

To make the butter sauce, soften the butter and mix with the remaining ingredients in a bowl. Set aside.

To make the spice mix, blend all the ingredients in a spice grinder to a powder. Set aside.

To make the cooking stock, add all the ingredients to a large saucepan and bring to a simmer. Cook for 30 minutes over a low heat to infuse. Strain, then set aside.

Heat the oil in a deep frying pan (skillet) and start to brown the chicken pieces for 3–4 minutes, then add the hotdog slices and cook for another 1–2 minutes. Add the cooking stock and continue to cook for 8 minutes. Meanwhile, melt the butter sauce in a separate pan until bubbling, then add to the frying pan with the spice mix.

Add the cooked rice noodles or rice cakes to the pan for the last 3 minutes to heat through. Pour into a large serving bowl and garnish with coriander, Vietnamese mint, a squeeze of lime juice and sliced spring onions.

THIGHS

TRACK FOUR

THE ORIGINAL DISCO BISTRO
FRIED CHICKEN SANDWICH

SERVES 1

96

WORTH THE EFFORT

T H I G H S

4 boneless chicken thighs, skin on

about 2 litres (70 fl oz/8 cups) vegetable oil, for deep-frying

2 very ripe avocados

juice of 2 limes

1 tablespoon chopped coriander (cilantro)

Maldon sea salt and freshly ground black pepper

8 slices of dry-cured streaky bacon

4 brioche or soft white potato bread rolls, toasted

melted butter, for brushing

100 g (3½ oz/scant ½ cup) Chef Patty Hot Sauce (page 128)

4 American cheese slices

2 tablespoons Pink Pickled Onions (page 165)

2 tablespoons Japanese Kewpie mayonnaise

FOR THE BUTTERMILK BRINE

500 ml (17 fl oz/2 cups) buttermilk

1 teaspoon salt

¼ teaspoon MSG (optional)

FOR THE WET BATTER

1 large egg

120 ml (4 fl oz/½ cup) milk

FOR THE FLOUR COATING

60 g (2 oz/½ cup) plain (all-purpose) flour

75 g (2½ oz/½ cup) rice flour or dried rice, ground to a fine powder in a spice mill

30 g (1 oz/⅔ cup) cornflour (cornstarch)

1 teaspoon salt

¼ teaspoon coarse ground black pepper (not fine)

A few years ago, I did a six-month pop-up restaurant called Disco Bistroabove an old pub in St Paul's in London. It was a lot of fun and it went on to cause quite a stir, but it was here that I first started my never-ending journey into the search for perfect fried chicken, which I continue to try and perfect to this very day. Along with my friends Pat and Glyn we created a super-crispy coating for the chicken that would stay crispy an hour later. We still use the same coating at both CHICK'N and Chick 'n' Sours today, although it has been constantly tweaked over the years in search of perfection. I obviously can't give you the exact recipe because there's only myself and The Colonel that know, but the one in this recipe does the trick. Pat came up with the hot sauce, so we named it Chef Patty Hot Sauce. As Pat will tell you himself, making a couple of hundred portions of the hot sauce every two days was definitely a labour of love but so worth it. We worked on the double-fry technique for quite some time and found it was the perfect way to get a beautifully textured, crispy-coated thigh. The end result was a fried chicken sandwich of dreams with every layer adding something different. It is everything a fried chicken sandwich should be – crispy chicken, warm toasted buttery bread roll, heat from the hot sauce, cooling avocado, crispy lettuce and some pickled onions for acidity to cut through it all.

To make the buttermilk brine, whisk all the ingredients together in a shallow bowl. Add the chicken thighs, cover with cling film (plastic wrap) and leave in the refrigerator for 12–24 hours.

The next day, to make the wet batter, whisk the egg and milk together in a bowl until combined. Set aside. For the flour coating, blend all the ingredients together in a medium bowl with a whisk.

Remove the chicken thighs from the brine and shake off the excess buttermilk. Lightly dip the thighs into the flour mix, then submerge them in the wet batter. Dredge them back into the flour and work in with your hands to give some texture almost like cornflakes.

Heat the oil for deep-frying in a deep-fryer or a large, deep saucepan to 140°C (284°F), or until a cube of bread dropped in sizzles in 40 seconds. Deep-fry the chicken in pairs for 7 minutes, then remove and set aside. Increase the temperature of the oil to 180°C (350°F), or until a cube of bread dropped in sizzles in 30 seconds. Deep-fry the chicken again for 3–4 minutes until golden brown and cooked through. Remove and drain on paper towels.

To build the sandwiches, cut the avocados in half and scoop the flesh out into a bowl. Add the lime juice, coriander, season with salt and pepper and mix together.

Preheat the grill (broiler) to medium. Grill (broil) the bacon to your liking. Cut the bread rolls in half and brush each half with melted butter, then toast under the grill or face down in a hot dry frying pan (skillet) for 2 minutes. Spread some of the avocado mix onto the base of each roll and top with a fried chicken thigh. Spoon over some of the hot sauce (be generous), top with a cheese slice and 2 slices of bacon each. Add some pickled onions on top.

Spread a little of the mayonnaise on the lid of the bread roll and close the sandwich. It's messy, but a killer sandwich.

T R A C K   F O U R

BULGOGI GRILLED CHICKEN WITH KIMCHI

SERVES 4

98

EASY PEASY

4 boneless chicken thighs, skin on

No Need to Wait Kimchi (page 175)

FOR THE MARINADE

6 tablespoons soy sauce

4 tablespoons light brown or granulated sugar

2 tablespoons honey or 2 teaspoons sugar

4 tablespoons Shaoxing rice wine, red wine or mirin

2 tablespoons sesame oil

4 tablespoons very finely chopped garlic

2 teaspoons ground black pepper

4 teaspoons toasted sesame seeds

2 tablespoons sliced spring onion (scallion)

1 very ripe pear, Asian if possible

T H I G H S

Bulgogi is also known as Korean barbecue meat and is mostly made with thin strips of marinated beef cooked over charcoal. It has regional variations and there are lots of different versions of the marinade and other cuts of meat can also be used, such as pork or chicken, which I have used here. The classic Korean marinade is made with only a few ingredients and is super easy to make. The trick is to find the right balance between saltiness and sweetness, then use generous amounts of garlic and sesame oil to create an authentic flavour. To add to the flavour and to tenderise the meat, Koreans traditionally add grated Korean pear, but if you can't find those a regular pear or even an apple will do the job.

Brine the chicken according to the instructions on page 24 (optional).

Meanwhile, to make the marinade, blitz all the ingredients together in food processor, then transfer to a shallow bowl and set aside.

Once the thighs are brined, pat dry with paper towels and place in the marinade. Cover with cling film (plastic wrap) and leave to marinate in the refrigerator for at least 4 hours, or preferably 24 hours.

To finish, preheat the grill (broiler) to medium. Place the chicken on a grilling (broiling) rack and grill (broil), skin-side up, for 7–8 minutes, then turn and grill for another 2–3 minutes, or until cooked through. Serve the chicken with some of the kimchi.

T R A C K   F O U R

CHICKEN THIGHS
WITH OYSTER SAUCE AND BROCCOLI

SERVES 4

4 skinless, boneless chicken thighs, thinly sliced crossways

120 ml (4 fl oz/½ cup) oyster sauce

4 tablespoons light soy sauce

1 tablespoon caster (superfine) sugar

4 tablespoons rice wine vinegar

4 tablespoons rapeseed (canola) oil

16 Tenderstem broccoli stalks

4 garlic cloves, thinly sliced

4 eggs, beaten

300 g (10½ oz) flat white rice noodles, cooked according to packet instructions

salt and ground white pepper

lime wedges, to serve

This is really one of the simplest recipes in the book. It takes no time at all and can be cooked in a wok without much preparation or any fuss. Oyster sauce tastes a little like a combination of soy sauce and BBQ sauce and is both salty and sweet. The saltiness comes from the fermented oysters and has a sweetness with hints of caramel. It is less salty than soy sauce and is full of umami flavour. Here, I have used beaten egg for another texture and wide flat rice noodles to create a quick, tasty and filling dish for after work or a quick, weekend dinner. The broccoli brings a nice earthiness and crunch to the finished dish. This recipe is for four people as I like to eat Chinese food together with others, but just scale it down as you wish to make this for just yourself.

Place the chicken thighs in a shallow bowl, add the oyster sauce, cover and leave to marinate for 1 hour, but preferably overnight.

Mix the soy sauce, sugar and vinegar together in a bowl and stir until the sugar dissolves.

Heat the oil in a wok or deep frying pan (skillet) over a medium heat. Add the broccoli and fry for 2 minutes, then add the garlic and fry for another minute. Add the chicken and oyster sauce and cook for 3–4 minutes until the chicken is cooked through. Transfer the chicken to a plate and set aside. Add the eggs to the wok and cook, without stirring, for a minute, then stir and chop into pieces for another 30 seconds. Add the cooked rice noodles to the pan along with the reserved chicken and stir-fry for another 2 minutes until heated through.

Serve with lime wedges on the side.

EASY PEASY

THIGHS

THIGH HIGH

HAKKA-STYLE CHILLI CHICKEN

SERVES 4

100

WORTH THE EFFORT

4 skinless, boneless chicken thighs, cut into small bite-sized 2.5 cm (1 in) pieces

1.5 litres (51 fl oz/6½ cups) rapeseed (canola) oil, for deep-frying, plus 2 tablespoons

120 g (4 oz/scant 1 cup) cornflour (cornstarch)

1 onion, sliced

1 green (bell) pepper, cut into chunks

good pinch of salt

FOR THE MARINADE

thumb-sized piece of fresh ginger root, peeled and sliced

3 garlic cloves

½ small onion

1½ tablespoons dark soy sauce

½ tablespoon Kashmiri chilli powder

1 teaspoon ground black pepper

4 tablespoons water

FOR THE SAUCE

3–4 green bird's eye chillies, sliced

1½ tablespoons dark soy sauce

2½ tablespoons light soy sauce

1 tablespoon rice wine vinegar

1 teaspoon ground cumin

1 tablespoon ground coriander

2 tablespoons tomato ketchup

1 tablespoon honey

½ teaspoon Kashmiri chilli powder

120 ml (4 fl oz/½ cup) water

6 tablespoons cornflour (cornstarch) mixed with a little water to form a paste

TO SERVE

400 g (14 oz/1¾ cups) cooked white rice

Pink Pickled Onions (page 175)

The Hakka are a cultural group of Chinese that migrated to countries such as Singapore, Hong Kong, Taiwan and India, where this dish originates. This is Indo-Chinese food, a fusion of Chinese ingredients and Indian spices. I have read somewhere that it was invented in 1975 by a guy called Nelson Wang in India who used the local ingredients of garlic, green chillies and ginger, but instead of garam masala he used soy sauce and ketchup among other Chinese ingredients. I'm not sure if that's a true story, but who cares anyway, my hat's off to whoever invented it as it is super easy to make and super tasty. Serve with plain white rice and some greens fried in garlic and soy, and you won't go far wrong.

To make the marinade, blitz the ginger, garlic and onion in a food processor to a fine paste. Reserve 2 tablespoons of this paste for browning the onions and green peppers later.

Place the chicken pieces in a bowl with the remaining ginger-garlic-onion paste, the soy sauce, chilli powder, black pepper and water, then cover with cling film (plastic wrap) and marinate in the refrigerator for 1 hour.

To cook the chicken, heat the oil for deep-frying in a wok, large, deep saucepan or deep-fryer to 180°C (350°F), or until a cube of bread dropped in sizzles in 30 seconds.

Meanwhile, remove the chicken from the marinade. Toss the chicken with the cornflour until combined and the chicken is lightly coated.

When the oil is hot, deep-fry the chicken in batches for 5–6 minutes, then remove and drain on paper towels. Keep warm.

Heat 2 tablespoons of rapeseed oil in a wok or frying pan (skillet) over medium heat. Add the reserved 2 tablespoons of the ginger-garlic-onion mix and cook for 2 minutes, or until toasty and brown. Add the onion and green pepper chunks and cook for about 2 minutes.

To make the sauce, put the ingredients, apart from the cornflour, into a small saucepan and bring to a simmer, then add the cornflour paste, a little at a time, until it starts to thicken and coat the back of a spoon. Once the sauce has thickened, add the chicken and mix through. Serve with the pepper mix, rice and some pickled onions on the side.

CHICKEN NUGGETS WITH KIMCHI BACON RANCH DIP AND SPICY SHAKE

SERVES 4

8 boneless chicken thighs, skin on or off, cut into 4 cm (1½ in) pieces

1.5 litres (51 fl oz/6½ cups) rapeseed (canola) oil, for deep-frying

FOR THE BRINE

100 ml (3½ fl oz/scant ½ cup) kimchi juice, drained from 1 jar of kimchi

225 ml (8 fl oz/scant 1 cup) buttermilk

1 teaspoon sea salt

1 tablespoon soy sauce

35 g (1¼ oz/½ cup) gochugaru or Korean chilli (hot pepper) flakes

FOR THE COATING

180 g (6 oz) tangy cheese Doritos

20 g (¾ oz/⅓ cup) panko breadcrumbs

400 g (14 oz/3½ cups) plain (all-purpose) flour

1 large egg

120 ml (4 fl oz/½ cup) milk

FOR THE KIMCHI BACON RANCH DIP

150 g (5 oz) kimchi

70 g (2¼ oz/¼ cup) mayonnaise (Japanese Kewpie is best)

2 tablespoons finely chopped chives

½ teaspoon onion powder

1 teaspoon runny honey

70 g (2¼ oz/¼ cup) sour cream

1 teaspoon white vinegar

¼ teaspoon American mustard

4 slices of cooked dry-cure streaky bacon, crumbled

pinch of fresh dill

sea salt and freshly ground black pepper

FOR THE SPICY SHAKE

1 tablespoon cayenne pepper

2 teaspoons gochugaru or Korean chilli (hot pepper) flakes

1½ teaspoons granulated sugar

1½ teaspoons fine salt

scant teaspoon MSG (optional)

1 teaspoon crumbled nori seaweed

1 teaspoon onion powder

1 teaspoon garlic powder

½ teaspoon smoked paprika

¼ teaspoon citric acid

Kimchi is a staple in any Korean diet. It's made from fermenting all different kinds of vegetables with a spice paste that generally has Korean fish sauce or salted shrimps in its base. Making kimchi is quite a lengthy process that requires careful preparation to avoid mould growing on the top, so I came up with a No Need to Wait Kimchi recipe for this book (page 175). The vegetables are salted then mixed with the spice paste and left at room temperature for anything from a couple of days up to a few months. The fermentation gives it a funky acidic taste that goes with just about anything. As kimchi is fermented, it also has lots of good health benefits, one being that it's a probiotic. In this recipe, I have used the kimichi in two parts, one in the brining of the chicken for flavour and the other in recreating a Korean version of the classic American ranch dressing. The spicy shake is inspired by my favourite instant noodles, Shin Cup, from Korea, which are really spicy. I used to just open the soup mix packet and put it on chips (fries) or fried chicken as a shake. My friend Ash, who does the food development with me at Chick 'n' Sours & CHICK'N, came up with our version, which is a banger. However, if you can't be bothered making the spicy shake then just grab some Shin Cup instant noodles and do the same. If you don't like it spicy, then sprinkle them with lots of Maldon sea salt instead. They will be banging whatever you use.

WORTH THE EFFORT

To make the chicken nuggets, whisk all the brine ingredients together in a large shallow bowl, then add the chicken, cover with cling film (plastic wrap) and leave to marinate in the refrigerator for at least 6 hours, if not 24 hours.

To make the spicy shake, combine all the ingredients in a small bowl. Set aside.

When ready to cook, to make the coating, blitz the Doritos in a food processor until crushed, then transfer to a bowl. Lightly crush the panko breadcrumbs between your hands and mix with the Doritos. Set aside.

Whisk the egg and milk together in a bowl until combined. Set aside. Place the flour for coating in another bowl.

Remove the chicken from the brine, then dip the chicken into the flour, shaking off excess, then in the wet batter and then in the Doritos coating until coated all over. Set aside in the refrigerator while you make the ranch dip.

To make the dip, drain the kimchi and give it a squeeze to remove as much liquid as possible. Place in a food processor with the mayonnaise, chives, onion powder, honey , sour cream, vinegar and mustard. Season with salt and pepper and blitz until smooth. Fold in the bacon bits and chopped dill and transfer to a serving bowl.

To cook the chicken, heat the oil for deep-frying in a deep-fryer or a large, deep saucepan to 160°C (325°F), or until a cube of bread dropped in sizzles in 30 seconds. Deep-fry the chicken, in batches, for 7–8 minutes until golden brown and cooked through. Remove and drain on paper towels.

Serve the chicken with the dip and spicy shake.

CHICKEN TIKKA KEBAB WITH NAAN BREAD, MINT CHUTNEY AND GUNPOWDER SHAKE

SERVES 4

102

WORTH THE EFFORT

**T
H
I
G
H
S**

2.5 cm (1 in) piece of fresh ginger root, peeled

4 garlic cloves

2 bird's eye green chillies, finely chopped

3 large tablespoons thick plain yoghurt or Greek yoghurt

2 teaspoons chickpea (gram) flour

1 teaspoon mild paprika

1 teaspoon Kashmiri chilli powder

½ teaspoon garam masala

1 teaspoon ground coriander

pinch of ground cinnamon

pinch of saffron threads soaked in a little warm water for 5 minutes

salt, to taste

450 g (1 lb) skinless, boneless chicken thighs, cut into bite-sized pieces

FOR THE NAAN BREAD

1½ teaspoons fast-action dried (active dry) yeast

1 teaspoon caster (superfine) sugar

150 ml (5 fl oz/scant ⅔ cup) warm water

300 g (11 oz/scant 2½ cups) strong white bread flour

1 teaspoon salt

5 tablespoons plain yoghurt

2 tablespoons melted ghee or butter, plus extra for brushing

vegetable oil, for oiling

1 teaspoon nigella or poppy seeds,

FOR THE MINT CHUTNEY

150 g (5 oz/⅔ cup) plain yoghurt

20 g (¾ oz) shop-bought mint sauce

salt, to taste

TO FINISH

3 tablespoons melted ghee

Gunpowder Shake (page 124)

juice of 1 lemon

Pink Pickled Onions (page 175)

handful of coriander (cilantro) leaves

I grew up in Birmingham so Indian food is part of my DNA and remains one of my favourite foods to eat to this day. This naan wrap takes me right back there. There's an Indian pub I know that serve masala fries, and this is where I got the idea for the gunpowder shake named after the traditional southern Indian spice blend. This recipe is not authentic like most recipes in this book – it's just my imagination running wild.

Place the ginger, garlic and green chillies in a food processor and blend to a smooth paste.

Mix the yoghurt and chickpea flour together in a large bowl to get rid of any lumps and until it is a thick paste. Add the ginger, garlic and chilli paste, paprika, chilli powder, garam masala, ground coriander, cinnamon, saffron and salt, to taste and stir well. Tip in the chicken and coat in the marinade. Cover with cling film (plastic wrap) and marinate in the refrigerator for a few hours, or overnight, if you prefer.

To make the naan bread, mix the yeast, sugar and 2 tablespoons of the warm water together in a bowl, then leave until it froths.

Whisk the flour and salt together in a large bowl to combine. Stir the yoghurt into the yeast mixture, then make a well in the middle of the flour and pour it in, plus the melted ghee. Mix, then gradually stir in the remaining water to make a soft, sticky mixture that is just firm enough to call a dough, but not at all dry. Tip out on a lightly floured surface and knead for 5 minutes, or until smooth and a little less sticky. Transfer to a large, lightly oiled bowl and turn to coat. Cover with a tea (dish) towel and leave in a draught-free place for 1½–2 hours until doubled in size.

Tip the dough back out onto a lightly floured surface and knock the air out, then divide into 8 balls. Meanwhile, heat a non-stick frying pan over a high heat for 5 minutes and put the oven on low.

Flatten one of the balls and roll it into a circle, slightly thicker around the edge, then put it in the hot pan. When it starts to bubble, turn it over and cook until the other side is browned in patches. Turn it back over and cook until there are no doughy bits remaining. Brush with melted ghee and sprinkle with seeds (if using), then keep warm in the oven and cook the remaining naan.

Meanwhile, soak 8 wooden skewers in a bowl of warm water. Mix all the ingredients for the mint chutney together in a small bowl, then cover and chill until ready to serve.

Preheat the grill (broiler) to medium. Shake the excess marinade off the chicken and thread onto the skewers, then place them on a wire rack. Cook under the grill for 15–20 minutes, turning the skewers every 5 minutes and basting with ghee until the chicken juices run clear and the pieces are cooked through.

To build the wraps, take a warm naan bread and brush with ghee, then liberally add the gunpowder shake. Lay the chicken on top and squeeze over the lemon and drizzle with the mint chutney. Lay the pickled onions on top, scatter with coriander and roll into a wrap.

**T
R
A
C
K

F
O
U
R**

BBQ CHICKEN PIZZA

SERVES 4

WORTH THE EFFORT

7 g (1 heaped teaspoon) fast-action dried (active dry) yeast

350 ml (12 fl oz/1½ cups) warm water

1 tablespoon honey

360 g (12¾ oz/scant 3 cups) '00' flour, plus extra for dusting

1 tablespoon Maldon sea salt

2 tablespoons olive oil, plus extra for oiling

FOR THE BBQ SAUCE

60 g (2 oz) marrow bone piece, split down the middle (optional)

1 small pigs' trotter (foot), split down the middle (optional)

250 ml (8½ fl oz/1 cup) tomato ketchup

4 tablespoons French's American mustard

1½ tablespoons cider vinegar

2 tablespoons Worcestershire sauce

1 teaspoon Tabasco sauce

100 ml (3½ fl oz/scant ⅓ cup) apple juice

4 tablespoons treacle (blackstrap molasses)

100 ml (3½ fl oz/scant ⅓ cup) chicken stock (broth)

3 tablespoons smoke powder (optional)

FOR THE PIZZA TOPPING

150 g (5¼ oz) cooked shredded chicken

1 tablespoon rapeseed (canola) oil

½ red onion, thinly sliced

handful of grated mozzarella

handful of grated fontina

2 tablespoons grated Parmesan

salt and coarse black pepper

A pizza stone works best for this, or cook the pizza directly on the oven rack at the highest temperature possible. When making the BBQ sauce, you can omit the pigs' trotter and marrow for a more straight-up version, if you prefer.

First, make the BBQ sauce. Preheat the oven to 180°C (350°F/gas 4), if using the marrow bones and pigs' trotter. Roast the marrow bones and trotter in a roasting pan for 30 minutes until golden, then tip into a pot, along with any fat, and add the ketchup, mustard, vinegar, Worcestershire sauce, Tabasco, apple juice, treacle and chicken stock. Bring to a simmer, then leave to bubble gently over a low heat for 2–3 hours until thickened. Strain the sauce through a fine sieve (strainer) into a bowl and discard the bones. Stir in the smoke powder. Allow to cool, then store in an airtight container in the refrigerator until ready to use – it will keep for 2 weeks.

To make the pizza dough, dissolve the yeast in the water in a small bowl, then add the honey and stir until cloudy. Combine the flour and salt together in a stand mixer fitted with a paddle attachment, then add the yeast and honey water with the oil and mix for 5–7 minutes to form a dough. Turn out onto a lightly floured surface and continue to knead by hand for another 4–5 minutes. Transfer the dough to a lightly oiled bowl, loosely cover with cling film (plastic wrap) and leave in a warm place for 30 minutes–1 hour.

Divide the dough into 4 equal balls, then loosely cover again with cling film and leave to prove on a baking tray (pan) for another 30 minutes in a warm place.

Meanwhile, to make the pizza topping, season the shredded chicken with salt and pepper and set aside. Heat the rapeseed oil in a frying pan (skillet) over a medium heat and fry the onion for 5 minutes until translucent but with some charred edges. Remove from the heat and set aside.

Preheat the oven to the highest temperature, with a pizza stone or baking tray in the oven.

Shape the dough balls into the required shape on a floured surface, then, working quickly, place on the stone or tray. Brush the base with some of the BBQ sauce, then sprinkle over the chicken mix and grated cheeses. Bake for 5–8 minutes until crispy on the base. Repeat with the rest of the dough and topping, serving as you go.

OOZE

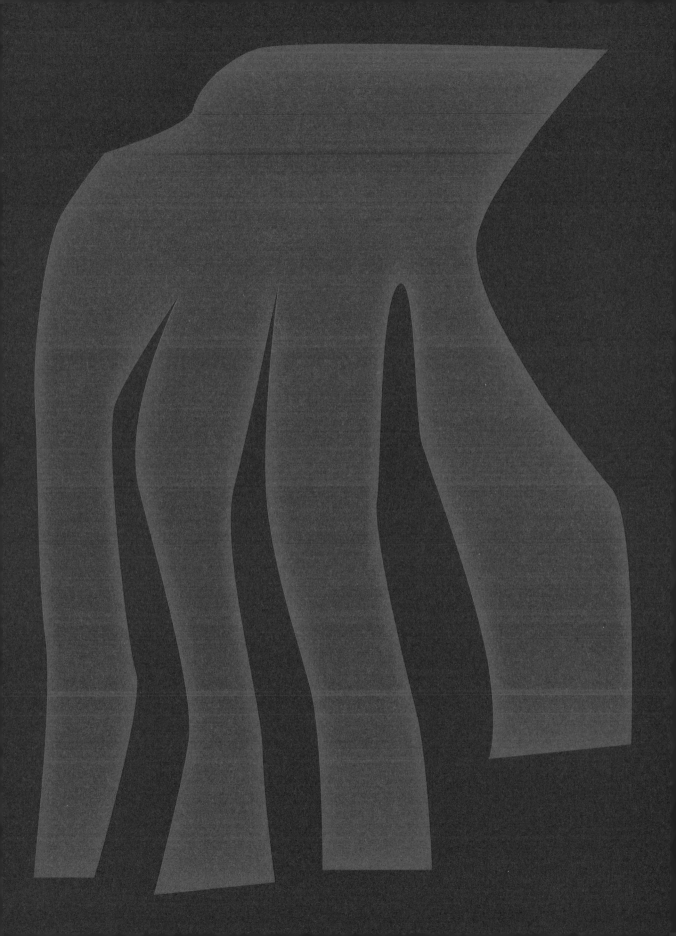

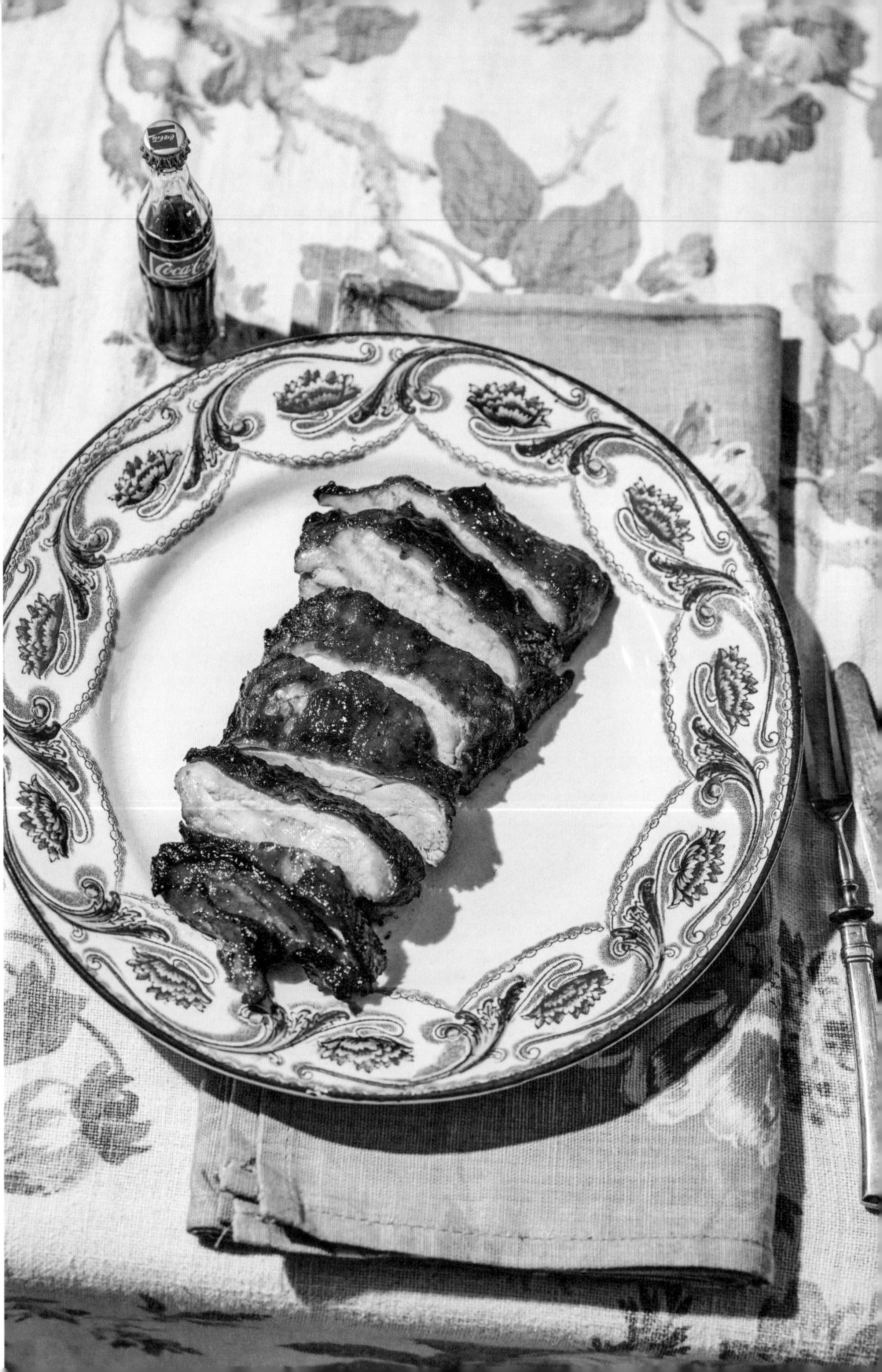
Coca-Cola

CHERRY COLA CHICKEN LEGS

SERVES 4

4 boned-out chicken legs, skin on
(ask your butcher to do this for you)

FOR THE CHAR SIU CHERRY COLA

4 tablespoons hoisin sauce

8 tablespoons cherry cola

2 pieces Chinese fermented
red bean curd, roughly chopped

4 tablespoons honey

4 tablespoons Shaoxing rice wine

4 tablespoons light soy sauce

3 tablespoons oyster sauce

2 teaspoons dark soy sauce

1 teaspoon five-spice powder

¼ teaspoon ground white pepper

TO SERVE

400 g (14 oz/1¾ cups) cooked
white rice

stir-fried Chinese greens (optional)

This recipe is inspired by Chinese roast char siu, which is one of my favourite roast meats to eat. It's traditionally made with pork shoulder that's marinated in a funky, sweet five-spice marinade then roasted. You may have seen it in the windows of many Chinese restaurants hanging with the array of crispy pork bellies and crispy ducks. It works beautifully with chicken legs as they take a little more time to cook, ending up with perfectly crispy, sticky, funky, sweet skin. The funkiness comes from the fermented bean curd, which is used as an ingredient in Chinese cooking. It's basically cubes of soybean curd that have been preserved in rice wine, fermented red rice and other seasonings. You will find it in any Asian supermarkets (grocery stores) and it is essential to this recipe. The cherry cola is my twist and it adds another sticky, sweet, cherry layer to the flavour of the marinade. Serve with plain rice and some stir-fried Chinese greens or even on a sandwich with sliced white bread, Kewpie mayo and some pickles.

To make the marinade, mix all the ingredients together in a shallow dish, add the chicken legs, cover with cling film (plastic wrap) and marinate in the refrigerator for at least 24 hours.

When ready to cook, preheat the oven to 180°C (350°F/gas 4).

Cook the chicken legs on a rack to allow the air to flow around the legs for 35–40 minutes, or until cooked through and crispy. Slice before serving with rice.

**EASY
PEASY**

**L
E
G
S**

**T
R
A
C
K

F
I
V
E**

CRISPY - STICKY - FUNKY

LETTUCE CUPS WITH CHICKEN, MANDARIN, GINGER AND SESAME

SERVES 4 (MAKES 4 CUPS EACH)

250 g (9 oz) Chinese (Napa) cabbage, shredded

100 g (3½ oz) red cabbage, finely shredded

50 g (2 oz) bean sprouts

500 g (1 lb 2 oz) leftover roast chicken leg, shredded (page 117)

handful of coriander (cilantro), leaves torn

handful of Thai basil, leaves torn

handful of fresh mint, leaves torn

50 g (2 oz) wakame seaweed (optional)

12 spring onions (scallions), finely sliced

295 g (10½ oz) tin mandarin segments, drained

1 head baby gem or English butter lettuce, leaves separated

FOR THE GINGER AND SESAME DRESSING

60 g (2 oz) pickled ginger, chopped

2⅔ tablespoons rice vinegar

2 tablespoons honey

2 tablespoons caster (superfine) sugar

1 tablespoon sesame oil

1 tablespoon soy sauce

¼ teaspoon Chinese five-spice powder

salt and ground white pepper

TO GARNISH (OPTIONAL)

200 ml (7 fl oz/¾ cup) rapeseed (canola) oil

handful of uncooked flat white rice noodles, broken into pieces

3 tablespoons roasted peanuts, crushed

1 tablespoon toasted black sesame seeds

There's something beautiful and enticing about canned mandarins and it's one of the few canned fruits that really work for me. This is a fun recipe to make and reminds me of one of those 1970s old-school cookbooks with the brown pictures. It is light and refreshing and a dish that's meant to be eaten with your hands, so ideal for a drinks party or to just plonk down on the table and eat with a group of friends. The lettuce cups are filled with the delicious, vibrant, fresh crunchy salad with fragrant herbs. The dressing can be used with just about any slaw you fancy for future creations.

To make the dressing, blend all the ingredients together in a food processor.

To make the crispy noodles for the garnish, heat the oil in a small saucepan to 180°C (350°F), or until a cube of bread dropped in sizzles in 30 seconds. Drop in the broken noodles and cook for 1 minute, until puffed up. Drain and set aside.

To build the lettuce cups, mix both cabbages, the bean sprouts, chicken, torn herbs, seaweed, spring onions and mandarin segments together in a large bowl. Add plenty of dressing and mix until everything is coated. Arrange 4 baby gem outer leaves or butter lettuce leaves on a plate, pile on the salad mix, then garnish with the crispy noodles, crushed peanuts and black sesame seeds.

CHICKEN, WHITE MISO AND TRUFFLE PIE

SERVES 4

WORTH THE
EFFORT

4 chicken legs, bone in, skin removed, cut into drumsticks and thighs

1 litre (34 fl oz/4 cups) chicken stock (broth)

3 tablespoons butter

15 g (½ oz) finely diced fresh ginger root

2 garlic cloves, finely chopped

150 g (5 oz) shiitake mushrooms

1 tablespoon plain (all-purpose) flour

50 g (2 oz/3 tablespoons) white miso paste

1 teaspoon white truffle oil

2 tablespoons light soy sauce

5 spring onions (scallions), finely sliced

20 g (¾ oz) black or white canned truffle shavings

375 g (13 oz) packet of all-butter puff pastry

1 egg, beaten

salt and ground white pepper

For me, any chicken pie needs to be made with the dark meat from the chicken and the legs work perfectly for this recipe. By poaching the legs first, you end up with a delicious chicken broth to use as the base to build this pie. I wanted to add ultimate luxury here by swapping out regular mushrooms and using truffles and meaty shiitakes. Truffles have a pungent smell and are one of the best things to eat on the planet. They are very expensive, but you can find trimmings in cans from any good delicatessen, which will work perfectly for this recipe. The white miso adds a slightly sweet funky flavour and works incredibly well with the creamy chicken sauce. If you don't want to make a pie, then just make the filling and eat it with rice for a delicious and comforting midweek dinner.

In a large saucepan, poach the chicken in the stock over a low heat for 20–30 minutes, or until cooked through. Remove the meat and set the stock aside.

Heat the butter in a frying pan (skillet) over a medium heat, add the ginger and garlic and sweat for 3 minutes, then add the mushrooms and flour and stir until everything is well coated, then add the stock, stirring until the sauce is thickened, and the consistency of double (heavy) cream. Add the white miso, truffle oil, soy sauce and spring onions, then remove from the heat.

Shred the poached chicken with two forks, reserve the drumstick bone and mix the meat with the sauce, then stir through the truffle shavings. Season to taste.

Divide the chicken mixture among 4 individual pie dishes.

Preheat the oven to 180°C (350°F/gas 4).

Roll out the pastry on a floured work surface, then cut circles slightly wider than your pie dishes. Poke a hole in the middle of each, cover each pie dish, then stick a drumstick bone through each hole, so that it's poking out the top. Brush each with a little of the beaten egg.

Bake for 20–30 minutes, until golden and piping hot in the middle.

MY SUNDAY NIGHT CHICKEN MADRAS

SERVES 6

**L
E
G
S**

6 chicken legs, jointed into drumsticks and thighs, skinned

rice, naan or roti bread, to serve

FOR THE LIME PICKLED ONIONS

2 red onions, thinly sliced

good pinch of Maldon sea salt

juice of 3 limes

toasted cumin seeds

whole coriander (cilantro) leaves

FOR THE MADRAS POWDER

1 teaspoon black peppercorns

1 cassia bark stick, about 7 cm (2¾ in long)

5 whole cloves

2 tablespoons coriander seeds

1 teaspoon fenugreek seeds

1 teaspoon mustard seeds

1 teaspoon white poppy seeds

1 teaspoon cumin seeds

½ teaspoon fennel seeds

2 tablespoons ground turmeric

1 teaspoon Kashmiri chilli powder

1 teaspoon salt, or to taste

FOR THE MASALA SAUCE

3 teaspoons vegetable oil

1 teaspoon black mustard seeds

10–12 fresh curry leaves

1 onion, finely diced

1 green chilli, finely chopped (2 for more heat)

2 cm (¾ in) piece of fresh ginger root, peeled and grated

2 garlic cloves, finely chopped

400 g (14 oz) tin plum tomatoes

2 teaspoons tamarind pulp

1 teaspoon hot red chilli powder (optional)

handful of coriander (cilantro)

For me, Sunday nights are all about curry. I don't know why, but it always feels like the right thing to eat to finish a weekend and sit on the sofa watching a movie. It goes back to my days of DJing when I would be away all weekend playing in various clubs and not get back until Sunday evening. All I wanted was a curry and some quiet time in front of the TV and I guess it has stuck since. I'm also a Brummie by birth and we know a thing or two about curries in Birmingham I'll have you know! This is a recipe that I have been making for years and it takes me back to Brum every time I make it. It's complex, spicy, comforting, and sweet and sour from the tamarind. You don't want to rush this curry, so take your time, roast all the spices properly and brown the onions slowly. It really is a curry with layers of flavour that come from the different stages of cooking. I always make this on Saturday, then leave it on the work surface and reheat it on Sunday evening. It gives all the spices a chance to settle down and the flavours to amalgamate and develop. In fact, any curry is better eaten a day or two after cooking. I like to eat this with freshly baked Naan Bread (page 102) brushed with garlic and green chilli butter. Brummie vibes!

To make the pickled onions, mix all the ingredients together in a bowl, then cover with cling film (plastic wrap) and leave to stand at room temperature for at least 1 hour, or more if possible. When ready to serve, drain the liquid and transfer to a serving bowl.

To make the Madras powder, grind the black peppercorns, cassia, cloves, coriander, fenugreek, mustard, poppy, cumin and fennel seeds in an electric grinder, blender or mortar and pestle to a fine powder. Stir in the turmeric and the chilli powder.

Place the chicken in a large bowl and rub with 2–3 tablespoons of the Madras powder and the salt until the meat is coated all over. Set aside. Transfer the remaining Madras powder to a well-sealed jar for another time – it will keep for 3 months.

To make the sauce, heat the oil in a large cast-iron saucepan with a lid over a medium heat until hot. Add the mustard seeds, then once they start to pop, stir in the curry leaves and then the onion and fry gently for 20 minutes until the onion turns dark brown. Add the green chilli and ginger along with the garlic and fry, stirring, as the mix has a tendency to catch on the base of the pan. If it does catch, add a splash of water. After a few minutes, add the tomatoes, tamarind and the hot chilli powder, if you like it very spicy. Bring to the boil, then reduce the heat and simmer to create a thick masala sauce.

Once the sauce is shiny and thick, add the chicken and stir to coat it in the sauce. Reduce the heat to the lowest setting, cover with a lid and cook very gently for 40 minutes–1 hour, stirring occasionally, until the chicken is cooked through and the sauce has thickened.

Serve with rice, naan or roti bread and the lime pickled onions.

COLD SESAME CHICKEN NOODLES

SERVES 4

4 chicken legs

1 tablespoon light soy sauce

1 tablespoon sesame oil

1 teaspoon salt

5 tablespoons cold water

3 tablespoons Chinese sesame paste or tahini

400 g (14 oz) fresh noodles (whatever, your choice)

½ tablespoon rapeseed (canola) oil

1 teaspoon caster (superfine) sugar

½ tablespoon Chinese black vinegar (Chinkiang)

FOR EACH SERVING

1 tablespoon light soy sauce

4 tablespoons Chinese sesame paste or tahini

5 spring onions (scallions), thinly sliced, plus extra to garnish

handful of torn coriander (cilantro)

½ tablespoon Explosive Chilli Oil (page 182), for drizzling

pinch of freshly ground Sichuan peppercorns each, plus extra to garnish

1 tablespoon chopped crushed peanuts each, plus extra to garnish

generous pinch of pickled carrot (optional)

1 finely sliced radish

1 teaspoon sesame seeds

There's something about eating cold noodles in the summer. They are more chewy than when served hot but just as satisfying. I have based this dish on the Sichuan sesame noodle dish called mala noodles, which is a chilled but fiery hot sesame noodle dish that uses half the amount of sesame paste used in this recipe. It has a creamy nutty flavour not far off from peanut butter if you close your eyes but way more complex. It is spicy and numbing from the chilli oil and Sichuan pepper and works a treat against the cold temperature of the chewy noodles. Not traditional, but I have topped this dish with some pickled carrot strips, spring onions (scallions) and sesame seeds for extra freshness and acidity. These cold noodles should be really spicy, so adjust the chilli oil level to whatever suits you and pimp up the topping with anything you like.

Brine the chicken legs according to the instructions on page 24 (optional).

The next day, preheat the oven to 180°C (350°F/gas 4). Roast the legs in the oven for 35–40 minutes, until cooked through. (Remove the skin if you like but I like them better with the skin on.) Leave to cool, then chill in the refrigerator for 30 minutes until cold. Once cold, shred all the chicken off the bones and set aside.

In a bowl, stir the soy sauce, sesame oil, salt and cold water into the sesame paste to combine well. The sesame paste should be runny but not thin. Set aside.

Bring a large saucepan of water to the boil, then add the noodles and cook according to the packet instructions.

Drain and immediately add ½ tablespoon of oil (this will help to avoid the noodles sticking to each other). Stir to mix well, then use chopsticks to stir the noodles repeatedly to help them cool down quickly. Chill the noodles in the refrigerator to cool completely.

Mix the cold noodles with the soy and sesame sauce and all the other serving ingredients, including the chicken, and divide among 4 bowls. Garnish with some extra chopped spring onion, coriander, chilli oil, freshly ground Sichuan peppercorn and toasted peanuts.

L
E
G
S

T
R
A
C
K

F
I
V
E

RAMEN-FRIED CHICKEN

SERVES 2

WORTH THE
EFFORT

2 chicken legs, cut into drumsticks,
and 2 chicken thighs, skin on, bone in

2 litres (70 fl oz/8 cups) rapeseed
(canola) oil, for deep-frying

1 quantity Spicy Shake mix (page 101)

FOR THE BUTTERMILK BRINE

500 ml (17 fl oz/2 cups) buttermilk

1 teaspoon salt

¼ teaspoon MSG (optional)

FOR THE NOODLE DREDGE

4 nests of Shin Cup instant
Ramen noodles

FOR THE WET BATTER

1 large egg

120 ml (4 fl oz/½ cup) milk

FOR THE SPICY RAMEN BROTH

4 Shin Cup Instant Ramen soup
mix sachets

boiling water as per packet
instructions

TO SERVE

No Need to Wait Kimchi (page 175)

Watermelon Rind Pickles (page 173)

**L
E
G
S**

I first saw this done by a chef I love called David Chang from Momofuku New York and *Lucky Peach* magazine. I love the way he looks at food and is incredibly creative. He also doesn't hide the fact that, although he is a serious chef and has a number of restaurants and three Michelin stars, he has a love for trashy fast food and sees the beauty in it. It was a very clever idea to blitz the instant noodles back down to a flour and coating fried chicken in it. However, I wanted to take it a step further and so have used my favourite instant noodles: spicy Shin Cup Ramen. If you need a chilli hit, then these are your baby. They were my best friend for a few years when I got home late at night after working long days in the kitchen and not eating. They are spicy and comforting at the same time and all you have to do is to boil a kettle! In this dish, I have used the spicy shake from the nuggets recipe (page 101) in the brine and to season the chicken after frying. I have also made a soup from the spicy shake so it ends up being something like an inside-out spicy ramen, if that makes any sense at all? The coating is super crispy from the blitzed dried noodles and is perfect served with some of the Pickled Watermelon Rinds (page 173) or the No Need To Wait Kimchi (page 175).

To make the buttermilk brine, whisk all the ingredients together in a shallow bowl, add the chicken legs, cover with cling film (plastic wrap) and leave in the refrigerator for 12–24 hours.

The next day, to make the noodle dredge, blitz the dry noodle nests in a food processor until it forms a powder. Transfer to a bowl and set aside.

For the wet batter, whisk the egg and milk together in a bowl until combined. Set aside.

Remove the chicken legs from the buttermilk brine and shake off excess buttermilk. Dredge the chicken in the noodle flour mix, then in the wet batter, then back into the noodle flour, working it in with your hands.

Heat the oil for deep-frying in a deep-fryer or a large, deep saucepan to 140°C (284°F), or until a cube of bread dropped in sizzles in 40 seconds. Deep-fry the chicken for 7–8 minutes until it starts to turn golden brown, then remove and set aside. Increase the temperature of the oil to 160°C (320°F), or until a cube of bread dropped in sizzles in 30 seconds. Deep-fry the chicken again for 4–5 minutes until cooked through. Remove and season the chicken liberally over all with the spicy shake. Set aside.

For the ramen broth, add the soup mix and enough water according to the packet instructions to a large saucepan. Bring to the boil, then remove from the heat and set aside.

To serve, divide the ramen broth between two Asian-style soup bowls. Place the fried chicken on a large plate and serve with kimchi and watermelon pickles on the side.

LIP SMACKIN' FLAVOUR

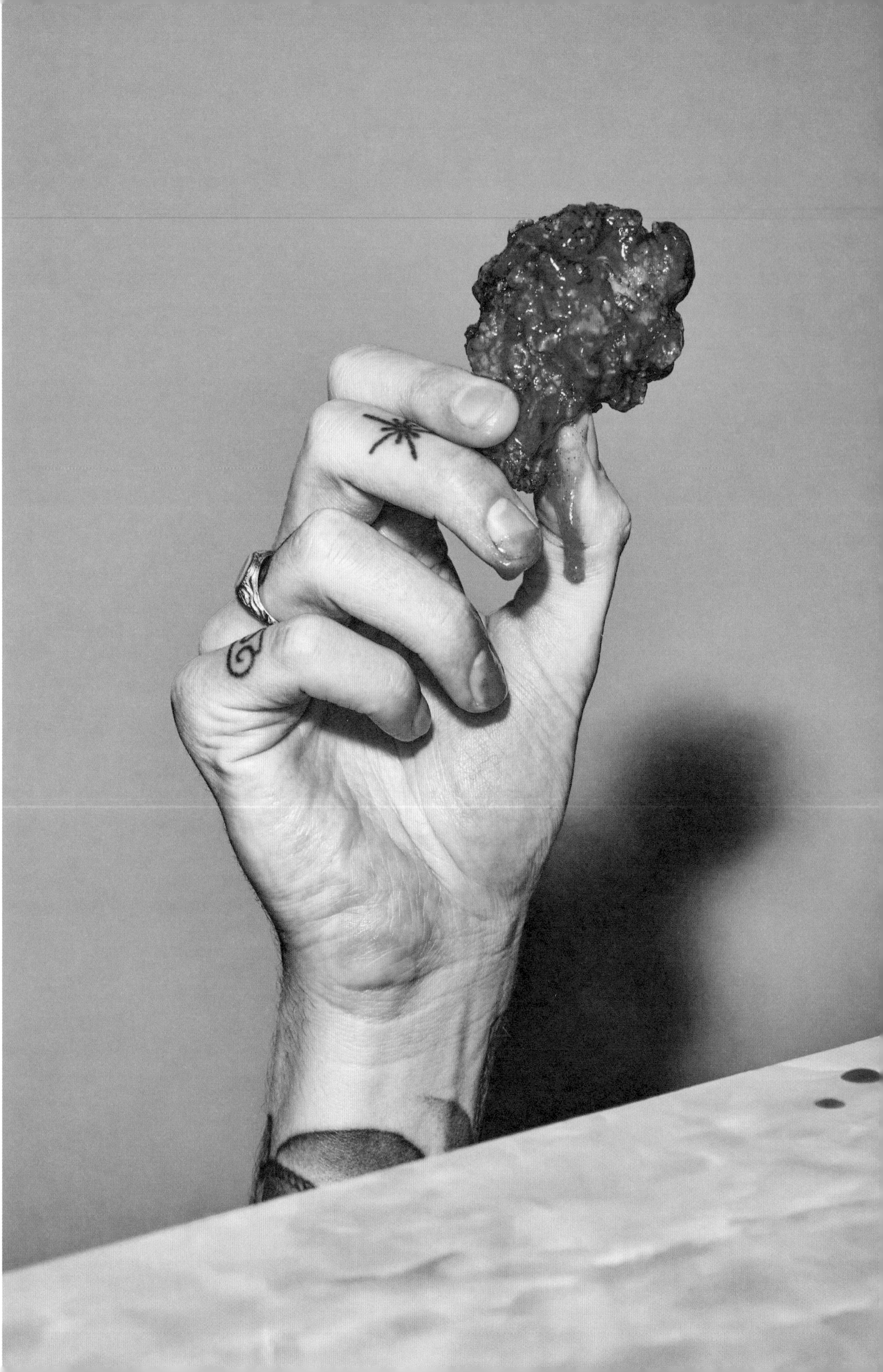

GENERAL TSO MY STYLE

SERVES 2

4 tablespoons baking powder

3 tablespoons Maldon sea salt

600 g (1 lb 5 oz) jointed chicken wings (you can ask your butcher to do this for you)

6 spring onions (scallions), thinly sliced, to garnish

FOR THE GENERAL TSO GLAZE

1 teaspoon dried red chillies, deseeded

20 g (¾ oz) garlic cloves

20 g (¾ oz) piece of fresh ginger root, peeled

60 g (2½ oz) spring onions (scallions)

160 g (5¾ oz/¾ cup) brown sugar

4 tablespoons light soy sauce

2 tablespoons dark soy sauce

2 tablespoons Sichuan toban paste (chilli bean paste)

140 ml (5 fl oz/⅔ cup) cider vinegar

1 tablespoon Chinese black vinegar (Chinkiang)

1½ tablespoons tomato ketchup

2 tablespoons Shaoxing rice wine

1 tablespoon cornflour (cornstarch) or tapioca flour

2 teaspoons sesame oil

It is said that General Tso chicken was invented by a Taiwanese chef called Peng Chang-kuei in the 1950s in New York while serving a group of US military, but there are many different stories and myths around these wings. It has been America's number-one-selling Chinese takeaway dish to this day more than 60 years later, and there's even a documentary movie about it called *The Search for General Tso,* following the search for the real story behind the legendary dish. It's a sweet, savoury and sticky dish that appeals to everybody. This recipe is my more grown-up version of this classic and is a lot more complex and has a lot more depth of flavour than the original. Once you have all the ingredients measured out then it's really simple to make in a matter of minutes. This glaze is also great with grilled (broiled) chicken thighs, fried chicken feet or just about anything really.

To make the glaze, add the chillies, garlic, ginger and spring onions to a blender or food processor and blitz to a purée.

Add the purée and the sugar, soy sauces, toban paste, both vinegars, ketchup and rice wine to a saucepan and bring to a simmer. Cook for 5 minutes. Mix 1 tablespoon of water into the cornflour in a small bowl to make a paste, then stir into the sauce to thicken. It should just be thick enough to coat the back of a spoon. Add the sesame oil.

To cook the wings, preheat the oven to 180°C (350°F/gas 4).

Mix the baking powder and salt together in a small bowl. Place the wings in a large bowl, add the baking powder mixture and, using your hands, toss the chicken until it is coated evenly all over. Place a roasting rack on top of a roasting tray (pan), then arrange the wings on the rack, side by side, leaving a small gap in between each wing to allow the air to circulate around them. Cook in the oven on the middle shelf for 30 minutes, then place the tray on the top shelf and increase the oven temperature to 250°C (475°F/ gas 9) and cook for another 10–15 minutes until the wings are crispy to the touch.

Reheat the sauce gently over a medium heat, then toss the wings in plenty of sauce in bowls and garnish with thinly sliced spring onions.

EASY PEASY

W I N G S

T R A C K

S I X

GUNPOWDER WINGS

SERVES 6–10

124

EASY
PEASY

2 kg (4 lb 8 oz) jointed chicken wings (ask your butcher to do this for you, if liked)

4 tablespoons baking powder

3 tablespoons Maldon sea salt

FOR THE GUNPOWDER SHAKE

2 tablespoons Madras curry powder (page 116)

1 teaspoon fine salt

2 teaspoons onion powder

1 tablespoon nigella seeds

1 scant tablespoon light soft brown sugar

1 teaspoon garam masala

1 teaspoon MSG (optional)

½ teaspoon chaat masala

¼ teaspoon garlic powder

FOR THE CRISPY SHIZZLE

3 tablespoons rapeseed (canola) oil

handful of curry leaves

2 tablespoons thinly sliced garlic

2 tablespoons thinly sliced shallots

1 tablespoon dried chillies, broken up by hand

Gunpowder seasoning is a southern Indian table seasoning made using various spices and dried pulses. I have no idea why it is called gunpowder, but I guess it's something to do with the heat from the dried chillies. It's very versatile and can be sprinkled on many things as a seasoning. To be honest, this recipe bears no resemblance to the authentic recipe, but I just love the name. My favourite way to use this spice mix is on chips (fries). At my fast food restaurant CHIK'N we use it on our loaded gunpowder fries and top the fries with tamarind chutney and mint chutney. They are incredible and loved by many customers. Here, I have used it to season the chicken wings and finished them off with a crispy curry leaf shizzle. They are delicious and if you are ever having friends round for a drink, then just add some roasted peanuts or cashews to the shizzle recipe and serve as a drinking snack.

Brine the chicken wings according to the instructions on page 24 (optional).

 To make the gunpowder shake, combine the ingredients in a spice grinder and pulse a few times to bring it together. Do not overblend as it will clump if it's a fine powder.

 To cook the wings, preheat the oven to 180°C (350°F/gas 4).

 Mix the baking powder and salt together in a small bowl. Place the wings in a large bowl, add the baking powder mixture and, using your hands, toss the chicken until it is coated evenly all over. Place a roasting rack on top of a roasting tray (pan), then arrange the wings on the rack, side by side, leaving a small gap in between each wing to allow the air to circulate around them. Cook in the oven on the middle shelf for 30 minutes, then place the tray on the top shelf and increase the oven temperature to 250°C (475°F/gas 9) and cook for another 10–15 minutes until the wings are crispy to the touch.

 To make the crispy shizzle, heat the oil in a small frying pan (skillet) over a medium heat, then fry the curry leaves, garlic, shallots and dried chillies one at a time, each for 1–3 minutes, until crisp.

 Season the cooked wings generously, using about 50–70 g (2–2½ oz) of the shake, then garnish with a handful of the shizzle.

**W
I
N
G
S**

**T
R
A
C
K

S
I
X**

STICKY CIDER VINEGAR AND
BLACK PEPPER WINGS

SERVES 6–10

2 kg (4 lb 8 oz) jointed chicken wings (ask your butcher to do this for you, if liked)

4 tablespoons baking powder

3 tablespoons Maldon sea salt

FOR THE STICKY BLACK PEPPER SAUCE

250 ml (8½ fl oz/1 cup) apple juice

250 ml (8½ fl oz/1 cup) apple cider vinegar

250 g (9 oz/1⅓ cups) dark brown sugar

1 tablespoon coarse ground pepper

125 g (4 oz) cold unsalted butter, cut into cubes

1 tablespoon cornflour (cornstarch)

½ tablespoon water

The origins of this recipe date back to the very beginning of my journey into the never-ending search for perfect fried chicken at DiscoBistro, the six-month pop-up restaurant I did a few years ago. When David and I first started Chick 'n' Sours we only had two types of wings on the menu – 'hot' and 'sticky', and they were on the menu for at least the first two years. These chicken wings are very simple to make and incredibly moreish. They are both sweet from the jaggery and sour from the cider vinegar. Use the best cider vinegar you can find as it makes all the difference. Even the everyday vinegar made from concentrated apple juice you find in any corner shop is best for this recipe because of the sugar content. The black pepper makes the sticky glaze beautifully fragrant. These wings are messy to eat with your hands but that's the way they are supposed to be, so make sure you have plenty of napkins to hand.

Brine the chicken wings according to the instructions on page 24 (optional).

For the sauce, place the apple juice, vinegar and sugar in a saucepan and cook over a medium heat for 10 minutes until it is reduced by half. Turn off the heat, add the black pepper and stir in the butter. Mix a little cornflour with a little water in a bowl. Heat the sauce very gently over a low heat until hot, then stir in the cornflour paste to thicken. It should just be thick enough to coat the back of a spoon. Turn off the heat and set aside.

To cook the wings, preheat the oven to 180°C (350°F/gas 4).

Mix the baking powder and salt together in a small bowl. Place the wings in a large bowl, add the baking powder mixture and, using your hands, toss the chicken until it is coated evenly all over. Place a roasting rack on top of a roasting tray (pan), then arrange the wings on the rack, side by side, leaving a small gap in between each wing to allow the air to circulate around them. Cook in the oven on the middle shelf for 30 minutes, then place the tray on the top shelf and increase the oven temperature to 250°C (475°F/gas 9) and cook for another 10–15 minutes until the wings are crispy to the touch.

Remove the wings from the oven and, while they are still hot and crispy, place them in a large bowl big enough to toss the wings around in the sauce. Reheat the sauce over a low heat, then pour the sauce over the wings. Toss around in the bowl so all the wings are evenly coated. Pile high on a large plate and dive in.

ALMOST
BREEZY

W
I
N
G
S

T
R
A
C
K

S
I
X

JOY LUCK CHICKEN WINGS

SERVES 2–4

126

WORTH THE EFFORT

W I N G S

600 g (1 lb 5 oz) jointed chicken wings (you can ask your butcher to do this for you)

1.5 litres (51 fl oz/6½ cups) rapeseed (canola) oil, for deep-frying

1 tablespoon sesame oil

1 tablespoon tapioca flour

FOR THE MARINADE

15 g (½ oz) piece of fresh ginger root, peeled

15 g (½ oz) shallots

6 garlic cloves

½ tablespoon caster (superfine) sugar

1 teaspoon salt

½ teaspoon white pepper

½ tablespoon light soy sauce

1 teaspoon dark soy sauce

1 tablespoon oyster sauce

1 tablespoon Worcestershire sauce

2 tablespoons Shaoxing rice wine

TO GARNISH

6–8 spring onions (scallions), thinly sliced

5 red chillies, thinly sliced

1 tablespoon deep-fried dried red chillies

1 tablespoon shop-bought crispy shallots

Joy Luck is one of my favourite Chinese restaurants on Gerrard Street in Chinatown, London. I have eaten at this family-run Northern Chinese restaurant for a long time and, although this recipe is not anything to do with them, I would like to pay homage for all the inspiration they have given me over the years. There are many variations for paper-bag wings, but I have simplified this method so you can make them at home. Traditionally, they are deep-fried in the bag, but make sure you watch very carefully and have either a deep-fat fryer or a very deep wok. These chicken wings are great fun to take to the table – cut the tops off the bags with a pair of scissors, add the extra garnish and there you have 'shake in the bag' wings for people to dive into. It's a little different, but one recipe your guests will be talking about for a very long time.

To make the marinade, blitz the ginger, shallots and garlic in a food processor to a paste or pound in a mortar and pestle. Mix with all the other marinade ingredients in a large shallow bowl, then add the chicken wings. Cover with cling film (plastic wrap) and marinate in the refrigerator for at least 6 hours, if not 24 hours.

Remove the chicken from the refrigerator, shake off a little of the marinade and put into a clean bowl. Add the sesame oil and tapioca flour and coat thoroughly. Divide the chicken wings among four brown paper bags and fold the tops of the bags over several times to seal in the chicken. Make sure there's not too much lingering marinade, as it will make the bags too wet.

To cook the chicken, you will need either a domestic table-top electric fryer or a deep wok. Add enough oil to the fryer or wok so the bags will be submerged while cooking and heat to 140°C (284°F), or until a cube of bread dropped in sizzles in 45 seconds. Deep-fry the chicken bags in pairs for 6 minutes, then remove and leave to rest for 10–15 minutes, then heat the oil to 180°C (350°F), or until a cube of bread dropped in sizzles in 30 seconds. Deep-fry again for 3–4 minutes until the chicken is cooked through.

Once cooked, place the bags on a plate, carefully cut open the tops of the bags with scissors and add the garnishes directly to the wings inside the bags. Give them a shake around and eat straight from the bag.

T R A C K

S I X

WINNER WINNER

TAMARIND CHILLI CARAMEL WINGS

SERVES 6–10

2 kg (4 lb 8 oz) jointed chicken wings
(ask your butcher to do this for you,
if liked)

4 tablespoons baking powder

3 tablespoons Maldon sea salt

FOR THE TAMARIND CHILLI CARAMEL

4 tablespoons fish sauce

1 bird's eye chilli

200 g (7oz/1cup) coconut palm sugar

1 tablespoon water

100 g (3½ oz) tamarind pulp

2 tablespoons lime juice

1 teaspoon cornflour (cornstarch)

TO GARNISH

small handful of coriander
(cilantro), torn

small handful of Thai basil

small handful of mint

2 tablespoons shop-bought
crispy shallots

These wings are simple to make and are probably my favourite wings on the planet. This recipe is based on the Thai chilli fish sauce caramel recipe, and once you start eating them you can't stop! It's everything a sticky glaze should be. The secret here is getting the balance right between the sweetness of the coconut palm sugar, the saltiness of the fish sauce and the sourness of the tamarind. You can add as little or as much chilli as you wish, but I like these fiery hot and so use the tiny fresh Thai bird's eye chillies, but any variety will do. The herbs add a fresh fragrance as a garnish and the crispy shallots add a nice crunch at the end. This glaze will work with just about anything fatty, from crispy pork belly or duck right through to oily mackerel – it really is a banger of a sticky glaze.

To make the caramel, combine all the ingredients, except the tamarind, lime juice and cornflour in a pot and bring to a simmer over a low medium heat for 10 minutes, or until the sugar has dissolved. Add the remaining ingredients and remove the pan from the heat. Leave to cool to room temperature to thicken slightly.

To cook the wings, preheat the oven to 180°C (350°F/gas 4).

Mix the baking powder and salt together in a small bowl. Place the wings in a large bowl, add the baking powder mixture and, using your hands, toss the chicken until it is coated evenly all over. Place a roasting rack on top of a roasting tray (pan), then arrange the wings on the rack, side by side, leaving a small gap in between each wing to allow the air to circulate around them. Cook in the oven on the middle shelf for 30 minutes, then place the tray on the top shelf and increase the oven temperature to 250°C (475°F/gas 9) and cook for another 10–15 minutes until the wings are crispy to the touch.

Remove the wings from the oven and, while they are still hot and crispy, place them in a large bowl big enough to toss the wings around in the sauce. Add the room temperature sauce, then pour over the wings and toss around. Garnish with torn coriander, basil, mint and crispy shallots. Pile high on a large plate and dive in.

**WORTH THE
EFFORT**

**W
I
N
G
S**

**T
R
A
C
K

S
I
X**

CHICKEN DINNER

ORIGINAL DISCO WINGS

SERVES 4

128

**ALMOST
BREEZY**

2 kg (4 lb 8 oz) jointed chicken wings (ask your butcher to do this for you, if liked)

4 tablespoons baking powder

3 tablespoons Maldon sea salt

FOR THE CHEF PATTY HOT SAUCE

1 kg (2 lb 4 oz) Scotch bonnet chillies, deseeded

1 kg (2 lb 4 oz) long red chillies, deseeded

50 g (2 oz) dried chipotle chillies

250 g (9 oz) chopped garlic

1 teaspoon allspice (pimento seeds)

2 star anise

2 litres (70 fl oz/8 cups) cider vinegar

1 litre (34 fl oz/4 cups) water

250 g (9 oz) butter

2 tablespoons cornflour (cornstarch), for thickening

**W
I
N
G
S**

These are the OG chicken wings from Disco Bistro, which is where it all started, although they were fried incredibly crispy. I have kept things simple in this chapter as I know it's difficult for people to deep-fry at home, but if you have the urge then just adopt the cooking method from the Korean Hot Wings (page 129), as it's really worth it. For this recipe, you may need to wear swimming goggles and disposable gloves due to prepping a lot of Scotch bonnets, which are a fiery flavoursome chilli common in Jamaican cooking. I'm talking from experience here. For me, these are the ultimate hot wings, as each variety of chilli adds its own unique flavour and heat. These wings are spicy but they are not 'blow your head off'. They are a perfectly balanced level of heat with a buttery, sour vinegary goodness to finish. It's like a grown-up buffalo sauce, but better.

To cook the wings, preheat the oven to 180°C (350°F/gas 4).

Mix the baking powder and salt together in a small bowl. Place the wings in a large bowl, add the baking powder mixture and, using your hands, toss the chicken until it is coated evenly all over. Place a roasting rack on top of a roasting tray (pan), then arrange the wings on the rack, side by side, leaving a small gap in between each wing to allow the air to circulate around them. Cook in the oven on the middle shelf for 30 minutes, then place the tray on the top shelf and increase the oven temperature to 250°C (475°F/gas 9) and cook for another 10–15 minutes until the wings are crispy to the touch.

Meanwhile, to make the sauce, place all the ingredients, except the butter and cornflour, in a large saucepan and simmer over a low heat for 20–30 minutes. Remove the star anise, transfer to a blender and blitz until smooth. Return to the pan, whisk in the butter, then make a paste with the cornflour and a splash of water. Use to thicken the sauce, stirring until it coats the back of a spoon.

Toss the wings in the sauce, then serve.

KOREAN HOT WINGS

SERVES 2–4

600 g (1 lb 5 oz) jointed chicken wings (you can ask your butcher to do this for you)

about 2 litres (70 fl oz/8 cups) vegetable oil, for deep-frying

5 spring onions (scallions), thinly sliced, to garnish

FOR THE FLOUR COATING

60 g (2 oz/½ cup) plain (all-purpose) flour

75 g (2½ oz/scant ½ cup) rice flour, or dried rice, ground to a fine powder in a spice mill

30 g (1 oz/¼ cup) cornflour (cornstarch)

FOR THE WET BATTER

1 large egg

120 ml (4 fl oz/½ cup) milk

FOR THE KOREAN HOT SAUCE

1.5 kg (3 lb 5 oz/6¾ cups) caster (superfine) sugar

1.55 litres (51 fl oz/6 cups) rice wine vinegar

750 g (1 lb 2 oz/2¼ cups) Sriracha (hot chilli sauce)

750 g (1 lb 10 oz/2½ cups) gochujang (Korean red chilli paste)

750 g (1 lb 10 oz/scant 3¼ cups) tomato ketchup

400 ml (13 fl oz/generous 1½ cups) sesame oil

300 g (10½ oz) ssamjang (Korean spicy paste)

200 g (7 oz) butter

400 g (14 oz) rendered chicken fat (page 23)

It was my good friend and chef Gizzi Erskine that first introduced me to the wonders of Korean food a few years ago. Now and again as a chef you find new ingredients and new cultures and it refreshes and unlocks your imagination, which is exactly what happened. Gizzi's Korean fried chicken is notorious and is truly the best I have ever eaten. She is also one of the loveliest and hardest-working chefs I know, and her creativity is endless. She has inspired me time and time again and continues to do so to this day. The Koreans use a double-fry method, which I use in my restaurants as it gives a super-crispy finish to the chicken. The sauce is funky and spicy from the fermented bean paste and I have enriched it with rendered chicken fat or Schmaltz (page 23), which really takes it to another level. When done right, I think Korean fried chicken is the best on the planet, and I hope I have paid homage to Gizzi's incredible Korean fried chicken here. Make these, pile them high on serving platters and eat with friends. These are made to be eaten with your hands, so lock the cutlery away and get the napkins out.

Brine the chicken wings according to the instructions on page 24 (optional).

To make the hot sauce, heat the sugar and vinegar together in a saucepan over a medium heat until the sugar has completely dissolved. Add all the remaining ingredients, except the butter and chicken fat, and bring to a simmer being careful not to burn the bottom of the pan. Once simmering, add the butter and chicken fat and whisk until combined. Set aside.

For the flour coating, blend all the ingredients together in a medium bowl with a whisk. Set aside.

For the wet batter, whisk the egg and milk together in a bowl until combined. Set aside.

Drain the chicken from the brine and rinse under cold running water, then pat dry with paper towels. In batches, add the chicken to the flour mixture, shaking all the excess flour off completely, then dip into the wet batter and then toss in the flour mixture again, really working the flour in with your hands until the chicken is coated and there is some texture on the wings. This will give you the crispy cornflake effect.

Heat the oil for deep-frying in a deep-fryer or a large, deep saucepan to 140°C (284°F), or until a cube of bread dropped in sizzles in 40 seconds. Deep-fry the chicken in batches for 7–8 minutes. These will not be cooked through. Remove from the fryer and set aside on a baking sheet. For the best results, leave the chicken to cool overnight in the refrigerator before the final fry.

Heat the oil again in a deep-fryer or a large, deep saucepan to 180°C (350°F), or until a cube of bread dropped in sizzles in 30 seconds. Deep-fry the wings in batches for another 3–4 minutes until golden brown and crispy. Drain, then transfer to a bowl and smother with the sauce – if you are eating the next day, gently reheat the sauce until warm. Garnish with thinly sliced spring onions and serve piping hot.

WORTH THE EFFORT

W I N G S

T R A C K S I X

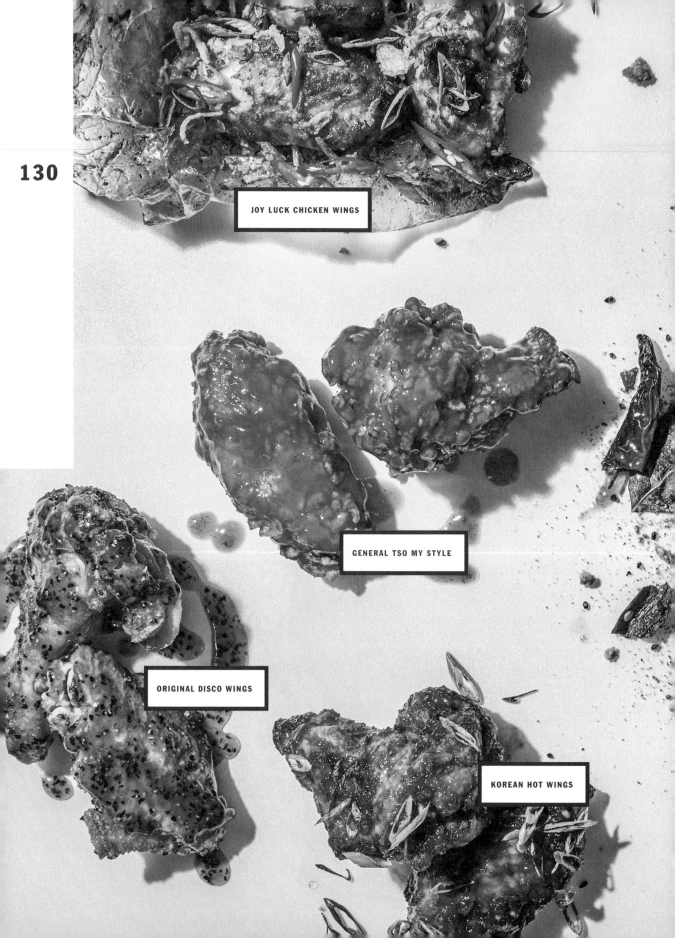

JOY LUCK CHICKEN WINGS

GENERAL TSO MY STYLE

ORIGINAL DISCO WINGS

KOREAN HOT WINGS

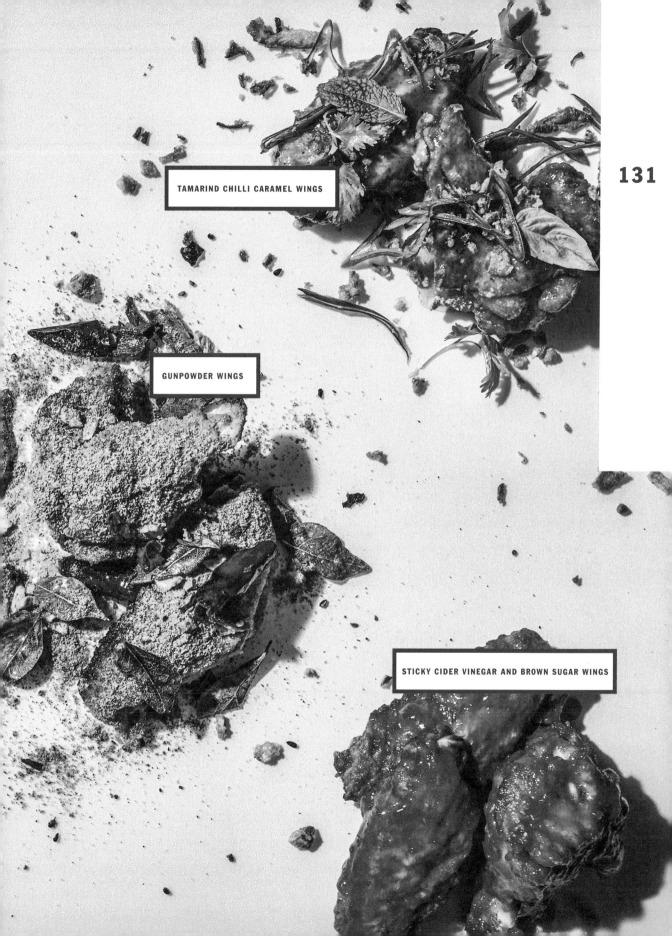

TAMARIND CHILLI CARAMEL WINGS

GUNPOWDER WINGS

STICKY CIDER VINEGAR AND BROWN SUGAR WINGS

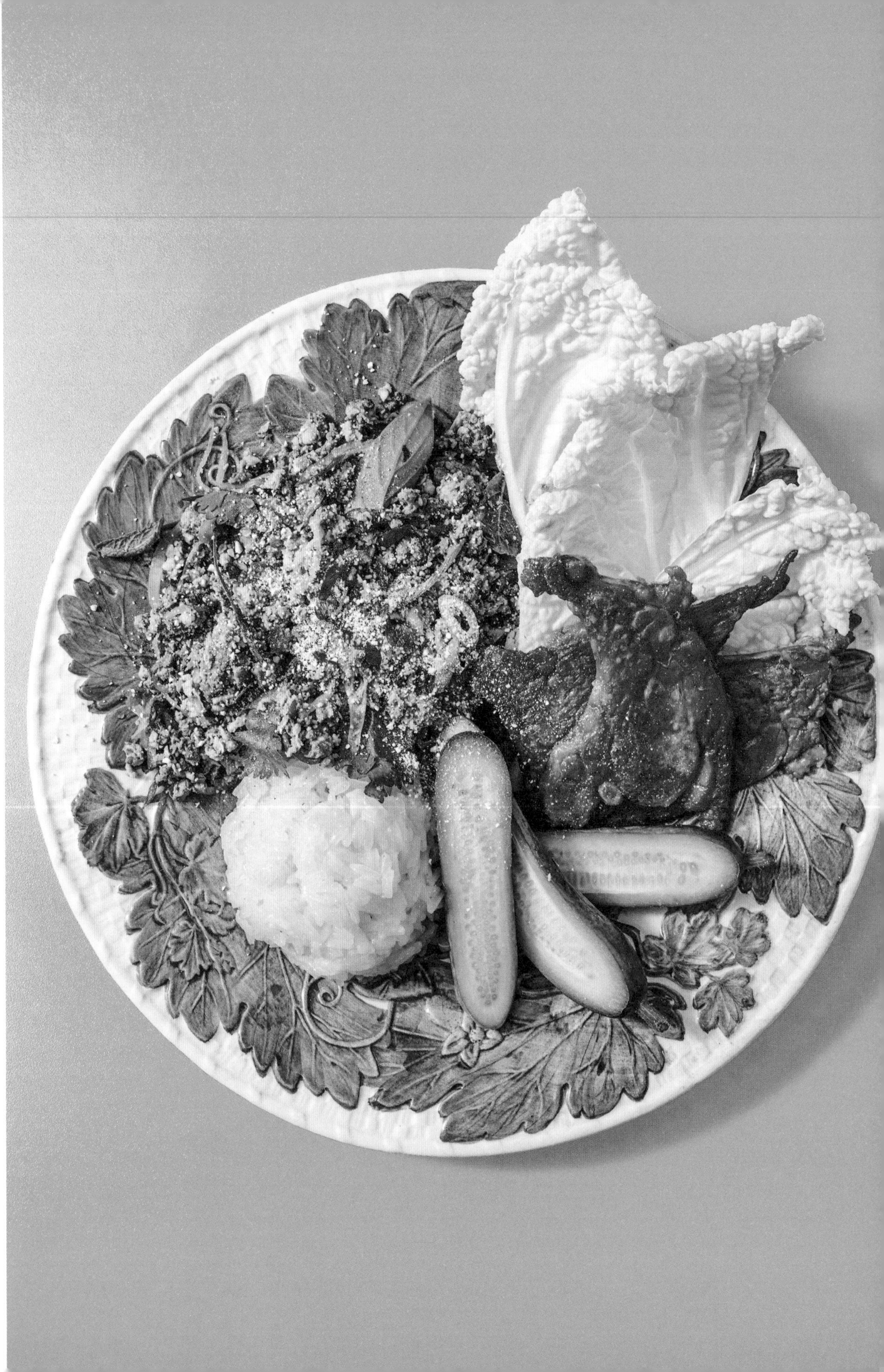

CHICKEN OFFAL THAI LARB

SERVES 2

150 g (5 oz/¾ cup) glutinous rice

4–5 thin slices of galangal

2 kaffir lime leaves, roughly torn

1 lemongrass stalk, tough outer layer removed and thinly sliced

200 g (7 oz) chicken offal (variety meat) (liver and heart), very finely chopped

100 g (3½ oz/½ cup) minced (ground) chicken thigh

60 ml (2 fl oz/¼ cup) chicken stock (broth)

1 teaspoon ground toasted dried small red chilli, plus extra whole to serve

½ tablespoon crushed coconut palm sugar or use caster (superfine) or brown sugar

2 tablespoons fish sauce

60 ml (2 fl oz/¼ cup) lime juice, or to taste

2 tablespoons thinly sliced Thai red shallots or just small round shallots

2 tablespoons sliced spring onions (scallions)

small handful of coriander (cilantro) leaves and stalks, chopped, plus extra to serve

small handful of mint, torn, plus extra to serve

small handful of Thai basil, torn, plus extra to serve

TO SERVE

3 Chinese (Napa) cabbage wedges, lettuce or salad leaves

½ small cucumber, sliced lengthways

Chicken Skin Crackers (page 157)

sticky rice

WORTH THE EFFORT

Larb is of Laotian origin, but eaten in various variations all over northern Thailand. There's even a fresh blood larb that I have seen, but wasn't brave enough to try it. It is a type of salad that's spicy, sour, sweet and fiery hot all at the same time. The heat levels in this dish aren't for the faint-hearted and some of the ones I have eaten in Thailand have almost made me hallucinate as they were so spicy. Here, I have used minced (ground) thigh meat and various chicken offal (variety meats) to give the larb a rich flavour. It's herbaceous and fragrant and, although spicy, it's refreshing to eat on a hot day. The toasted ground rice adds an interesting nutty texture, but take your time when toasting the rice before you grind it, as it can be gritty in the mouth if not toasted correctly. This dish can be served with sticky rice or in lettuce cups where you can build your own larb straight into the crisp lettuce leaf. This contrast of cold crunchy lettuce and spicy warm larb works really well.

Roast the glutinous rice in a dry frying pan (skillet) over a low-medium heat, tossing or stirring, for 4–5 minutes until it is evenly pale gold in colour. Add the galangal, lime leaves and lemongrass and cook, keeping it moving, for another 2–3 minutes until evenly golden brown and fragrant. The inside of the rice should still be white. Leave to cool completely, then grind in a spice grinder or use a mortar and pestle. Set aside.

Mix the chicken offal and minced chicken together in a large bowl.

Bring the stock to a gentle boil in a non-stick frying pan (skillet) over a medium heat. Add the meat, then, using a large metal spoon, work quickly to toss the chicken so it cooks evenly, about 3–4 minutes. Once the chicken is cooked through and no longer pink, remove the pan from the heat. Don't let it overcook.

Drain off most of the liquid, keeping a little so it just covers the chicken like a thin blanket – this stops the chicken drying out and adds the intense chicken flavour to the finished dish.

Transfer the chicken to a bowl and, while still warm, add 1 tablespoon of the ground glutinous rice, then the toasted chilli. Stir and toss to distribute evenly through the chicken mixture, then add the sugar, fish sauce and lime juice to taste.

To finish, add the shallots, spring onions and all the soft herbs and toss gently until evenly incorporated. Top with extra chillies and herbs and serve with wedges of Chinese cabbage or lettuce, or salad leaves, sliced cucumber, chicken skin crackling and sticky rice.

CHICKEN HEART ALMOND SATAY

SERVES 6–8

136

WORTH THE EFFORT

O
F
F
A
L

1 kg (2 lb 4 oz) whole chicken hearts, cleaned

FOR THE MARINADE

2 tablespoons coriander seeds

6 garlic cloves, finely chopped

thumb-sized piece of fresh ginger root, peeled and finely chopped

6 lemongrass stalks, finely chopped

4 kaffir lime leaves, torn

2 tablespoons vegetable oil

2 tablespoons kecap manis (Indonesian sweet soy sauce)

2 teaspoons soy sauce

FOR THE SPICE PASTE

1 teaspoon dried red chilli

¾ tablespoon shrimp paste

1 large onion, roughly chopped

2 cm (1 in) piece of fresh galangal, peeled and roughly chopped

3 garlic cloves, roughly chopped

5 stalks lemongrass, tough outer layer removed and roughly chopped

1 tablespoon cashew nuts

¼ teaspoon ground coriander

¼ teaspoon ground cumin

¼ teaspoon ground turmeric

pinch of sweet paprika (not smoked)

½ teaspoon salt

FOR THE ALMOND SATAY DIP

3 tablespoons vegetable oil

100 g (3½ oz/⅔ cup) almonds, toasted

80 ml (2½ fl oz/⅓ cup) water

2 teaspoons kecap manis

¼ teaspoon salt

2 teaspoons coconut palm sugar

100 g (3½ oz/scant ½ cup) good-quality almond butter

100 ml (3½ fl oz/scant ½ cup) coconut milk

15 g (½ oz) tamarind paste

2 teaspoons lime juice

There is a little prep to be done to get chicken hearts just right, but once finished they are a real treat when grilled (broiled) to medium rare. They are very lean and are similar to the dark meat of chicken, but they are quite chewy because of their zero fat content. Satay sauce is everyone's favourite, right? Traditionally made with peanuts, I have adapted this recipe and used toasted almonds and almond butter for a twist. They give the finished sauce a delicate creamy nutty flavour and provide a very nice alternative to the classic peanuts. There's a bit of work in this recipe but it's worth taking some time to do this properly as the results are incredible. You can always freeze some leftover paste once you have made it, so your next batch of satay will be even easier. This satay recipe is also good used with chicken thighs or breasts. Just follow the recipe and swap out for either. It's great as a snack or starter (appetiser) with a group of friends served on large serving plates so they can just sit around and dip away.

To make the marinade, toast the coriander seeds in a dry frying pan (skillet) over a medium heat for a few minutes. Transfer to a mortar and pestle or food processor with the remaining ingredients and pound or blitz. It doesn't need to be smooth.

Place the chicken hearts in a bowl and add the marinade. Cover with cling film (plastic wrap) and chill in the refrigerator for at least 6 hours, or overnight.

When ready to cook, soak 12 bamboo skewers in a bowl of warm water for 30 minutes to prevent them burning during cooking.

To make the spice paste, soak the dried chillies in a bowl of cold water for 1 hour, then drain and place in a blender with the remaining ingredients and blend to a paste. Set aside.

To make the dip, heat the oil in a wok or deep frying pan (skillet) over a medium heat and fry the spice paste for about 15 minutes, or until caramelised and fragrant. Blitz the toasted almonds in a food processor, keeping them quite chunky and crunchy. Add the water, kecap manis, salt and palm sugar to the paste and whisk until the sugar has dissolved. Add the almonds, almond butter and coconut milk and bring to a simmer. Add the tamarind paste and continue to cook for 2 minutes. Remove from the heat and stir in the lime juice. Set aside in a serving bowl.

To cook the skewers, thread a few marinated chicken hearts onto each soaked skewer. Heat a frying pan over a medium heat and cook the skewers for about 2 minutes on each side or however you like them, in batches. It is best to serve a little pink. Serve the skewers and dip with the room temperature sauce.

T
R
A
C
K

S
E
V
E
N

SPICY CHICKEN LIVERS
WITH BLACK VINEGAR

SERVES 4

138

EASY PEASY

4 tablespoons rapeseed (canola) oil, plus extra if needed

300 g (10½ oz) chicken livers

2 spring onions (scallions), cut into 1 cm (½ in) pieces

2.5 cm (1 in) piece of fresh ginger root, peeled and thinly sliced

1 onion, thinly sliced

10 dried red chillies

1 tablespoon whole Sichuan peppercorns

2 tablespoons chilli bean paste (Toban djan)

2 tablespoons Chinese black vinegar (Chinkiang)

These chicken livers are super quick and easy to make and provide a comforting late-night supper or a speedy lunch any time. They are spicy from the chilli bean paste and dried chillies, numbing from the Sichuan pepper and the black vinegar cuts through the richness of the livers. Chinese black vinegar is a complex mild vinegar made from glutinous rice with quite a unique flavour, similar in some ways to balsamic. It is commonly used in Chinese stir-fries, braises and sauces. Serve the chicken livers with rice or noodles or simply on some grilled (broiled) sourdough and you won't go far wrong.

Heat the oil in a wok over a medium high heat until it is smoking, then add the livers and stir-fry for about 60–90 seconds. Remove the livers from the wok and set aside.

Return the wok to the heat and stir-fry the spring onions and ginger for 30 seconds. Add the onion and continue to stir-fry for 7–8 minutes until the onion is soft and slightly caramelised. Remove from the wok and set aside. Add a little more oil and stir-fry the dried chillies and peppercorns for about 20 seconds. Add the chilli bean paste, black vinegar and all the reserved ingredients back to the wok and stir-fry over a very high heat for 1–2 minutes.

Serve in a large serving bowl.

POPCORN CHICKEN GIZZARDS
WITH SEAWEED SHAKE

SERVES 4

400 g (14 oz) chicken gizzards, cleaned

about 2 litres (70 fl oz/8 cups) vegetable oil, for deep-frying

FOR THE BRINE

90 g (3¼ oz/⅔ cup) salt

2 litres (70 fl oz/8 cups) water

FOR THE WET BATTER

1 large egg

120 ml (4 fl oz/½ cup) milk

FOR THE FLOUR COATING

60 g (2 oz/½ cup) plain (all-purpose) flour

75 g (2¼ oz/scant ½ cup) rice flour, or dried rice, ground to a fine powder in a spice mill

30 g (1 oz/¼ cup) cornflour (cornstarch)

FOR THE SEAWEED SALT

120 g (4 oz/¾ cup) sesame seeds

120 g (4 oz) nori seaweed sheets, toasted

2 tablespoons Maldon sea salt

WORTH THE EFFORT

Chicken gizzards are cut from the digestive tract of a chicken and their function is to grind up the foods the chicken eats. They need to be cleaned and prepped thoroughly to get rid of any leftover grit. You can find them already prepared in most butchers, so go for this option if you can. Chicken gizzards are very small with a distinctive flavour that resembles the dark meat of the chicken, but with a chewy texture. You can find them sold as street food all over the world, from Mexico to Africa, where they are served in lots of different ways. In this recipe I have turned them into a fun popcorn chicken dish and who doesn't love popcorn chicken? The seaweed salt gives it a great sea-salty flavour and there is a nutty taste from the sesame. You can pile these high in bowls for everyone to snack on and they are also good with just about any of the dips in this book (pages 178–185).

To make the brine, mix the salt and water together in a large bowl until the salt has dissolved. Add the chicken gizzards, cover with cling film (plastic wrap) and brine for at least 1–2 hours.

To make the wet batter, whisk the egg and milk together in a large bowl until combined. Set aside.

For the flour coating, mix all the ingredients together in a bowl and set aside.

To make the seaweed salt, toast the sesame seeds in a dry non-stick frying pan (skillet) over a medium heat for 2–3 minutes, then transfer to a food processor with the remaining ingredients and blitz until smooth. Set aside.

To cook the chicken gizzards, heat the oil for frying in a large pan or deep wok to 160°C (325°F), or until a cube of bread dropped in sizzles in 40 seconds.

Remove the gizzards from the brine. Using your hands, lightly coat the gizzards in the flour mix, then dip into the wet batter then into the flour again, working it in with your hands to create texture. Shake off excess flour and carefully lower into the hot oil in batches. Fry for 3–4 minutes, or until crispy and golden brown. Remove with a slotted spoon and drain on paper towels. Season generously with the seaweed salt before serving.

OFFAL

TRACK SEVEN

CRISPY FEET WITH CHILLI VINEGAR SAUCE

SERVES 6–8

140

WORTH THE EFFORT

500 g (1 lb 2 oz) chicken feet

1 teaspoon Maldon sea salt

2 tablespoons dark soy sauce

1 tablespoon caster (superfine) sugar

3 garlic cloves, very finely chopped

1 cinnamon stick

1.5 litres (51 fl oz/6 cups) rapeseed (canola) oil, for deep-frying

FOR THE BATTER

1 large egg

120 g (4 oz/1 cup) plain (all-purpose) flour

120 g (4 oz/1 cup) cornflour (cornstarch)

200 ml (7 fl oz/scant 1 cup) very cold fizzy water

½ teaspoon salt

FOR THE CHILLI VINEGAR SAUCE

360 ml (12 fl oz/scant 1½ cups) rice vinegar

200 g (7 oz/scant 1 cup) gochujang (Korean red chilli paste)

80 g (3 oz/⅓ cup) tomato ketchup

Chicken feet are quite scary to look at but don't let that put you off in any way. Once prepared correctly, they are as tasty a snack as any other part of a chicken. When I was developing this recipe, I was thinking about buffalo chicken wings and that's what this recipe reminds me of. Once the chicken feet are prepared and cooked it's a super easy recipe to make. The sauce only has three ingredients but the depth of flavour is incredible with just about the right amount of heat from the fragrant gochujang paste, acidity from the rice vinegar and sweetness from the ketchup. In fact, if you added a few knobs of butter to this sauce at the end and served it with fried chicken wings it would stand up to any buffalo sauce on the planet, so why not give that a go as well if chicken feet just aren't your thing.

Place the chicken feet in a deep pot and add enough water to cover. Add all the remaining ingredients, except the oil, and simmer over a low heat for 2 hours. Remove the feet from the cooking liquid and, using a pair of pliers, pull the claws out and discard. Chill on a plate in the refrigerator for 2 hours.

To make the batter, whisk all the ingredients together in a large bowl. It doesn't need to be smooth, texture is better.

To make the sauce, blend all the ingredients in a food processor to emulsify. Set aside.

To cook the chicken feet, heat the oil for frying in a large, deep saucepan or wok to 160°C (325°F), or until a cube of bread dropped in sizzles in 40 seconds. Dip the feet into the batter and deep-fry for 5 minutes, or until golden and crispy.

In a separate pan, gently heat the sauce but don't let it boil, then pour into a heatproof bowl. When the feet are fried, toss in the bowl until they are coated in plenty of sauce. Serve in a pile on a large plate.

O
F
F
A
L

HAPPY FEET

T
R
A
C
K

S
E
V
E
N

∞ FLE NIC BO

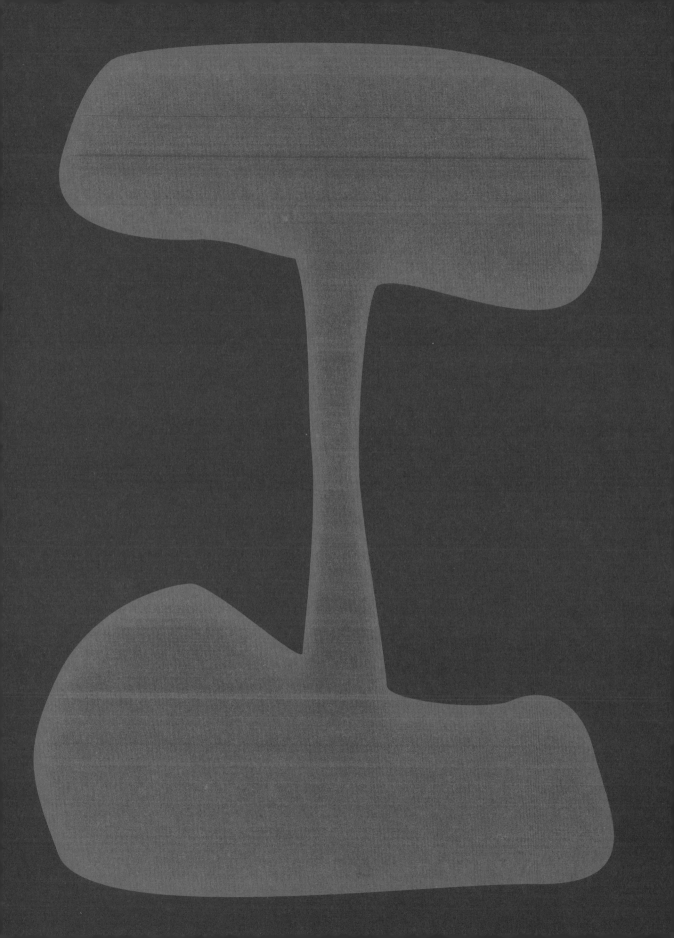

THAI BONE BROTH

SERVES 6

2 tablespoons coconut oil

1 onion, finely diced

2 tablespoons finely chopped fresh ginger root

4 garlic cloves, chopped

30 g (1 oz) galangal root, thinly sliced

2 litres (70 fl oz/8 cups) chicken stock (broth) (page 146)

1 teaspoon salt

6 kaffir lime leaves

3 lemongrass sticks, left whole, then flattened and bruised with a knife

120 g (4 oz) mushrooms, sliced (optional)

4 red bird's eye chillies, split in half lengthways but left whole

300 g (10½ oz) vermicelli rice noodles

600 g (1 lb 5 oz) cooked and shredded chicken meat

2 pak choi (bok choi), cut into quarters

2–3 teaspoons fish sauce

lime juice, to taste

4 spring onions (scallions), thinly sliced

FOR THE SHIZZLE

handful of coriander (cilantro), torn

6 handfuls of bean sprouts

3 fresh red chilies, thinly sliced

1 lime, cut into wedges

This broth is super-tasty, filling and nourishing. It's very fragrant from the galangal, lime leaves and fish sauce. The base is an already prepared chicken stock (broth) from the recipe in the book (page 146), but if you can find a decent shop-bought fresh stock then that will do the trick as well. This broth has a decent amount of heat in it from the bird's eye chillies, but you can adjust the heat levels to suit your own taste. The rice noodles add a nice texture to slurp and you can use just about any leftover cooked chicken you have in the refrigerator to add to this delicious Thai broth.

Heat the oil in a large saucepan over a medium low heat. Add the onion and cook for 2–3 minutes until soft and golden. Add the ginger, garlic and galangal and cook for 1–2 minutes. Add the chicken stock, salt, lime leaves, lemongrass, mushrooms, if using, and the chillies and simmer for about 20 minutes, or until fragrant. Add the noodles and cook for a further 7–8 minutes until cooked through. Add the shredded chicken and pak choi and cook for 3 minutes. Season with fish sauce and the lime juice at the last minute, then add the spring onions.

Divide between six Asian-style soup bowls, adding coriander, a handful of bean sprouts, a few slices of red chilli and a lime wedge to each bowl.

ALMOST BREEZY

BONES

TRACK EIGHT

TWO KINDS OF CHICKEN STOCK

EACH MAKES ABOUT 1 LITRE (34 FL OZ/4 CUPS)

EASY PEASY

FOR THE BASIC WHITE CHICKEN STOCK

1 chicken carcass

1 onion, roughly chopped

1 carrot, roughly chopped

1 celery stalk, roughly chopped

1 leek, cut into 3 sections

1 sprig of thyme

3 bay leaves

FOR THE BASIC BROWN CHICKEN STOCK

2 kg (4 lb 8 oz) chicken wings

2 tablespoons rapeseed (canola) oil, plus extra for frying

2 onions, quartered

3 carrots, thickly sliced

100 g (3½ oz) button mushrooms, quartered

2 garlic cloves, bashed and peeled

**B
O
N
E
S**

These are the two basic stock (broth) recipes that are always to hand in my refrigerator. The white stock has a lighter, cleaner flavour that is perfect for more delicately flavoured dishes, risottos, or even seafood-based recipes, whereas the brown stock, because of the roasting of the bones, produces a much richer, umami-packed stock that you can use as the base of any noodle dish in this book.

To make the white chicken stock, put all the ingredients into a large pot and cover with cold water. Bring to a simmer, skimming off any impurities with a spoon and discarding. Do not boil as you will emulsify the fat and create a cloudy stock. Continue to simmer for 3–6 hours. When finished, pass through a very fine sieve (fine mesh strainer), discarding the solids, and leave to cool. Chill in the refrigerator overnight. The next day, remove the solidified fat from the top of the stock.

For the brown chicken stock, preheat the oven to 200°C (400°F/gas 6). Add the chicken wings to a deep roasting tray (pan) with the oil and roast for 1 hour, or until golden and crispy. Remove the tray from the oven and pour away the fat, then transfer the wings to a plate. Place the roasting tray on the stove and heat, then add 200 ml (7 fl oz/¾ cup) water and scrape with a wooden spoon to loosen all the bits stuck on the bottom of the pan. Set aside.

Heat a little oil in a large saucepan over a medium heat and cook the carrots, onions and mushrooms for 10 minutes until they start to caramelise and turn a dark brown colour. Add the wings and enough water to cover, then bring to a simmer. Cook for at least 3 hours, but 6 hours is better. When finished, pass through a sieve (fine mesh strainer), discarding the solids, and leave to cool. Chill in the refrigerator overnight. The next day, remove the solidified fat from the top of the stock.

Both stocks will keep in an airtight container in the fridge for 1 week.

**T
R
A
C
K

E
I
G
H
T**

FROM THE BOWL

CHICKEN BROTH WITH SHIITAKE AND SEAWEED

SERVES 4

20 g (¾ oz) dried wakame seaweed, rehydrated in cold water for 10 minutes

2 teaspoons Maldon sea salt

2 teaspoons sesame oil

a large pinch of dried baby shrimp (optional)

ground white peppercorns

2 eggs

FOR THE SHIITAKE, CHICKEN AND GINGER BROTH

85 g (3 oz) dried shiitake mushrooms, rinsed

8 chicken feet (optional)

2 chicken carcasses

thumb-sized piece of fresh ginger root, peeled and thinly sliced

4 litres (136 fl oz/16 cups) filtered water or bottled mineral water

This is a real soul cleanser of a broth that would go down a treat at any zen monk's dinner party. The flavours are clean and the seaweed and baby shrimp give it a back note of the ocean. The dried shiitake mushrooms really add depth of flavour to the broth and complement the ginger perfectly. I have also used chicken feet to give the broth a more gelatinous mouthfeel, but if you are not keen on them then just leave them out. Like all these broth recipes, you can make a batch and freeze into portions for using later. I use an electric pressure cooker to cook mine so if you have one give it a try on the slow cook preset for around three hours for a more intense-flavoured broth.

To make the broth, soak the shiitake mushrooms in enough hot water to rehydrate for 30 minutes, or until soft, then drain, setting the soaking liquid aside.

Place the feet and chicken carcasses in a large pot of cold water and bring to the boil. Remove the feet and carcasses and throw away the water. Add the ginger to the large pot with the mushroom soaking liquid, the chicken carcasses and feet. Add the filtered water to the pot and bring to a simmer. Simmer for 3–6 hours. The longer the broth is simmered the better. Use a sieve (fine mesh strainer) to strain the broth, discarding the carcasses, feet and ginger.

Pour 2 litres (70 fl oz/8 cups) of the broth into a large saucepan and add the seaweed, salt, sesame oil, dried shrimp, if using, and peppercorns. Bring to a simmer and simmer for about 5 minutes.

Whisk the eggs in a bowl. Divide the broth between four warmed serving bowls and stir in the egg at the last minute.

WORTH THE EFFORT

B O N E S

T R A C K   E I G H T

TO THE SOUL

CHINESE CHICKEN AND INSTANT NOODLE SOUP

SERVES 4

148

**WORTH THE
EFFORT**

4 litres (136 fl oz/16 cups) filtered or mineral water

1 whole chicken, jointed (page 12)

3 white onions, cut into quarters

3 garlic cloves, bashed with skin on

1 carrot, halved

3 spring onions (scallions), finely sliced

1 tablespoon Maldon sea salt

1 tablespoon black peppercorns

1 star anise

2 tablespoons light soy sauce

TO GARNISH

2 eggs

1 packet instant noodles

2 spring onions (scallions), sliced

½ teaspoon toasted sesame oil

TO SERVE

Sriracha sauce or favourite chilli oil

greens of your choice (optional)

This is one-pot broth that you can just put on a very low simmer and forget about for a few hours. It's very simple to make but the finished broth is very light, cleansing and full of flavour. The instant noodles add a nice chewy twist and, along with the soft-boiled eggs, make a delicious filling lunch or late supper. The Sriracha is optional, so if you don't like it too spicy, just leave it out or even use your favourite brand of chilli oil.

Pour the filtered water into a large pot, then add the chicken pieces and the remaining ingredients. Bring to the boil and, using a spoon, spoon off any scum that rises to the top. Reduce the heat and simmer for 3–6 hours. The longer the broth is simmered the better. The liquid should have reduced considerably. Once cooked, strain the broth through a sieve (fine mesh strainer), discarding all the solids and set aside from the broth. Once the chicken is cool enough to handle, using your hands, remove all the meat you can and set aside.

In a separate pan, soft-boil the eggs for 6 minutes, then remove and leave until cool enough to handle, then peel, halve and set aside. Cook the instant noodles according to the packet instructions and divide between four Asian-style soup bowls. Add the hot broth to the bowls and place the halved eggs, the sliced spring onions and a touch of toasted sesame oil to the top of each. Serve with Sriracha or your favourite chilli oil with greens of your choice, if you like, on the side.

**B
O
N
E
S**

**T
R
A
C
K

E
I
G
H
T**

DAVID'S MUM'S JEWISH CHICKEN SOUP

SERVES 6–8

150

WORTH THE EFFORT

BONES

1 boiler chicken (spent hen)

1 chicken carcass

1 bunch of celery

2 parsnips

4 leeks

3 large onions

5 large carrots

2 garlic cloves

1 bunch of parsley

2 heaped tablespoons Jewish chicken soup seasoning mix

250 g (10½ oz) vermicelli or broken pasta (optional)

squeeze of lemon juice, to serve

FOR THE MATZO BALLS

275 g (10 oz/2½ cups) medium matzo meal

6 eggs

100 g (3½ oz) chicken fat from the broth (see above)

20 ml (1½ tablespoons) chicken soup

1 large tablespoon Jewish chicken soup seasoning

salt, to taste

David is my business partner and my brother in both our fried chicken restaurant brands Chick 'n' Sours and CHIK'N. I have had the pleasure of being invited to Jewish New Year dinner at his parent's house, and his mum's food is incredible. She makes the best baked cheesecake I have ever had. In fact, everything I have eaten has been incredibly delicious. David's mum is Jewish and was born in Egypt, so her style of cooking comes with a more North African influence. This is her chicken soup recipe, and it's also the best I have ever tasted, so I asked her if I could include it in my book. I was delighted when she said yes and now I want to share this delicious soup with you. You really should try to make this soup with spent hens, which you will find in any halal butcher, as they are more gamey and have much more depth of flavour for soups, while the matzo balls are made using schmaltz or rendered chicken fat (page 23). You don't need to wait for Jewish New Year to make this and it's guaranteed to make you feel better when you are feeling ill.

Bring the chicken and carcass to the boil in a large saucepan of water and continue to boil, skimming off all the scum that floats to the top until all the scum has gone and the liquid is clear. Add all the vegetables and the Jewish seasoning, then reduce the heat and simmer for 3 hours. Strain through a fine sieve (fine mesh strainer) into a bowl and leave to cool before placing in the refrigerator. Once the fat has solidified, remove and use to make the matzo balls.

To make the matzo balls, beat the eggs together in a large bowl, then add all the remaining ingredients. Place in the refrigerator to firm up. Once firm, using wet hands, shape the mixture into 16 balls. Bring a large pan of salted water to the boil, add the matzo balls and cook for 5–6 minutes. Drain and set aside.

To serve, pour the soup into a large pan and bring to the boil. Add the matzo balls and cook for 5–10 minutes. You can also add vermicelli or broken pasta until cooked. Add a squeeze of lemon juice and serve.

BUBBLE
BUBBLE
BUBBLE

CHICKEN SKIN PAD THAI

SERVES 2

1 teaspoon dried shrimp (optional)

120 g (4 oz) cooked fat rice noodles

2 tablespoons Schmaltz (page 23) or rapeseed (canola) oil

200 g (7 oz/1 cup) minced (ground) or very finely chopped chicken thigh or breast

1 egg

50 g (2 oz) smoked tofu

handful of bean sprouts, plus extra to serve

100 g (3½ oz) Chicken Scratchings, crushed (page 21)

2 tablespoons chopped unsalted peanuts

FOR THE SAUCE

150 ml (5 fl oz/scant ⅔ cup) tamarind water (page 62)

90 g (3¼ oz/½ cup) solid coconut palm sugar, shaved

40 ml (1¼ fl oz/2⅔ tablespoons) fish sauce

TO SERVE

small handful of roasted salted peanuts

1 tablespoon finely chopped garlic chives

2 lime wedges

If you asked anyone to name one Thai dish, they would probably say pad Thai. It is a popular street food as it's cheap and affordable and was created in the 1930s when the country changed its name from Siam to Thailand. As the country was focused on nation building and defining its identity, the then prime minister held a competition to find a 'national' dish, and this noodle dish was the winning entry. It's a sweet, sour and salty dish made with fat rice noodles. Most pad Thai served in Thai restaurants here bear no resemblance to the authentic version and are usually overly sweet without the sourness of the tamarind water. Pad Thai can be made with chicken, pork or prawns (shrimp), but I have come up with a novel way of using crispy chicken skin. The crispy Chicken Scratchings (page 21) work really well and add a nice crunch to the soft rice noodles alongside the peanuts. As long as the base is right you can take away or add just about any protein you like. Pad Thai is a dish for any time of the day and can also work well as a different weekend brunch dish.

If using the dried shrimp, then soak them in a small bowl of boiling water for 1 hour, then drain and set aside.

Meanwhile, to make the sauce, place the tamarind water and sugar in a small saucepan and heat over a low heat for 3 minutes until the sugar has dissolved. Using a whisk, whisk in the fish sauce to combine. Set aside.

To cook the pad Thai, place the rice noodles in a bowl, cover with boiling water and leave to stand for about 30 minutes, or until soft. Once soft, drain and set aside.

Place a wok over a medium-high heat, add the chicken fat or oil and heat for 1–2 minutes until it begins to smoke. Add the minced chicken and cook, breaking it up with a spatula as it cooks, for 8–10 minutes. Push the meat to one side of the wok and add the egg. Leave it to set without moving until the edges are crispy. Add the smoked tofu, beansprouts and dried shrimp (if using), then flip the egg over and break it up with the spatula. Stir everything together with the chicken and shrimp. Add the noodles, then stir in the sauce. Cook for 30 seconds. At the last minute, add the crushed Chicken Scratchings and peanuts and toss around to combine. Serve on warmed plates with extra bean sprouts, roasted unsalted peanuts, garlic chives and lime wedges.

BLUE CHEESE SALADWITH PICKLED APPLE & CRISPY CHICKEN SKIN

SERVES 4

ALMOST
BREEZY

S
K
I
N

FOR THE PICKLED APPLE

2 Granny Smith apples

50 g (2 oz/scant ¼ cup) caster (superfine) sugar

50 ml (1¾ fl oz/3 tablespoons) water

50 ml (1¾ fl oz/3 tablespoons) cider vinegar

FOR THE BLUE CHEESE DRESSING

100 g (3½ oz) St Agur blue cheese

65 ml (2¼ fl oz/¼ cup) buttermilk or plain yoghurt

65 g (2¼ oz/¼ cup) Japanese Kewpie mayonnaise

1 tablespoon cider vinegar

pinch of salt

FOR THE SALAD

2 baby gem lettuces, outer leaves removed

50 g (2 oz) slices of smoked streaky bacon, cooked until crispy

50 g (2 oz) Chicken Crispies (page 21)

very finely chopped chives, for sprinkling

Saint Agur is a creamy commercial blue cheese that is sold in most supermarkets (grocery stores). It's a modern take on the famous Roquefort cheese, but nowhere near as strong and much creamier. It's also a cheese that lends itself to making the perfect blue cheese dressing. This recipe was on at my restaurant Chick 'n' Sours from day one as we thought it was the perfect one for crispy fried chicken. The pickled apples add a nice acidity and extra crunch to the salad but it still works well with just raw strips of Granny Smith apples. This is the ultimate blue cheese salad with lots of delicious crispy bits, such as the bacon, cold wedges of iceberg or baby gem lettuce and the dressing. The crispy chicken skin adds a salty crunch that tops the salad off very nicely. Serve on its own for one or in a large bowl in the middle of the table with a few other dishes from this book.

To make the pickled apple, slice the apples very thinly on a mandoline or by hand. Bring the sugar, water and vinegar to the boil in a medium pan, then turn off the heat and leave to cool completely in the refrigerator. Cut the sliced apples into batons, then place in the pickle liquor and set aside.

To make the dressing, blend all the ingredients in a food processor until smooth. Set aside.

To make the salad, pull the baby gem leaves apart, being careful to keep them whole, and place them in a large bowl. Add some of sauce to the bowl and toss until all the leaves are coated in the sauce. Add the pickled apple and toss again. Arrange in a pile on a chilled serving plate and sprinkle the crispy bacon over the top. Crunch up the chicken skin with your hands and scatter on top. Finally, sprinkle with plenty of very finely chopped chives.

T
R
A
C
K

N
I
N
E

CHINESE HUMMUS
WITH CHICKEN SKIN CRACKERS

SERVES 6–10

1 kg (2 lb 4 oz) chicken skin, scraped

Maldon sea salt

FOR THE HUMMUS

150 g (5 oz/generous ⅔ cup) dried chickpeas (garbanzo beans)

1 teaspoon bicarbonate of soda (baking soda)

2 garlic cloves, unpeeled

2 tablespoons plus 2 teaspoons lemon juice

75 g (2½ oz/¼ cup) Chinese sesame paste

75 g (2½ oz/¼ cup) white miso paste

2 tablespoons ice-cold water

½ teaspoon ground cumin

1 tablespoon toasted sesame oil

TO SERVE

2 tablespoons Explosive Chilli Oil (page 182), to serve

prawn (shrimp) crackers (optional)

WORTH THE EFFORT

First, this recipe is in no way whatsoever Chinese in origin, it's just a fun twist on everyday hummus. I have swapped out the traditional tahini, which is the sesame paste that hummus is made with, for Chinese sesame paste and added white miso, which gives it a funky flavour. If you have a pressure cooker, then use it to cook the raw chickpeas (garbanzo beans) to ensure they are soft and cooked through. If you don't have one, then just make sure the chickpeas are cooked through or you will end up with a chalky, grainy hummus, which is not very pleasant to eat. I have served this hummus with crispy chicken skin crackers, which work a treat, but there is some work required to prepare them, so if you are serving this dish to a large group of people then another fun way to serve it is with prawn (shrimp) crackers.

To make the hummus, place the chickpeas and ½ teaspoon of the bicarbonate of soda in a medium bowl and pour in enough cold water to cover. Leave to soak overnight until the chickpeas have plumped up and doubled in size.

The next day, to prepare the chicken skin, preheat the oven to 160°C (325°F/gas 3).

Cut some greaseproof (wax) paper the same size as a shallow roasting tray (pan) and lay one sheet on the base. Lay a layer of scraped chicken skin onto the paper and sprinkle with sea salt. Put another sheet on top and repeat until all the chicken skin is seasoned on the tray. Place another piece of paper on top and weigh down with another tray the same size. Place in the oven for about 30–40 minutes, checking occasionally, until the skin is golden brown and crispy. Set aside.

Drain the soaked chickpeas for the hummus and rinse under cold running water, then place in a large saucepan with the remaining bicarbonate of soda. Pour in enough cold water to cover and bring to the boil. Reduce the heat and simmer for 45–50 minutes until the chickpeas are soft. Drain and set aside.

Blend the garlic, 2 tablespoons of lemon juice, sesame paste and miso in a food processor or blender until smooth. Add the ice-cold water, 1 tablespoon at a time, and continue to blend until pale and thick. Add the cooked chickpeas, cumin and sesame oil and continue to blend for about 4 minutes, adding a little more water if it is too thick. Season to taste with the remaining lemon juice and scrape into a bowl. Spoon over the chilli oil and serve with the chicken skin crackers. Prawn crackers are equally as good to serve as well.

S K I N

T R A C K   N I N E

NOTE

You can buy Chinese sesame paste in specialist Asian grocery stores and online.

CHINESE HUMMUS WITH CHICKEN SKIN CRACKERS

XIAN-SPICED CHICKEN SCRATCHINGS

SERVES 6–10

160

WORTH THE EFFORT

100 ml (3½ fl oz/scant ½ cup) rapeseed (canola) oil

1 kg (2 lb 4 oz) fatty chicken skin

500 ml (17 fl oz/2 cups) rapeseed oil, for deep-frying

FOR THE XIAN SPICE

25 g (1 oz) dried red chillies

50 g (2 oz/½ cup) cumin seeds

50 g (2 oz/generous ¾ cup) coriander seeds

1 tablespoon Sichuan peppercorns

1 tablespoon brown sugar

½ teaspoon MSG (optional)

I can remember as a young kid the smell of the scratching factories in Birmingham, which wasn't very pleasant as the vats of pork skin bubbled away. They do, however, taste much better than they smell. In this recipe, I have taken the same cooking method and rendered the chicken skins down in their own fat in a technique the French call confit. For this recipe you want to use chicken skin with plenty of fat from round the legs or the undercarriage by the spine. Serve these chicken scratchings with drinks at a party or with a few beers on movie night.

Place the oil and chicken skins in a deep, large, cold pot and heat over the lowest heat for 60–90 minutes, until the skins render off all their fat, are golden brown and should float to the top of the fat. Strain off and keep the rendered fat (schmaltz) in a jar in the refrigerator for future recipes.

To make the spice, toast the chillies in a dry frying pan (skillet) over a low medium heat for 2–3 minutes until they are slightly blackened and giving off oil. Remove and set aside, then toast all the remaining spices in the pan for 2–3 minutes, or until fragrant. Leave to cool, then add all the ingredients to a mortar and pestle and grind to a powder.

To finish, heat the oil for deep-frying to 170°C (340°F), or until a cube of bread dropped in sizzles in 30 seconds. Deep-fry the chicken skin in batches for 2–3 minutes, until golden, then remove and drain on paper towels. They will crisp up as they cool. Once cooled to room temperature and are crisp, transfer to a bowl and douse liberally with Xian spice tossing them around in the bowl until they are all evenly coated.

S
K
I
N

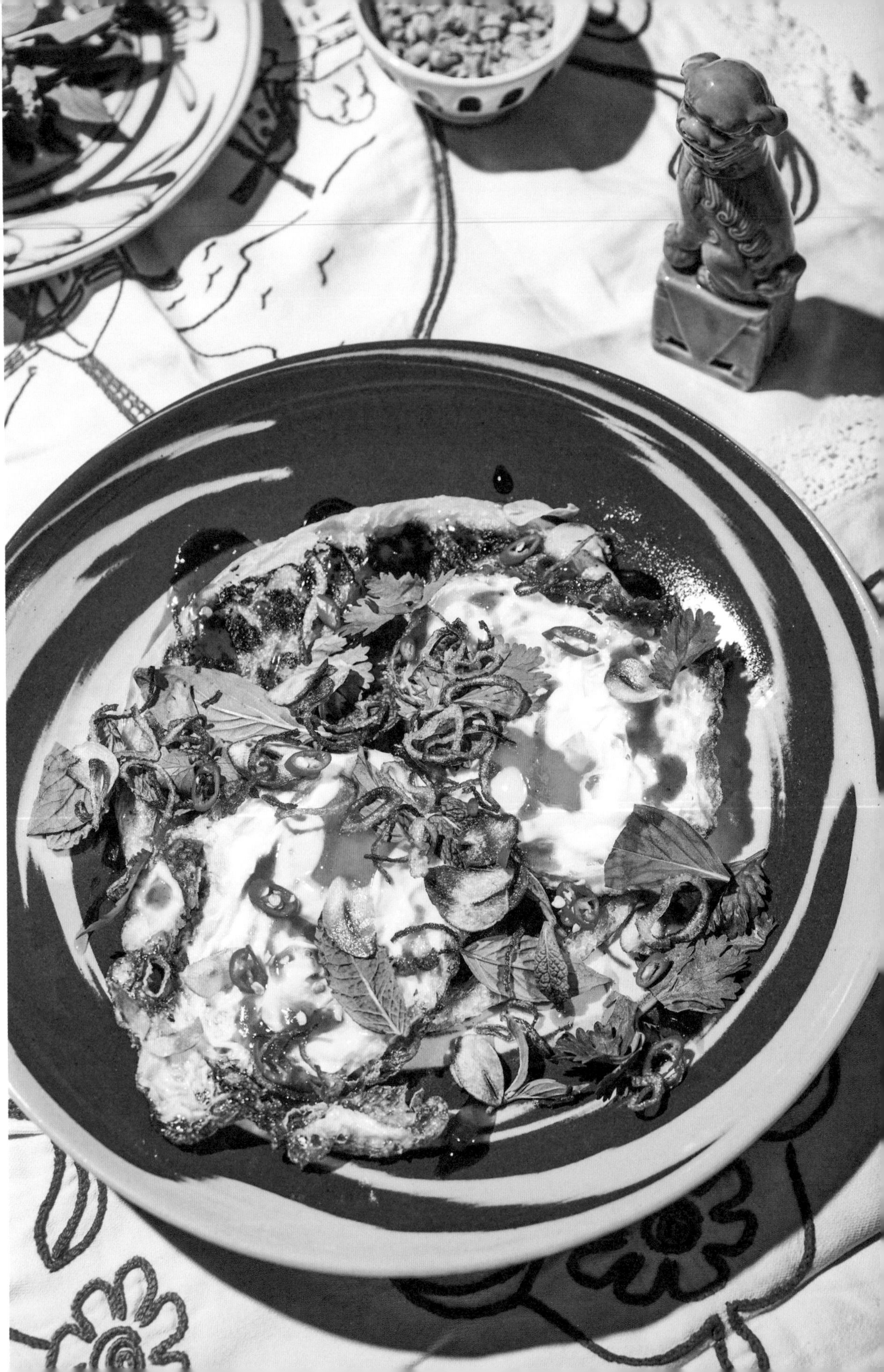

SON-IN-LAW EGGS

SERVES 1

200 ml (7 fl oz/scant 1 cup) rapeseed (canola) oil

1 garlic clove

1 shallot

2 eggs

1 shop-bought paratha or roti bread (available in good Indian supermarkets)

1 long fresh red chilli, sliced

handful each of coriander (cilantro), Thai basil and mint, roughly torn

1 tablespoon chopped roasted peanuts

FOR THE DRESSING

2 large tablespoons Thai fish sauce

2 red bird's eye chillies, finely chopped

140 g (5 oz/¾ cup) palm sugar

65 g (2¼ oz) tamarind pulp

2 tablespoons water

This is a Thai recipe that I have adapted. Legend has it that it is served to the new son-in-law joining the family as a warning to be good to their daughter! Not sure how true that is, but these are really delicious. The sweet, salty, sour caramel works beautifully with the eggs, herbs and all the crispy bits. It's super easy to make and is a great alternative breakfast or brunch for lazy weekends.

To make the dressing, combine all the ingredients in a small saucepan and heat over a medium heat for 5 minutes until the sugar has melted and become a light syrupy texture. Set aside and keep warm.

Heat the oil in a shallow saucepan to 160°C (325°F), or until a cube of bread dropped in sizzles in 40 seconds. Meanwhile, ideally using a Japanese mandoline, slice the garlic as thinly as you possibly can and set aside. Repeat this process with the shallots. Once the oil is hot, fry the garlic for 1 minute until golden and crisp. Remove with a slotted spoon and drain on paper towels, then fry the shallot for 2–3 minutes, or until golden and crispy. Drain on paper towels.

Heat a large frying pan (skillet) over a medium heat until very hot, then fry the eggs very fast so the edges are crispy and the yolk is still soft. In another dry frying pan, toast the roti for 2 minutes until crispy and golden brown, then transfer to a plate. Place the fried eggs on top of the roti bread, then dress the eggs and roti bread generously with the dressing. Sprinkle the crispy shallots, garlic and sliced chilli on top and garnish with the herbs and chopped roasted peanuts.

ALMOST BREEZY

E G G S

T R A C K T E N

SPICED CHICKEN OMELETTE SANDWICH WITH SAMBAL OELEK

SERVES 2

WORTH THE EFFORT

5 eggs, beaten

250 g (9 oz/1¼ cups) minced (ground) chicken

1 tablespoon Madras curry powder (page 116)

½ red onion, finely chopped or grated

1 tablespoon grated garlic

1 tablespoons grated fresh ginger root

pinch of salt

2 soft large submarine rolls

1 tablespoon rapeseed (canola) oil

25 g (1 oz) butter

FOR THE SAMBAL OELEK

50 g (2 oz) fresh red chillies

90 g (3¼ oz) piece of fresh ginger root, peeled

1 lemongrass stalk, tough outer layer removed

90 g (3¼ oz) garlic cloves

90 ml (3 fl oz/generous ⅓ cup) rice wine vinegar

120 g (4 oz/½ cup) sugar

½ tablespoon lime zest

salt

TO GARNISH

½ cucumber, sliced

2 tomatoes, sliced

1 small red onion, thinly sliced

handful of shredded lettuce

4 spring onions (scallions), finely sliced

1 fresh red chilli, finely sliced

This is a twist on the Malaysian street-food classic, roti john, as I have used chicken minced (ground) chicken instead of pork or beef. It is a spicy, filling sandwich that really does suit any time of the day or night, and it's up to you how spicy you make it by adding more or less of the fiery sambal oelek. Try to use soft submarine rolls as opposed to crusty baguette, as the sandwich just eats better that way.

To make the sambal oelek, blend the chillies, ginger, lemongrass and garlic in a food processor, slowly adding the vinegar until it forms a smooth paste. Transfer the paste to a saucepan and bring to the boll over a medium heat, being careful not to let it burn. Once boiling, reduce the heat, add the sugar and stir until it dissolves. Remove from the heat, add the lime zest and season with salt. Leave to cool to room temperature. It is best served a day later from the refrigerator.

Thoroughly mix the eggs, chicken, curry powder, onion, garlic, ginger and salt together in a large bowl. Cut the rolls in half lengthways and cover both sides of the bread with plenty of the chicken mixture. Heat a large frying pan (skillet) over a medium heat, then add the oil first, then the butter. When the butter is foaming, place the bread, chicken mixture-side down, into the pan, pushing it down with the back of a spatula. Cook for 6–8 minutes until cooked through, being careful not to burn the butter.

To serve, lay one half of the bread roll open on a large plate and dress with as much sambal oelek as you can handle. Arrange cucumber slices, sliced tomatoes and red onion on top, followed by the lettuce, spring onion and chilli. Close with the other half of the roll. Cut into 3 sections and serve.

THE SUN HOUSE FRIED CHILLI EGGS

SERVES 1

1 tablespoon rapeseed (canola) oil

½ red onion, finely diced

2 green bird's eye chillies, finely chopped

2 very ripe tomatoes, diced

2 eggs

30 g (1 oz/⅓ cup) grated mild Cheddar

1 tablespoon chopped coriander (cilantro)

salt and freshly ground black pepper

chilli (red pepper) flakes, to garnish (optional)

warm roti bread or good-quality sourdough toast, to serve

The Sun House in Sri Lanka is probably my favourite place to stay in the world and is owned by my friend Geoffrey Dobbs, who is one of the finest hosts on the planet. It has the most beautiful terraced restaurant I have ever seen, and I was lucky enough to cook there as a guest chef once, which was one of the best cooking experiences I have ever had. In the mornings, the monkeys come to say hello, and in the evenings, the famous Dick's bar serves arak sours before dinner. These spicy fried eggs are served on the breakfast menu alongside the usual bacon and eggs, but the spicy fried eggs are my go-to every time. They are super easy to make and are a very tasty alternative weekend breakfast or brunch dish. Serve these as Geoffrey would, with hot buttered toast and extra green chillies on the side.

Preheat the grill (broiler) to medium high.

Heat an ovenproof frying pan (skillet) over a medium heat and add the oil. When hot, add the onion and chillies and sweat for a few minutes, then add the tomatoes and fry for another 2–3 minutes. Make 2 wells for the eggs, then break into the pan and continue to fry. Sprinkle the grated cheese on top, then grill (broil) until the cheese has melted slightly but the yolks are still soft, around 2–3 minutes. Using a spatula, transfer it all in one go onto a warmed serving plate. Top with coriander, salt and pepper and chilli flakes, if using, then serve with warm roti or sourdough toast.

EASY PEASY

E G G S

T R A C K

T E N

TAKE A WALK ON THE SUNNY SIDE

KIMCHI CORNBREAD WAFFLES
WITH HONEY BUTTER AND FRIED EGGS

SERVES 1–2

168

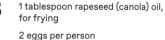

WORTH THE EFFORT

1 tablespoon rapeseed (canola) oil, for frying

2 eggs per person

FOR THE WAFFLES

90 g (3¼ oz/¾ cup) plain (all-purpose) flour

90 g (3¼ oz/⅔ cup) cornmeal

15 g (½ oz/4 teaspoons) brown sugar

½ teaspoon baking powder

2 eggs

70 ml (2¼ fl oz/generous ¼ cup) full-fat (whole) milk

65 ml (2¼ fl oz/scant ¼ cup) kimchi juice

10 g (½ oz) butter, melted

90 g (3¼ oz) kimchi, roughly chopped

1 teaspoon Maldon sea salt

neutral oil or bacon fat, for oiling

FOR THE HONEY BUTTER

50 g (2 oz) unsalted butter

50 g (2 oz/¼ cup) honey

TO SERVE

1–2 tablespoons shop-bought kimchi

Sriracha (hot chilli sauce), to taste

gochugaru (Korean chilli (red pepper) flakes), for sprinkling

You can put just about anything in a waffle iron, and not just sweet Belgian-style waffles. Here, I have made a savoury cornbread batter and added kimchi. The finished cornbread waffle is then drenched in honey butter and served with a couple of fried eggs. If you want to add bacon, as I often do, then please be my guest. Like all the egg recipes in this book, eat this any time you fancy for breakfast, brunch or even dinner.

To make the waffles, mix the flour, cornmeal, sugar and baking powder together in a large bowl. Whisk the eggs, milk and kimchi juice together in a separate bowl, then add the melted butter and mix to a smooth batter. Fold the kimchi through the batter with a pinch of salt, then add the dry ingredients.

Heat a waffle iron until it is ready to cook and lightly oil. Once hot, ladle in the mixture, close the lid and cook until golden brown and slightly crispy around the edges, or the green light on your machine flicks on.

To make the honey butter, gently heat the butter and honey together in a small saucepan for 2 minutes, whisking well to slightly thicken. Set aside.

Heat the oil for frying in a large frying pan (skillet) over a high heat and fry the eggs. You want to fry them fast, so the edges are crispy, but the yolk is still soft. Remove the waffles from the waffle iron and slather generously with the honey butter. Lay the fried eggs on top and serve with a little kimchi, Sriracha and a sprinkle of Korean chilli flakes on top.

PICKLES & KILLS

172

SPICY MANGO AND PINEAPPLE PICKLE

PICKLED WATERMELON RINDS

SPICY MANGO AND PINEAPPLE PICKLE

MAKES 1 JAR

1 teaspoon cumin seeds

1 teaspoon coriander seeds

1 teaspoon black mustard seeds

10 black peppercorns

3 tablespoons rapeseed (canola) oil

2 small onions, finely chopped

1 pineapple, peeled, cored and cut into 1 cm (½ in) dice

2 large ripe mangoes, peeled, stoned and cut into 5 mm (¼ in) dice

1 long fresh red chilli, chopped

thumb-sized piece of fresh ginger root, peeled and grated

50 g (2 oz/¼ cup) dates or dried figs, cut into small pieces

1 tablespoon Maldon sea salt

100 g (3½ oz/½ cup) coconut palm or dark brown sugar

150 ml (5 floz/scant ⅔ cup) cider vinegar

½ teaspoon Kashmiri chilli powder

I adore this pickle, which was inspired by my love of Indian food. The pineapple and mango add a beautiful fruity flavour that works perfectly with all the spices and chilli. Kashmiri chillies are a bright vibrant red, and very fragrant. Be sure to cook this gently so as not to catch it on the bottom of the pan, otherwise it will burn and become bitter. This is a sweet and sour sticky pickle that will go perfectly with my Sunday Night Madras recipe (page 116) or just about any other curry you fancy. Keep for up to three months in the refrigerator.

Toast the cumin seeds, coriander seeds, mustard seeds and black pepper in a dry frying pan (skillet) for 2 minutes, or until fragrant. Heat the oil in a pan or wok over a medium heat and heat the oil with the spices for 2 minutes until the seeds start to pop. Add the onions, pineapple, mangoes, chilli and ginger and heat through, stirring constantly. Add the dried fruit, salt, sugar, vinegar and chilli powder and bring to the boil. Reduce the heat to low and simmer, stirring occasionally, for 25–30 minutes. Transfer to a sterilised Kilner (mason) jar and chill in the refrigerator. The pickle will keep for up to 3 months.

PICKLED WATERMELON RINDS

MAKES 1 JAR

300 g (10½ oz) watermelon skin

FOR THE PICKLE LIQUOR

100 ml (3½ fl oz/scant ½ cup) good-quality cider or rice wine vinegar

100 g (3½ oz /scant ½ cup) caster (superfine) sugar

100 ml (3½ fl oz/scant ½ cup) mineral water

thumb-sized piece of fresh ginger root, unpeeled and sliced into pieces

1 star anise

1 tablespoon Sichuan peppercorns

½ sheet of kombu seaweed, torn into small sheets

I first came across pickled watermelon rinds when I worked in Savannah, Georgia, years ago. They are sold in jars and very popular in the southern states of the US. At Chick 'n' Sours we serve a Thai watermelon salad and cubes of pickled watermelon with our fried chicken. It has been on the menu since day one and one that will never come off the menu. We pickle the peeled rinds in a sweet and sour pickle flavoured with ginger and serve them when you sit down at a table. The secret is to cook them for long enough that the tough skin breaks down and becomes a pleasant crunchy texture. They are great as a side dish or with any fried chicken on the planet.

Using a very sharp knife or a mandoline, slice the watermelon skin across the width into 2 mm (1⁄16 in) thick slices maximum.

Place all the liquor ingredients, except the seaweed, into a large saucepan and bring to a simmer over a medium heat. Simmer gently for 15 minutes, or until the skin softens but still has a bite. Once done, remove from the heat and leave to cool to room temperature.

Once cooled, transfer to sterilised Kilner (mason) jars, add the seaweed, cover with the lids and leave to pickle for at least 24 hours. This will last, and get better, for about 3 months.

EASY PEASY

MALAYSIAN NYONYA PICKLES

MAKES 1 JAR

EASY PEASY

5 tablespoons rapeseed (canola) oil

300 g (10½ oz) cucumber, skin on and cut into 2.5 cm (1 in) lengths, deseeded

150 g (5 oz) Chinese (Napa) cabbage, cut into 2.5 cm (1 in) pieces

50 g (2 oz) carrots, cut into 5 mm (¼ in) wide batons

100 g (3½ oz) French beans, cut in half lengthways

50 g (2 oz/⅓ cup) roasted crushed peanuts

salt, to taste

caster (superfine) sugar, to taste

FOR THE SPICE PASTE

5 shallots

12 long fresh red chillies

1 cm (½ in) piece of fresh turmeric, peeled

10 cashew nuts

120 ml (4 fl oz/½ cup) tamarind water (page 62)

These pickles are delicious and full of crunchy textures and different flavours. They have a nutty flavour from the crushed peanuts and a drier texture to the overall finished pickle than most. The spice paste has a beautiful fragrance from the fresh turmeric, which is really worth using if you can find it, some heat from the chillies and a sour creamy flavour from the cashews and tamarind water.

To make the spice paste, blitz all the ingredients, except the tamarind water, together in a food processor until smooth.

Heat the oil in a wok over a medium heat and, when hot, add the spice paste and fry for 10 minutes until golden brown and fragrant. Add the tamarind water and bring to the boil. Add the vegetables and peanuts, then turn off the heat and leave to cool completely in the pickle liquid.

Transfer to sterilised Kilner (mason) jars. This can be eaten the same day or it will get better over the following week, if you can wait. The pickles will keep for 3 months.

SPICY AND NUMBING BREAD AND BUTTER PICKLES

MAKES 1 JAR

3 English cucumbers, sliced into 5 mm (¼ in) rounds

1 white onion, thinly sliced

2 tablespoons sea salt

FOR THE PICKLE LIQUOR

600 ml (20 fl oz/2½ cups) cider vinegar

300 g (10½ oz/1⅔ cups) light brown sugar

1 teaspoon yellow mustard seeds

2 tablespoons Sichuan peppercorns

½ teaspoon ground turmeric

4 red bird's eye chillies, cut in half lengthways

1 teaspoon gochugaru (Korean chilli flakes) (optional)

These are my twist on the American classic bread and butter pickles, which are commonly served in the US with smoked barbecue meats. The crunchy cucumbers are both sweet and sour and are great on just about any sandwich you fancy. They are both spicy from the chilli and flagrantly numbing from the Sichuan pepper. I like to eat these with Chinese-style barbecue meats and rice, so these will work perfectly with my Peking Chicken (page 30) or Cherry Cola Chicken Legs (page 111).

Place the cucumber and onion in a colander and rub salt into them. Place the colander over a tray or bowl and leave to stand for 3–6 hours until the water has been released. Rinse the salt off under cold running water and leave to stand again for a while in the colander until the water has drained.

Bring all the pickling ingredients to the boil in a large saucepan. Once boiling, add the cucumbers and onions and bring back to the boil, then turn off the heat and leave to cool before transferring to sterilised jars. This will keep for up to a month in the refrigerator.

NO NEED TO WAIT KIMCHI

MAKES 1 JAR

1 kg (2 lb 4 oz) Chinese (Napa) cabbage

100 g (3½ oz/¾ cup) Maldon sea salt

½ cucumber, skin on and cut in half lengthways, deseeded and cut into 5 mm (¼ in) thick pieces

3 spring onions (scallions), cut into 2 cm (¾ in) pieces

sesame seeds, for sprinkling

FOR THE KIMCHI PASTE

5 tablespoons gochugaru (Korean chilli powder)

3 tablespoons very finely chopped garlic

2 tablespoons grated fresh ginger root

300 g (10½ oz) mooli (daikon), grated

1 tablespoon fish sauce

100 ml (3½ fl oz/scant ½ cup) sesame oil

5 tablespoons rice wine vinegar

5 tablespoons caster (superfine) sugar

This is a tasty little kimchi recipe that needs no fermentation time and is ready as soon as it's made. The trick here is to make sure you rub the salt into the cabbage leaves thoroughly and also wash them really well afterwards in plenty of cold water to remove the excess salt. As you have probably figured out, I love kimchi. It is such a versatile pickle that goes with just about anything, so try this on sharp cheese, as a kimchi toastie or in a healthy rice bowl.

Cut the cabbage into quarters and then quarter again so you have 8 pieces. Place in a bowl, add the salt and rub the salt into the leaves, making sure they are completely covered. Place a plate on top and leave for 24 hours, or until the cabbage releases water. Rinse the salt from the cabbage well under cold running water and cut into pieces.

To make the paste, mix all the ingredients together in a bowl. Add all the vegetables and spring onions to the bowl and mix well. Place in a serving dish, sprinkle with sesame seeds and serve.

PINK PICKLED ONIONS

MAKES 1 JAR

3 large red onions, very thinly sliced

FOR THE PICKLE LIQUOR

1 teaspoon black peppercorns

1 teaspoon cumin seeds

1 teaspoon dried oregano (Mexican, if you can get it)

4 garlic cloves, crushed

2 bay leaves

1 teaspoon Maldon sea salt

150 ml (5 fl oz/scant ⅔ cup) cider vinegar

150 g (5 oz/⅔ cup) caster (superfine) sugar

150 ml (5 fl oz/scant ⅔ cup) mineral water

I have made and used this recipe for years in all my restaurants in some form or another. In Mexico, they serve them with everything from quesadillas to tacos. If done right, the colour is a beautifully vibrant pink that always adds a smile to the dish you are serving them with. Do try to use Mexican oregano if you can, which is available online. It is more robust in flavour and closer to lemon verbena than ordinary oregano.

Bring all the pickle liquor ingredients to the boil in a large saucepan. Place the sliced onions in a separate heatproof container large enough to hold all the liquid. As soon as the pickle liquid boils to pour it straight over the onions. Weigh them down with something heavy, such as a small plate, and leave to cool to room temperature.

Once cooled, chill in the refrigerator overnight. They should be a vibrant pink within a few hours. They will keep for at least 3 months.

EASY
PEASY

P
I
C
K
L
E
S

176

MALAYSIAN NYONYA PICKLES

NO NEED TO WAIT KIMCHI

PINK PICKLED ONIONS

SAUCES

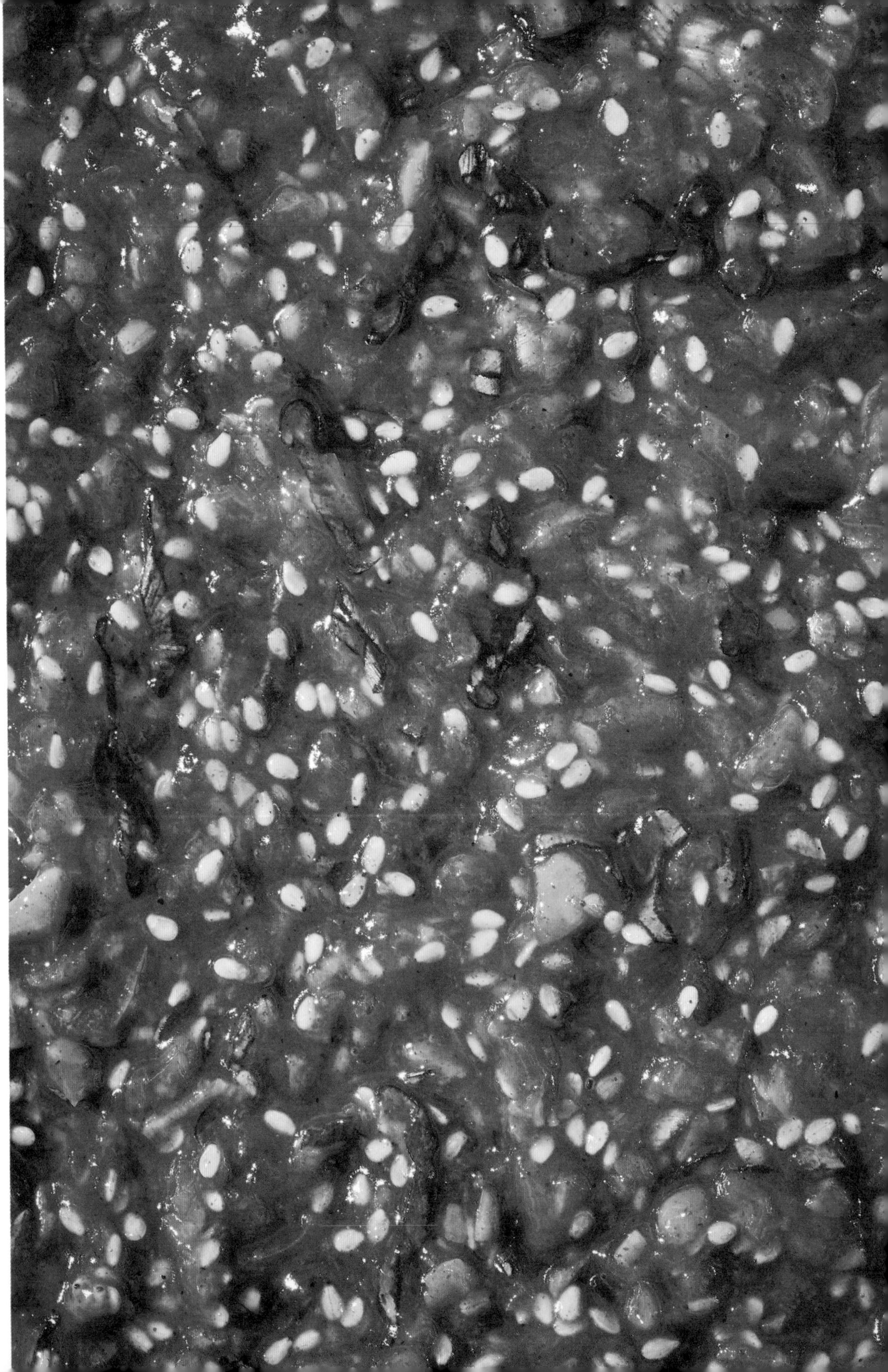

EVERYDAY SWEET, SOUR & SPICY AS YOU LIKE DRESSING

MAKES 100 G (3½ OZ)

2 tablespoons dried shrimp (optional)

2 garlic cloves, chopped into small pieces

1–6 red bird's eye chillies, seeds in (how hot can you go!), chopped into small pieces

3 tablespoons lime juice

1 tablespoon tamarind water (page 62)

2 tablespoons fish sauce

3 tablespoons coconut palm sugar, shaved if solid

An everyday dressing to make as spicy as you like with the flavours of Thailand. Try this on cold watermelon and thank me later.

Add all the ingredients to a blender and blitz until smooth. This will keep in an airtight container for 3 days.

SSAMJANG RELISH

MAKES 100 G (3½ OZ)

1 tablespoon rapeseed (canola) oil

1 small red onion, finely diced

3 garlic cloves, very finely chopped

100 g (3½ oz) ssamjang (Korean spicy paste)

1 tablespoon runny honey

2 tablespoons toasted sesame seeds

50 g (2 oz/scant ¼ cup) gochujang (Korean red chilli paste)

1 teaspoon sesame oil

4 spring onions (scallions), thinly sliced

This is a pimped-up funky ssamjang relish, which is a great alternative to BBQ sauce to use on anything you fancy, especially with crispy chicken wings.

Heat the rapeseed oil in a small pan over a medium heat and fry the red onion for 1–2 minutes. Add the garlic, ssamjang, honey and sesame seeds and cook for 2 minutes. Add the gochujang and sesame oil, mix together for another minute, then remove the pan from the heat. Add the spring onions and mix together. Leave to cool to room temperature or refrigerator temperature before serving. This will keep in an airtight container for 3 days.

EASY PEASY

S A U C E S

T R A C K   T W E L V E

'ALIVE' KETCHUP

MAKES 500 ML (17 FL OZ/2 CUPS)

182

EASY PEASY

60 g (2¼ oz/⅓ cup) muscovado (soft brown) sugar

80 ml (2½ fl oz/⅓ cup) water

2 x 175 g (6 oz) tins tomato purée (paste)

2 tablespoons raw cider vinegar

2 tablespoons shop-bought whey powder (optional)

1 tablespoon gochujang (Korean red chilli paste)

⅛ teaspoon ground cinnamon

⅛ teaspoon ground cloves

⅛ teaspoon freshly ground black pepper

sea salt, to taste

This is a very tasty fermented spicy ketchup recipe, that's as good as just about anything that you can buy, but is much better for you!

Combine the sugar and water together in a small saucepan and cook over a medium heat, stirring frequently, for 5 minutes until the sugar has dissolved. Pour into a heatproof bowl, add the remaining ingredients and mix together to combine.

Transfer to a sterilised Kilner (mason) jar, cover with a lid and leave to ferment at room temperature for 2–5 days, depending on how funky you like it, but basically until bubbly and fermented. It will keep in the refrigerator for 2 weeks.

EXPLOSIVE CHILLI OIL

MAKES 500 ML (17 FL OZ/2 CUPS)

270 g (9½ oz/1 cup) peanut chilli oil (Laoganma brand)

50 g (2 oz) shop-bought crispy shallots

100 g (3½ oz/½ cup) Toban Djan (Sichuan chilli bean sauce)

300 ml (10 fl oz/1¼ cups) chilli oil

1 tablespoon ground Sichuan pepper

This chilli oil has a real depth of flavour from the fermented black beans and crispy shallots. It's another classic dumpling dipper or great as a rice condiment.

Whisk all the ingredients together in a bowl until well combined. This will keep in an airtight container for 6 months.

S A U C E S

IT'S ALIVE

ME XO SAUCE

MAKES 500 ML (17 FL OZ/2 CUPS)

75 g (2½ oz) dried shrimp

1 guajillo dried chilli, halved
lengthways and seeded

2 small chipotle dried chillies, halved
lengthways and seeded

1 ancho dried chilli, halved
lengthways and seeded

10 g (½ oz) sliced fresh ginger root

1 garlic clove, peeled

1 shallot

1 long fresh red chilli,
roughly chopped

½ small Chinese sausage, sliced

2 slices any cured ham

½ cinnamon stick

1 star anise

2 teaspoons caster (superfine) sugar

1 tablespoon Shaoxing rice wine

100 ml (3½ fl oz/scant ½ cup)
rapeseed (canola) oil

2 teaspoons dark soy sauce

1 tablespoon fish sauce

1 teaspoon sea salt

½ teaspoon crushed
Sichuan peppercorns

This Mexican twist on a Chinese classic is rich, funky and spicy from the Mexican chillies.

Soak the dried shrimp in a bowl of water for at least 1 hour, but longer is better, until plump. Drain, setting aside 2 tablespoons of the soaking water.

Heat a frying pan (skillet) over a high heat, then when very hot, add the dried chillies and toast for 2–3 minutes until a little charred and their oils have been released. Transfer the toasted chillies to a bowl of cold water and leave to soak for about 30 minutes, or until softened.

Blitz the ginger, garlic, shallot, fresh chilli and soaked shrimp in a food processor until finely chopped, then add the sausage and ham and blitz to a paste. Set aside.

Add the reserved shrimp soaking water to a small saucepan. Add the cinnamon, star anise, sugar and rice wine and bring to a simmer, then remove from the heat and set aside.

Add the ginger and shrimp paste to another pan with 4 tablespoons of the oil and fry over a medium heat for about 4 minutes. Add the shrimp water mixture, then add the soy sauce and fish sauce and simmer for 30 minutes over a low heat, stirring frequently to ensure that the sauce isn't sticking to the base of the pan or burning. Add the remaining oil and mix through, then season with salt and Sichuan pepper, to taste. Remove and discard the whole spices, then leave to cool and pour into a sterilised Kilner (mason) jar. It will keep for 6 months.

ALMOST
BREEZY

EVERYDAY, SPICY AS YOU LIKE DRESSING

ME XO SAUCE

'ALIVE' KETCHUP

184

EXPLOSIVE CHILLI OIL

185

8 STUDIES 8

THAI WATERMELON SALAD

SMACKED CUCUMBERS WITH SESAME AND SEAWEED

THAI WATERMELON SALAD

SERVES 4

EASY PEASY

½ small watermelon, peeled and refrigerated (keep skins for pickling, page 173)

handful of roasted unsalted peanuts, plus extra to serve

handful of coriander (cilantro) leaves

handful of mint leaves, torn

5 spring onions (scallions), very thinly sliced

FOR THE DRESSING

2 tablespoons dried shrimp (optional)

2 garlic cloves, chopped

1–6 red bird's eye chillies, chopped (how hot can you go!)

3 tablespoons lime juice

1 tablespoon tamarind water (page 62)

2 tablespoons fish sauce

3 tablespoons solid coconut palm sugar, shaved

This is a real crowd-pleaser of a salad. It's a little unusual and not what you would expect as it's salty, sour and sweet from the watermelon and also fiery hot from the bird's eye chillies. This dish is best when the watermelon is served icy cold, so be sure to put the serving bowl in the refrigerator for a few hours before serving.

To make the dressing, blitz all the ingredients in a blender until smooth. Set aside.

To make the salad, remove all the seeds from the watermelon with a wooden skewer. Dice the watermelon into 1 cm (½ in) cubes and place in a large bowl. Add all the remaining ingredients and plenty of dressing and mix together. Put into a refrigerator-cold serving bowl and sprinkle a few more peanuts on top before serving.

SMACKED CUCUMBERS WITH SESAME AND SEAWEED

SERVES 4

1 cucumber

1 tablespoon Maldon sea salt

10 g (½ oz) wakame seaweed (optional)

thumb-sized piece of fresh ginger root, peeled and grated

5 garlic cloves, grated or very finely chopped

25 g (1 oz/2 tablespoons) caster (superfine) sugar

50 ml (1¾ fl oz/3 tablespoons) sesame oil

35 ml (1¼ fl oz/heaping 2 tablespoons) light soy sauce

50 ml (1¾ fl oz/3 tablespoons) rice wine vinegar

pinch of gochugaru (Korean chilli (red pepper) flakes), optional

Cucumbers and seaweed are like cheese and onion – they go together so well. The crunchy cucumbers work beautifully with the salty, zingy and fragrant dressing from the ginger and sesame, with just a touch of heat from the Korean chilli flakes.

Smash the cucumber with a rolling pin, then cut into 5 cm (2 in) batons. Place them in a colander and sprinkle with the salt. Leave to stand for at least 3 hours at room temperature, but overnight is better. Once finished, rinse the cucumber under cold running water, then pat dry with paper towels.

Place the dehydrated seaweed in a bowl and cover with cold water. Leave for 20 minutes until rehydrated and plump.

To make the dressing, mix all the ingredients, except the chilli flakes, together in a bowl until the sugar has dissolved. Add the chilli flakes (if using) and set aside.

To serve, transfer the cucumber to a bowl, then add plenty of dressing. Add the seaweed and mix until the cucumber is coated. Serve in refrigerator-cold small bowls.

CHARRED BROCCOLI WITH SEAWEED MAYO AND PINK PICKLED EGGS

SERVES 4–6

800 g (1 lb 12 oz) purple sprouting broccoli

salt

FOR THE SEAWEED MAYO

5 g (¼ oz) nori seaweed, toasted

170 g (6 oz/scant ¾ cup) Japanese Kewpie mayonnaise

1½ teaspoons light soy sauce

2 tablespoons buttermilk or plain yoghurt

1 tablespoon water

FOR THE PINK PICKLED EGGS

500 ml (17 fl oz/2 cups) cider vinegar

500 ml (17 fl oz/2 cups) water

5 g (¼ oz/1 teaspoon) Maldon sea salt

250 g (9 oz/1 cup) caster (superfine) sugar

½ teaspoon fennel seeds

½ teaspoon cloves

½ teaspoon coriander seeds

½ teaspoon chilli (red pepper) flakes

200 g (7 oz) raw beetroot (beets), peeled and grated

10 eggs

This is a colourful side dish as the pink pickled eggs add a ray of sunshine from the grated yolks against the purple whites. The charred broccoli takes on a smoky flavour that works so well with the seaweed mayo.

Cut the woody bases from the broccoli stalks. Have a large bowl of ice-cold water ready nearby. Bring a large saucepan of salted water to the boil, add the broccoli and blanch for 1 minute. Remove from the water and drop straight into the bowl of iced water to stop cooking and help retain the bright green colour. Set aside.

To make the mayo, blitz the seaweed to a powder in a spice grinder or blender, then transfer to a bowl and add all the remaining ingredients. Whisk together to combine. Set aside.

To make the pickled eggs, bring the vinegar, water, salt, sugar, spices and grated beetroot to the boil in a large saucepan, then set aside to cool.

In a separate pan, cook the eggs in boiling water for 7 minutes, then cool under very cold running water. Once cooled, carefully peel the eggs to keep their shape and add to the pickle liquor. Refrigerate for at least 48 hours. They will keep for up to 3 months.

To finish, heat a cast-iron or heavy-based frying pan (skillet) over a medium heat until it is very hot. Add the broccoli to the pan and cook for 2–3 minutes on each side until it heats through and becomes charred around the edges, almost burnt. Arrange the broccoli on a serving plate, spoon over some of the seaweed mayo, then grate the pickled egg on top to serve.

WHOEVER THOUGHT CABBAGE COULD TASTE SO GOOD SALAD

WHOEVER THOUGHT CABBAGE
COULD TASTE SO GOOD SALAD

SERVES 4

194

**EASY
PEASY**

¼ head red cabbage

¼ head Chinese (Napa) cabbage

1 beetroot (beet), unpeeled

salt (optional)

2 tablespoons shredded nori seaweed (optional)

2 tablespoons white sesame seeds, toasted

FOR THE DRESSING

2 tablespoons white miso paste

1 teaspoon miso soup powder

3 tablespoons tahini

1 teaspoon red wine vinegar

1 teaspoon rice wine vinegar

juice of 1 lemon

8 anchovy fillets, coarsely chopped

1 tablespoon light soy sauce

3 tablespoons rapeseed (canola) or olive oil (not virgin)

This is an unusual chunky cabbage slaw that will blow any bad memories away of overcooked cabbage at school dinners. The crunchy cabbage has a nutty flavour from the sesame paste, while the anchovies are salty and the earthy beetroot gives it some colour.

Remove the core from the cabbages and cut into large pieces. Slice the beetroot as finely as possible on a mandoline, then cut into thin matchsticks and set aside with the cabbage.

To make the dressing, mix the white miso, miso soup powder, tahini, both vinegars and lemon juice together in a bowl, then add the chopped anchovies, then whisk in the soy sauce and rapeseed oil. Mix well, until it has the texture of mayonnaise. Set aside.

To make the salad, add both the cabbages to a large bowl with the beetroot and mix the dressing through. Taste and season with a little salt if needed. Place in a pile in a serving bowl and sprinkle the shredded nori seaweed (if using) on top, then sprinkle with sesame seeds to serve.

S
I
D
E
S

T
R
A
C
K

T
H
I
R
T
E
E
N

MASALA SWEET POTATO WEDGES
WITH TAMARIND KETCHUP AND MINT CHUTNEY

SERVES 4

3 large sweet potatoes, cut into thick wedges, skin on

2 tablespoons rapeseed (canola) oil

small handful of chopped coriander (cilantro), for sprinkling

FOR THE MASALA SEASONING

85 g (3 oz/ ¾ cup plus 2 teaspoons) Madras curry powder

2 teaspoons fine salt

25 g (1 oz/¼ cup) onion powder

25 g (1 oz/¼ cup) nigella seeds

25 g (1 oz/1 tablespoon plus 2 tsp) soft light brown sugar

1 heaped tablespoon garam masala

1 heaped tablespoon MSG (optional)

1 heaped tablespoon chaat masala

1 heaped teaspoon garlic powder

FOR THE TAMARIND KETCHUP

1 teaspoon rapeseed (canola) oil

1 teaspoon cumin seeds

large pinch of asafoetida powder

200 g (7 oz) tamarind pulp

100 ml (3½ fl oz/scant ½ cup) water

10 dried dates, pitted

1 tablespoon chaat masala powder

100 g (3½ oz/½ cup plus 1 tablespoon) jaggery or muscovado (soft brown) sugar

1 teaspoon Kashmiri chilli powder

2 teaspoons ground cumin

1 teaspoon garam masala

FOR THE MINT CHUTNEY

200 g (7 fl oz/scant 1 cup) thick plain yoghurt

1 tablespoon shop-bought mint sauce

pinch of salt

NOTE

You can buy chaat masala from specialist Asian grocery stores or online.

These wedges are inspired by the Indian pubs of Birmingham and are just like another well-known brand of crisps (potato chips) as 'once you pop you can't stop!'. Once you've made these the first time, I'm sure you will make them time and time again.

Preheat the oven to 180°C (350°F/gas 4).

To make the masala seasoning, blitz all the ingredients together in a spice grinder.

Lay the sweet potato wedges in a large roasting tray (pan) and rub over the oil. Season with 2 tablespoons of the masala seasoning and roast in the oven for 30–40 minutes until soft and caramelised on one side. Turn only once.

To make the ketchup, heat the oil in a saucepan over a medium heat, add the cumin seeds and asafoetida powder and fry for 2–3 minutes, until the cumin starts to pop. Add the tamarind pulp, water, dates, chaat masala, jaggery, chilli powder and ground cumin. Bring to the boil, stirring constantly, so it doesn't burn, then reduce the heat to a low simmer and continue to cook for 20 minutes until it coats the back of a spoon, as it will thicken more when it is chilled. At the last minute, stir in the garam masala, then remove from the heat and leave to cool before pouring into a sterilised Kilner (mason) jar.

To make the chutney, mix all the ingredients together in a bowl until combined. Set aside.

To finish the sweet potatoes, remove them from the roasting tray (pan) and generously season again with the masala seasoning. Spoon over the tamarind ketchup, then the mint chutney. Add a good pinch more of masala seasoning on top and sprinkle with the chopped coriander to serve.

ALMOST BREEZY

TRACK THIRTEEN

SIDES

DESSERTS

HIP HIP HOORAY

DEEP-FRIED BIRTHDAY CAKE ICE CREAM

MAKES 4 LARGE OR 8 SMALL BALLS

WORTH THE EFFORT

250 ml (8½ fl oz/1 cup) double (heavy) cream

1 vanilla pod (bean), split in half lengthways and seeds scraped out

500 ml (17 fl oz/2 cups) condensed milk

100 g (3½ oz) packet vanilla sponge cake mix

3 tablespoons raspberry jam

3 tablespoons unicorn cake sprinkles, plus extra to serve

blue food colouring (optional)

neutral oil, for deep-frying

FOR THE SOUR CHERRY SAUCE

500 g (1 lb 2 oz) frozen morello cherries

100 g (3½ oz/scant ½ cup) caster (superfine) sugar

1 g (¼ teaspoon) citric acid

FOR COATING THE ICE CREAM

3 eggs

175 ml (6 fl oz/¾ cup) milk

120 g (4 oz/1 cup) plain (all-purpose) flour

30 g (1 oz/¼ cup) cornflour (cornstarch)

30 g (1 oz/2 tablespoons) sugar

2 g (scant ½ teaspoon) salt

150 g (7 oz/4 cups) crushed cornflakes, for coating

Deep-fried ice cream is one of those forgotten things of beauty. I love it and my favourite ice-cream flavour is birthday cake by far! I mean, who doesn't love birthday cake? Here, I have created a super-easy, no-churn ice cream that uses a mix of double (heavy) cream and condensed milk for a very rich, luxurious mouthfeel. The ice cream contains all the great things that a birthday cake is made of – raspberry jam, vanilla cake batter and sprinkles. It's coated in crunchy cornflakes, then served with a sour cherry sauce and even more sprinkles, because you can never have enough sprinkles. The contrast of the hot crunchy coating and cold sweet ice cream will have you thinking 'take me to the space rave' every time you eat this.

To make the ice cream, place the cream and vanilla seeds in a large bowl or in a stand mixer and whip the cream to very soft peaks. Add the condensed milk and stir together to combine. Mix in the sponge cake mix.

In a separate saucepan, add a little water to the raspberry jam and heat gently to loosen the jam's consistency, then pour into the ice cream mixture, making swirls with the back of a spoon. Add the sprinkles and blue food colouring, if using, and swirl again with a cocktail stick (toothpick) to get streaks of blue. Transfer the mixture to a freezerproof container and freeze for about 5–6 hours, or until firm.

For the sauce, place the cherries and sugar together in a pan and cook over a medium-low heat for 2–3 minutes, or until it is reduced and coats the back of a spoon. Transfer to a food processor and blend until smooth, then stir in the citric acid. Pass the sauce through a fine sieve (fine-mesh strainer).

To make the ice cream coating, blend all the ingredients, except the cornflakes, together in a bowl until a smooth batter forms. Place the crushed cornflakes in another bowl.

Scoop out the ice cream into balls or cut into 3 cm (1¼ in) slices. Dip each portion of ice cream into the batter, then roll in the cornflakes until coated and return to the freezer for at least 1 hour.

Heat enough oil for deep-frying in a deep-fryer or in a large, deep saucepan to 180°C (350°F), or until a cube of bread dropped in sizzles in 30 seconds. Deep-fry the ice cream balls, one at a time, for 30 seconds until golden and crispy. Place on a pool of sour cherry sauce, top with more sauce, then sprinkle unicorn sprinkles over the top.

CARL AND BRAD'S BANANA MISO CREAM PIE

SERVES 6–8

WORTH THE EFFORT

2–3 very ripe bananas, thinly sliced

FOR THE BANANA CREAM

2 very ripe bananas, frozen and then defrosted so the skins are blackened and soft

180 ml (6 fl oz/¾ cup) single (light) cream

60 ml (4 fl oz/¼ cup) full-fat (whole) milk

100 g (3½ oz/scant ½ cup) caster (superfine) sugar

25 g (1 oz/scant ¼ cup) cornflour (cornstarch)

3 egg yolks

½ teaspoon Maldon sea salt

40 g (1½ oz) softened butter, cut into chunks

80 g (3 oz) white miso paste

2 gelatine leaves, softened in water for 15 minutes

½ teaspoon yellow food colouring

80 ml (3 fl oz/⅓ cup) double (heavy) cream

160 g (5½ oz/1¼ cups) icing (confectioners') sugar

FOR THE CHOCOLATE PIE CRUST

70 g (2¼ oz/ ½ cup) plain (all-purpose) flour

¼ teaspoon cornflour (cornstarch)

40 g (1½ oz/ ⅓ cup) good-quality dark cocoa (unsweetened chocolate) powder

½ teaspoon salt

75 g (2½ oz) butter, melted, plus 15–20 g (½–¾ oz) extra if needed

75 g (2½ oz/⅓ cup) caster (superfine) sugar

FOR THE BANANA JELLY

oil, for oiling

125 ml (4¼ fl oz/½ cup) crème de banane liqueur

1 teaspoon agar agar

1 edible gold leaf, plus extra to serve

Brad Carter and his wife Holly run the Michelin-starred restaurant Carters of Moseley in Birmingham, which is probably one of my favourite restaurants on the planet. They are the most lovely, down-to-earth people you will ever meet in the restaurant business and I have so much love for them and what they do. Their restaurant is situated on an inconspicuous row of shops in an inner city part of Birmingham called Moseley and walking into their restaurant is like walking into their home. Brad is a self-taught chef and the first time I saw him cook on *Saturday Kitchen* it bowled me over. I knew I not only had to eat his food but had to meet the man himself. Brad asked me to bring Chick 'n' Sours to Birmingham and take over his restaurant for a day, so I obviously jumped at the chance. This was the dessert we served, which is a take on the American classic banana cream pie. For me, this is Brad's very funny Brummie lionheart sense of humour in a pie.

To make the banana cream, purée the bananas, single cream and milk together in a blender until completely smooth. Add the caster sugar, cornflour, yolks and salt and blend until smooth. Transfer to a saucepan and whisk constantly over a low-medium heat for about 2 minutes, being careful not to let the yolks scramble or get caught on the base of the pan. The mixture will now look like a thick paste. Transfer the mixture to a clean blender, and add the softened butter and miso paste. Remove the gelatine from the water and squeeze out any excess water. Add to the blender with the food colouring and blend. Transfer to a container and refrigerate until completely cool. In a separate bowl, whisk the double cream and icing sugar together until very soft peaks form. Remove the mixture from the refrigerator and stir in the cream mixture until everything is combined. Chill.

Preheat the oven to 150°C (300°F/gas 2).

Mix all the pie crust ingredients with just 65 g (2¼ oz/¼ cup) of the sugar together in a bowl or in an electric mixer until combined. Add 60 g (2 oz) of the melted butter and beat the mixture until clusters form. Spread the mixture out on a baking tray and bake for 20 minutes, breaking up the crumbs occasionally. Once done, remove from the oven and pulse in a food processor until no clusters remain. Transfer the mixture to a bowl, add the remaining sugar and butter, then knead to form into a ball. If it isn't moist enough, then knead in the extra 15–20 g (½–¾ oz) butter. Press the mixture into a 20 cm (8 in) pie mould and chill.

To make the jelly, lightly oil a very shallow tray. Boil the banana liqueur and agar agar together in a small saucepan for 2 minutes, then add the gold leaf and whisk constantly to break up the gold leaf and keep the jelly smooth. Pour the jelly into the prepared tray and leave to set at room temperature for 10 minutes. Once set, turn the jelly out onto a board and cut into 1 cm (½ in) cubes.

To assemble the pie, spoon half of the banana cream into the pie case and cover with a layer of sliced bananas, then cover with the remaining banana cream mixture. Layer another layer of sliced bananas over the top, then cover with the jelly cubes and serve.

DRINKS

BANANA AND ABSINTHE COLADA

SERVES 1

204

EASY
PEASY

20 ml (¾ fl oz) absinthe

15 ml (½ fl oz) dark rum

1 teaspoon crème de banane liqueur

30 ml (1 fl oz) chilled pineapple juice

20 ml (¾ fl oz) coconut syrup

15 ml (½ fl oz) lemon juice

crushed ice

1 sprig of mint, to garnish

This fun drink was inspired by a visit to Maison Premiere in Brooklyn, New York. It's one of the best cocktail bars in the world and I could sit there for hours just watching the skills of the bartenders. One of the drinks they are famous for is the absinthe colada and every time I drank one, I thought this would be great with banana, so here's my twist on their classic. It is a great party drink to enjoy on a sunny day among friends in the garden.

Combine the absinthe, rum, crème de banane, pineapple juice, coconut syrup and lemon juice in a large tall glass. Fill with crushed ice and swizzle with a bar spoon to mix. Top with more crushed ice and a mint sprig.

CHICK'N'CLUB MK1

SERVES 1

1 raspberry

25 ml (¾ fl oz) gin

10 ml (¼ fl oz) dry Martini

20 ml (¾ fl oz) chilli raspberry vinegar
(the Womersley Farm one is called Golden Raspberry and Apache Chilli Vinegar)

15 ml (½ fl oz) lemon juice

15 ml (½ fl oz) sugar syrup

30 ml (1 fl oz) apple juice

15 ml (½ fl oz) egg white

ice cubes

freeze-dried raspberries, to garnish

This was the first-ever cocktail that our good friend Sam invented for our menu at Chick 'n' Sours. At the restaurant we serve sour cocktails. We wanted the sours to be fun, colourful, and easy to drink with well-considered ingredients. Here, I have used naturally fermented vinegar from Womersley Farm, where they produce incredible natural drinking vinegars for the sours elements. This is an easy to drink cocktail that's not too strong, so you can enjoy a few with friends. Drink these with any of the fried chicken recipes you fancy in this book.

Muddle the raspberry in a cocktail shaker, then build the ingredients, making sure to add the egg whites last. Once all the ingredients are incorporated, muddle with 3 ice cubes. Pour over fresh ice, making sure there is about 8 mm (3½ in) of dense foamy head. Crumble freeze-dried raspberries over the centre of the foam to garnish.

DRINKS

TRACK FIFTEEN

BLUE HAWAIIAN
FISH BOWL

SERVES 1

45 ml (1½ fl oz) white rum

25 ml (¾ fl oz) blue curaçao

15 ml (½ fl oz) Koko Kanu coconut rum or Coco Lopez
or other good-quality coconut rum

30 ml (1 fl oz) fresh pineapple juice

ice cubes

Prosecco, for topping up

TO GARNISH

1 pineapple wedge

1–2 maraschino cherries

2 cocktail umbrellas

1 indoor sparkler

**Fish bowls are great fun to share (or not) with
a friend. We make them at Chick 'n' Sours as
they are a real showstopper that just make
you smile when you see them coming across
the restaurant floor. Fish bowls remind me of
youthful holidays in days gone by, going on
endless bar crawls and forgetting where I was
staying most of the time. This drink has a real
holiday vibe with rum and coconut as the lead
flavours to remind you of faraway beaches.
The garnish for this cocktail is just a guide,
and the more OTT the better, so get your
shades on and go crazy for fish bowls.**

Put all the ingredients, except the Prosecco,
into a cocktail shaker and shake over ice. Fill
a fish bowl glass with ice cubes and pour over
the drink. Top up with Prosecco. Garnish with
a pineapple wedge, 1–2 maraschino cherries,
a couple of cocktail umbrellas and an indoor
sparkler for holiday vibes.

MSG
MARTINI

SERVES 1

30 ml (1 fl oz) good-quality gin

15 ml (½ fl oz) dry vermouth

pinch of MSG

ice cubes

TO GARNISH

olives on cocktail sticks

**Yes, it's MSG, and yes, MSG makes everything
taste better. Here, I have created an MSG
martini based around the classic gin recipe.
By adding MSG, it adds a layer of complexity
making it much more interesting to drink. MSG
might not be your thing, but don't believe the
hype about it being not good for you because in
essence it is a natural ingredient, but I will leave
that one there. This is a more grown-up drink
than the others and pretty high in strength, too,
so is probably best enjoyed before dinner as an
aperitif, but if you fancy smashing a few, then
be my guest.**

Stir the gin, vermouth and MSG together with
ice. You must make sure everything is really cold
for this to work properly. Strain into a chilled
martini coupe and garnish with an olive or two.

**EASY
PEASY**

BANANA AND ABSINTHE COLADA

MSG MARTINI

BLUE HAWAIIAN FISH BOWL

CHICK'N'CLUB MK1

THE WHOLE CHICKEN PLAYLISTS

CARL'S TURNMILLS END OF AN ERA

French Kiss – The Original Underground Mix ....**LilLouis, The World**
This is Acid................................**Maurice Joshua, Hot Hands Hula**
Higher State of Consciouess..
..........................**Josh Wink, Higher State of Consciousness**
The Age of Love..................................**Age of love, Jam & Spoon**
Da Punk..**Daft Punk**
Windowlicker..**Aphex Twin**
Papua New Guinea..................**The Future Sound of London**
Phat Planet..**Leftfield**
Spastik..............................**Plastikman, Richie Hawtin**
Acperience 1..**Hardfloor**
Positive Education..**Slam**
Flash (Eats Everything Remix)..................**Green Velvet**
Chime – Edit..**Orbital**
Rez – Remastered..**Underworld**
Blue Jeans – Josh Wink Mix..................................**Ladytron**
Space Invaders Are Smoking Grass................................**I-F**
I Feel Love – 12" Version..........................**Donna Summer**
Energy Flash..**Joey Beltram**
Acid Phase..**Emmanuel Top**
Your Love – (Remastered)..............................**The Prodigy**
Strings of Life..**Derrick May**
Hey Boy Hey Girl..........................**The Chemical Brothers**
Chemical Beats................................**The Chemical Brothers**
Hayling (feat. Hafdis Huld)............**FC Kahuna, Hafdis Huld**
Pacific State..**808 State**
Sweet Harmony (original mix)..................................**Liquid**
Sweet Sensation..........................**Shades of Rhythm**
Your Love – 12" Version..........................**Frankie Knuckles**

PARTY HOUSE PLAYLIST

The Bomb! (These Sounds Fall Into My Mind).....**Kenny Dope**
Rhythm is a Mystery..............**Non-Stop Edit K-Klass**
Move Your Body..**Xpansions**
Open up..**Leftfield**
Is There Anybody Out There? – Radio Edit............**Bassheads**
Sweet Harmony (Original Mix)..................................**Liquid**
Born Slippy..**Underworld**
Hey Boy Hey Girl..........................**The Chemical Brothers**
Firestarter..**The Prodigy**
Satisfaction (Isak Original Extended) – Benny Benassi Presents
The Biz..**Benny Benassi, The Biz**
Professional Widow – Armands Star Trunk Funk Mix............
..........................**Tori Amos, Armand Van Helden**
Good Life..**Inner City**
Yeke Yeke – Short Mix..**Mory Kante**
Big Fun..**Inner City**
I Need Your Lovin..............................**Marc and Claude**
III House You................................**Jungle Brothers**
Infinity..**Guru Josh**
Going Back to My Roots................................**Richie Havens**
Love Cant Turn Around (Original Mix)............................
..................**Farley "Jackmaster" Funk, Darryl Pandy**
Love Cant Turn Around – Houseapella............**Darryl Pandy**
III Be Your Friend – Glamourous Mix............**Robert Owens**
Can You Feel It – New York Dub..................**Chez Damier**
Was That All it Was – Def Mix Edit 2............**Kym Mazelle**
Unfinished Sympathy – Paul Oakenfold Mix............

..........**Massive Attack, Paul Oakenfold, Steve Osborne**
Jack Your Body – 1986 Club Mix............**Steve "Silk" Hurley**
Can You Feel It (Chuck D, Mix)............**Mr. Fingers, Chuck D**
Love Cant Turn Around – Long Mix..................**Darryl Pandy**
Good Life..**Inner City**

SUNDAY VIBES

Lets Stay Together..**Al Green**
Something – Remastered 2009..................**The Beatles**
Maggie May..**Rod Stewart**
My Sweet Lord – 2014 Mix..................**George Harrison**
Your Song..**Elton John**
Here Comes the Sun – Remastered 2009............**The Beatles**
Aint No Sunshine..**Bill Withers**
Dreams – 2004 Remaster..................**Fleetwood Mac**
Smokebelch 2 (Beatles Mix)..........**The Sabres of Paradise**
Fire and Rain – 2019 Remaster..................**James Taylor**
Jolene..**Dolly Parton**
Rocket Man (I Think Its Going to be a Long, Long Time)............
....**Elton John**
Tiny Dancer..**Elton John**
Harvest Moon..**Neil Young**
We Dont Have to Take Our Clothes Off – Remastered 2015............
....**Ella Eyre**
Josephine..**Chris Rea**
Green Green Grass of Home..................................**Tom Jones**
Dont You Want Me............**Bahamas, The Weather Station**
Rather Be................................**Jasmine Thompson**
Fast Car (feat. Tall Heights)..................**Ryan Montbleau**
Perfect Places – Live from BBC Radio 2............**First Aid Kit**
I Believe in a Thing Called Love..............................**Branches**
How Can You Mend a Broken Heart..................**Al Green**
Just the Way You Are..................................**Barry White**
Kiss and Say Goodbye..................**The Manhattans**
50 Ways to Leave Your Lover..................**Paul Simon**
Young Americans – 2016 Remaster............**David Bowie**
Dreadlock Holiday..**10cc**
Walk on the Wild Side..**Lou Reed**
Dreams – 2004 Remaster..................**Fleetwood Mac**
Think for a Minute..................**The Housemartins**
Gabriel – Live Garage Mix............**Roy Davis Jr., Peven Everett**
Road To Zion..................................**Damian Marley, Nas**
One..**U2**
Valerie – Live at BBC Radio 1 Live Lounge, London / 2007............
....**Amy Winehouse**
Youre So Vain..**Carly Simons**
Wuthering Heights..**Kate Bush**
I Wish You Were Here..................................**Alpha Blondy**
In The Ghetto..**Dolly Parton**
Son Of A Preacher Man..................**Dusty Springfield**
Make Me Smile (Come Up and See Me) – 2014 Remaster............
..........**Steve Harley, Steve Harley & Cockney Rebel**
Unfinished Sympathy – 2012 Mix/Master......**Massive Attack**
Shout to the Top – USA Remix....**The Style Council, Jay Mark**
Angie..**The Rolling Stones**
Movin on Up..**Primal Scream**
The Masterplan..**Oasis**
The Earth Dies Screaming – 12"Version/2010 Digital Remaster
....**UB40**
I Think Its Going to Rain Today – 12" Version/Remastered 2010

	UB40
Reach Your Peak – 12" Version	Sister Sledge
Give Me the Night	George Benson
Teardrops	Neil Frances
Pale Blue Eyes	The Velvet Underground
Somewhere Only We Know – Live from Spotify, London	
	Lily Allen
Half the World Away	AURORA
Strange – Edit	Celeste
Heres Where the Story Ends	The Sundays
Pachamama	Beautiful Chorus
The First Time I Ever Saw Your Face	Roberta Flack
Wild Horses	The Rolling Stones
At Last	Etta James
(You Make Me Feel Like) A Natural Woman)	Aretha Franklin
Its All Over Now Baby Blue	Marianne Faithfull

ACID HOUSE BOOGIE

Coco Cabana – The Plagiat Remix	Lizzara & Tatsch, Plagiat
Nine to Nine – Nicone Remix	Spoony Talker, Nicone Remix
Uprising	Namtrak
Shadowndancer	Purple Disco Machine
Daylight	Kellerkind
Horizontal	Tobias W.
Slippery When Wet	Andreas Bergmann
A Jealous Heart Never Rests	The Black Madonna
We Can Never Be Apart	The Black Madonna
Electronic Germany	DJ Hell
Phuture Bound – Ame Mix	Akabu, Ame
La La Land – Original Mix	Green Velvet
Theme From Q	Objekt
Gabriel – Live Garage Mix	Roy Davis Jr., Peven Everett
Papua New Guinea	The Future Sound of London
Chime – Edit	Orbital
Rez – Remastered	Underworld
Cirrus	Bonobo
Push Pull	OFFAIAH
Light Up The Sky – Special Request Remix/ Edit	
	The Prodigy, Special Request
Get Up	Dole & Kom
Nuit	Alek Sander
Paris Is For Lovers (My Love)	Terranova, Tomas Hoffding
Deer In the Headlights – DJ Hell Remix	Chelonis R. Jones
Losing It	FISHER
Temptation – Remastered	Heaven 17
Discogirls – Discofunk Version	Timewarp Inc
Move Your Body – Club	Marshall Jefferson
Playing With Knives [Quadrant Mix]	Bizarre Inc
Belfast	Orbital
Sweet Sensation	Shades of Rhythm
On A Ragga Tip 97 (original Mix)	SL2
Searchin For My Rizla	Ratpack
Limewire – Original Mix	Bramo & Hamo
Dont Go (Original Mix)	Awesome 3
Sound of Eden	Shades of Rhythm
Windowlicker	Aphex Twin
Blue Jeans – Josh Wink Mix	Ladytron
Space invaders Are Smoking Grass	I-F
I Feel Love – 12" Version	Donna Summer
Sweet Harmony (Original Mix)	Liquid
Strings Of Life	Derrick May
Higher State of Consciousness	Tweekin Acid Funk
The Bomb! (These Sounds Fall Into My Mind)	
	The Bucketheads, Kenny Dope
Night Falls	Booka Shade
Remedy	Agoria, NOEMIE
Parallaxis – Traumprinzs Over 2 The End Version	
	Efdemin, Traumprinz
Positive Education	Slam
In White Rooms	Booka Shade
In My Head	Superpitcher, Fantastic Twins

Cold Song 2013 – DJ QQ China Rework	DJ Hell, Klaus Nomi
Circus Bells – Hardfloor Remix	Robert Armani
Bird	Kelly Lee Owens
Ageispolis	Aphex Twin

BLM

Feel Like Jumping	Marcia Griffiths
Concrete Jungle	Bob Marley & The Wailers
Wonderful World, Beautiful People – Single version	Jimmy Cliff
Isrealites	Desmond Dekker
Up Town Top Ranking	Althea and Donna
007 (Shanty Town)	Desmond Dekker & The Aces
Sensee Party	Eek-A-Mouse
Police in Helicopter	John Holt
Talkin' Blues	Bob Marley
Return of Django	The Upsetters
Woman of the Ghetto	Phyllis Dillon, The Tommy McCook Band
Bam Bam	Sister Nancy
Gangsters	The Specials
True and Big Love	Two Tone Club
Welcome to Jamrock	Damian Marley
Cocaine in My Brain	Dillinger
Monkey Man	The Maytals
Funky Kingston	Toots & The Maytals
War/No More Trouble – Medley/ Live at the Pavilion De Paris, 1977	Bob Marley & The Wailers
Wa-Do-Dem	Eek-A-Mouse
The Harder They Come	Jimmy Cliff
54-46 That's My Number	The Maytals
Skylarking	Horace Andy
Money Money	Horace Andy
Ali Baba	John Holt
I'm Still in Love With You	Marcia Aitken
Never Be Ungrateful – 12" Mix	Gregory Isaacs
Dread Are the Controller	Linval Thompson
Gypsy Man	Marcia Griffiths
The Upsetter	Lee "Scratch" Perry
Set Them Free	Lee "Scratch" Perry
Want Fi Goh Rave	Linton Kwesi Johnson
Ghost Town – Extended Version	The Specials
The Guns of Navarone	The Skatalites, Laurel Aitken
Soul Shakedown Party	Jamaica Reggae Band
Here I Come	Barrington Levy
Mount Zion Medley	Capleton, Jah Cure, Morgan Heritage, LMS, Ras Shiloh, Bushman
Sinsemilla	Black Uluru
Under Mi Sensi ('84 Original Spliff)	Barrington Levy
This Music Got Soul	The Trojans (Gaz Mayall)
Train to Skaville	The Ethiopians
Pressure Drop	The Maytals
You Can Get It If You Really Want	Jimmy Cliff
Sun is Shining	Bob Marley & The Wailers

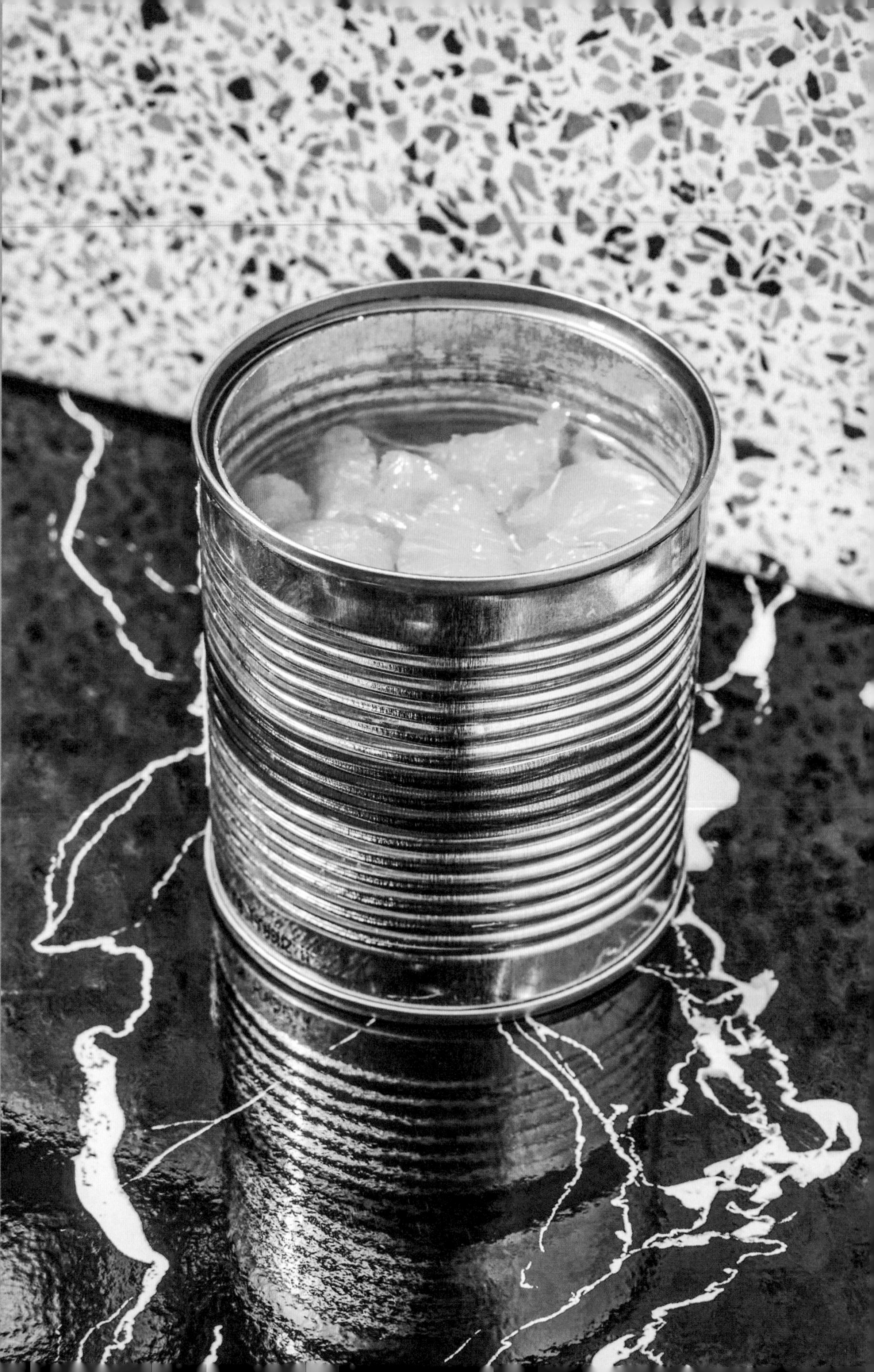

GLOSSARY

Achiote paste
Mexican flavouring made from annatto seeds, cumin, pepper, coriander, oregano, cloves, and garlic. Available in some large supermarkets, online and from specialist food shops.

**Amchoor powder
(dry mango powder)**
Indian mango powder made from dried, unripe mangoes. Available in some large supermarkets, online and from Asian supermarkets.

Ancho chillies
Dried Mexican Poblano chillies. Available online and from specialist food shops.

Asafoetida powder
Made from dried gum from the roots of plants of the celery family, the powder adds a smooth savoury flavour. Available in some supermarkets, online and from Asian supermarkets and health food shops.

Asian red shallots (Thai red onions, hom-daeng)
Red onions can be substituted. Available online and from Asian supermarkets.

Belacan shrimp paste
Shrimp paste dried and sold as blocks. Available online and from Asian supermarkets.

Black bean paste
Chinese mung bean paste Available in some large supermarkets, online and from Asian supermarkets.

Black vinegar
Chinese aged vinegar, with a woody, smoky flavour. Available online, from Asian supermarkets and specialist food shops.

Cassia bark stick
Chinese variety of cinnamon stick. Harder than Sri Lankan, with a more savoury flavour. Available in some large supermarkets, online and from Asian supermarkets.

Chaat (chat) masala
Indian spice mix of amchoor (dried mango powder), cumin, coriander, dried ginger, salt (often kala namak), black pepper, asafoetida and chilli powder. Available in some large supermarkets, online and from Asian supermarkets.

**Chinese (Napa) cabbage
(Chinese leaves)**
A Chinese variety of cabbage. Widely available.

Chinese sausage (lap cheong)
A hard, dried, smoked sausage of pork and pork fat with rosewater, rice wine and soy sauce. Available online and from Asian supermarkets.

Chinese sesame paste (zhī ma jiàng)
A thick paste made from toasted white sesame seeds. Available online and from Asian supermarkets.

Chipotle chillies
Smoke-dried Mexican jalapeño chillies. Available in some large supermarkets, online and from specialist food shops.

Crispy shallots
Fried sliced shallots, used as topping. Available online and from Asian supermarkets.

Dried mung bean vermicelli noodles (cellophane noodles, glass noodles, fensi)
The Chinese variety are usually made with mung bean starch and remain transparent when cooked. Available online and from Asian supermarkets.

Dried shrimp
Sundried shrimp, used as flavouring, often crushed first. Available in some large supermarkets, online and from Asian supermarkets.

Fermented black beans (douchi, tochi)
Chinese fermented salted black beans. Available in some large supermarkets, online and from Asian supermarkets.

Fish sauce
Liquid condiment made from fish or krill that have been coated in salt and fermented. Available in some large supermarkets, online and from Asian supermarkets.

Fresh turmeric
Root-like subterranean stems (rhizomes) from of the turmeric plant. Available in some large supermarkets, online and from Asian supermarkets and specialist food shops.

Fermented red bean curd
Soya bean curd preserved in rice wine with red rice and seasonings. Available online and from Asian supermarkets.

Galangal (Thai ginger, Siamese ginger)
Similar to ginger in appearance but with a different, spicier flavour. Available online and from Asian supermarkets in fresh, dried, powdered or paste form.

Ghee
Clarified butter. Available in some large supermarkets, online and from Asian supermarkets.

Gochugaru
Powdered, crushed, or flaked Korean dried chillies. Available in some large supermarkets, online and from Asian supermarkets.

Gochujang
Savoury sweet and spicy red chilli paste made with chilli powder, glutinous rice, fermented soybean powder, barley malt powder and salt. Available in some large supermarkets, online and from Asian supermarkets.

Guajillo chillies
Dried Mexican Mirasol chillies. Available online and from specialist food shops.

Hoisin sauce
Made of soya beans, fennel, red chilli peppers, and garlic. Vinegar, Chinese five-spice powder and sugar are also often added. Widely available.

Hokkien noodles
Oiled wheat and egg noodles popular in Malaysian cooking but originating in China. Available in some large supermarkets, online and from Asian supermarkets.

Instant ramen noodles
Instant variety of the Chinese wheat noodles popular in soup in Japan. Available in some large supermarkets, online and from Asian supermarkets.

Jaggery
Unrefined cane or palm sugar largely made in the Indian subcontinent. Available in some large supermarkets, online and from Asian supermarkets.

**Kecap manis
(Indonesian sweet soy sauce)**
Sweetened soy sauce. Make your own by simmering soy sauce with palm sugar or brown sugar until syrupy. Available in some large supermarkets, online and from Asian supermarkets.

Kewpie mayonnaise
A Japanese brand of mayonnaise made with egg yolks and apple and malt vinegar. Available in some large supermarkets, online and from Asian supermarkets.

Kimchi
Spicy Korean salted, fermented vegetables. Available in some large supermarkets, online and from Asian supermarkets.

Kombu (edible kelp, dasima, haidai)
Dried seaweed widely used as a flavouring in Japan. Available in some large supermarkets, online and from Asian supermarkets.

Labneh (Greek-style yoghurt, strained yoghurt)
Yoghurt that has been thickened by straining. Widely available.

Matzo meal
Ground, unleavened kosher bread, mostly used to make dumplings for soup. Available in some supermarkets, online and from specialist shops and delis.

Mirin
Japanese rice wine, similar to sake but lower in alcohol and higher in sugar. Widely available.

Miso paste
A cultured mixture of soybeans, a grain such as barley or rice, salt and koji (a mould). Used as a flavouring in many Japanese dishes. Available in some large supermarkets, online from Asian supermarkets and specialist food shops.

Mooli (daikon, white radish, winter radish, oriental radish, long white radish)
Long, thick, white, Asian winter radish. Available in some large supermarkets, online and from Asian supermarkets.

MSG (monosodium glutamate, ajinomoto, Chinese salt)
Raises the savouriness, or umami, flavours of a dish. Available in some large supermarkets, online and from Asian supermarkets and specialist food shops.

Panko breadcrumbs
Japanese-style breadcrumbs made without crusts – lighter and crisper than other types. Widely available.

Nori
Japanese edible seaweed, dried and sold in sheets, mainly used to wrap sushi and onigiri. Available in some large supermarkets, online and from Asian supermarkets.

Queso fresco
Soft Mexican cheese similar to Indian paneer or very light feta cheese. Available in some large supermarkets, online and from specialist food shops.

Red Kashmiri chilli powder
Vibrant red chilli powder made from Kashmiri chillies. Available in some large supermarkets, online and from Asian supermarkets.

Shaoxing wine
Chinese rice wine from Shaoxing. Available online and from Asian supermarkets.

Shichimi togarashi
Japanese mixture of seven spices – chilli, sansho (Japanese pepper), roasted orange peel, black and white sesame seeds, hemp seed, ginger, nori or aonori seaweed and poppy seed. Available in some large supermarkets, online and from Asian supermarkets.

Shiso (parilla) leaves
Japanese herb of the mint family with a light scent of cinnamon and clove. Available online and from Asian supermarkets. Easy to grow.

Shrimp paste (prawn sauce)
Finely crushed shrimp or krill mixed with salt and fermented. Available in some large supermarkets, online and from Asian supermarkets.

Sriracha sauce
Thai hot chilli sauce made from chilli peppers, vinegar, garlic, sugar and salt. Widely available.

**Sichuan chilli bean paste
(see toban djan, below)**

Smoke powder
Smoke flavouring, often of hickory smoke. Available online.

Ssamjang
A thick, spicy Korean paste made of doenjang (fermented bean paste), gochujang, sesame oil, onion, garlic, spring onions (scallions), and sometimes brown sugar. Available online and from Asian supermarkets.

Tapioca starch
Starch extracted from the cassava plant. Available online and from health-food shops.

Thai basil
A type of basil native to Southeast Asia with liquorice or anise-like qualities. Available online and from Asian supermarkets.

Toban Djan (Sichuan chilli bean sauce, doubanjiang, douban, broad-bean chilli sauce)
Chinese bean paste made from fermented broad beans, soya beans, salt, rice and spices. Available online and from Asian supermarkets.

Tomatillos (Mexican husk tomatoes)
Mexican savoury fruit of the nightshade family, often sold in cans. Available in some large supermarkets, online and from specialist food shops.

Udon noodles
Thick Japanese wheat-flour noodles. Widely available.

Vietnamese mint (Vietnamese coriander, hot mint, laksa leaf, praew leaf, larb)
Southeast Asian herb. Available from Asian supermarkets, or as seed or a growing plant online or from specialist nurseries.

Wakame seaweed
Edible Japanese seaweed, often used in soups and salads. Available in some large supermarkets, online and from Asian supermarkets.

R

S

ACKNOWLEDGEMENTS

220

When I was asked to write this book, I got chronic anxiety thinking 'How the f@&k do I write a book?' Followed by the critical voice 'Who the f@&k wants to read a book I wrote?' I then went to Thailand for a month with every intention of starting to write, but decided to do a ten-day *Vipassana* silent meditation course (as you do) instead, followed by a lot of eating and thinking about it. When I look back, it was actually the best way for this to ever happen. I think a lot. In fact, when I was away my very good friend Gemma Jane sent me her creative timeline and it went a little something like this:

PROJECT STARTS ... THINK ABOUT IT ... DO NOTHING ... PANIC ... START WORK ... PROJECT DEADLINE ... FINISH PROJECT.

I liked that very much, and have accepted that that's just the way I work. But I always get there in the end, and hopefully the results here are as rewarding to you, the readers, as they are to me.

I'm eternally grateful for the opportunity to write this, which has very much been a collaboration of some seriously creative and talented people, and I would like to say thank you to a few for the enormous effort they have all put in to make this happen, and putting up with my noodle head ideas at times telling me everything will be ok:

My Mum and Dad, Ann and Paddy Clarke, for giving me life.

Holly Arnold for making this happen, and her kindness, putting up with my crazy ideas, believing in me, and looking after me.

Eve Marleau for her tireless work, and for giving me the creative freedom to make this happen. For our lockdown chats and helping me on my quest to find out exactly 'what cheese the moon is really made of' ...

Evi O for her mad design skills, and somehow managing to get inside my head and bring stuff to life.

Kate Pollard, for her vision and for giving me the opportunity to write this book. Also for the Wim Hof method tips, which have came in very handy at times during the writing process.

The creative genius of the team who made me look good, and the laughs we had in the studio: Rob Billington; Nicole Herft; Alexander Breeze; Ben Boxhall and Stu 'the hands' Capper.

My beautiful Sister Michelle Leahy, for believing in me. One love. x

My Business partner and brother-in-arms David Wolanski, and his family Emma, Sam and Eva for always being there for me in good times and bad. For giving me the start on this incredible path I tread today, I'm eternally grateful. I love you all. xx

My ex-wife Victoria for putting up with me for so many years, telling me I could do anything, believing in me and keeping me alive. x

Jono, Stu, Ben, Tom and everyone else at Otherway for the daily inspiration, giving me a desk and the opportunity to go on the next incredible Future Noodles adventure.

My incredible, beautiful friend Gemma Jane for the love, kindness, laughter and joy. Love and light. x

To the ex-Vietnam Vet who told me 'everything was going to turn out ok' when I was on my arse in Savannah, Georgia, as we drank a late-night beer sitting in the gutter many moons ago. Jah love brother. x

There are so many more people I could mention that have helped me on my path today and believed in me. For this I am eternally grateful, and I hope if your reading this then you know that you are one of them. Thank you all.

Finally, I want to thank my Higher Power for keeping me safe and guiding me on my beautiful path through life's adventures. I offer gratitude and thanks to a kind and loving universe. x

Sending love, light and happiness to you all.

Be happy!

CARL XXX

WORLD-FAMOUS DJ CARL CLARKE REFERS TO HIMSELF AS AN 'ACCIDENTAL CHEF'.

Hailing from Handsworth in Birmingham, Carl ran away at fifteen to Jersey with just a small amount of money. After spending all his money in a casino, he was offered a job in a hotel by an Austrian chef, peeling 8,000 potatoes a day. Carl saw food as a necessity, with his passion for cooking to follow later on in life. After working in hotels and the military, Carl ditched it all to become a world-famous DJ.

Throughout his career, Carl travelled the world and ate at top-end restaurants, where he realised he had an interest in food. In the 1990s, Carl began working for Marco Pierre White, U2 and Simon Rogan before launching his pop-up restaurant business.

With pop-ups such as Rock Lobsta, God Save the Clam and Disco Bistro under his belt, Chick 'n' Sours was the first restaurant for Carl and his partner David Wolanski, opening in 2015 with their 'Secret Hot Sauce' becoming a local phenomenon! They've most recently opened their third Chick 'n' Sours in Islington.

Carl describes himself as an 'old raver who wanted to bring what we had in the clubs into the restaurant environment. The demographic of people that come to a place like Chick 'n' Sours want a good soundtrack and good visuals around them. They want the vibe. Food is important but it's just one part of the jigsaw'.

Aiming to change fried chicken for the good – Carl & David launched their new fast-casual fried chicken concept, aptly named 'Chik'n', in July 2018 and recently opened their second Chik'n in Soho. It's 'all about happy people serving kick-ass fried chicken to a banging soundtrack in an awesome environment'.

CARL CLARKE

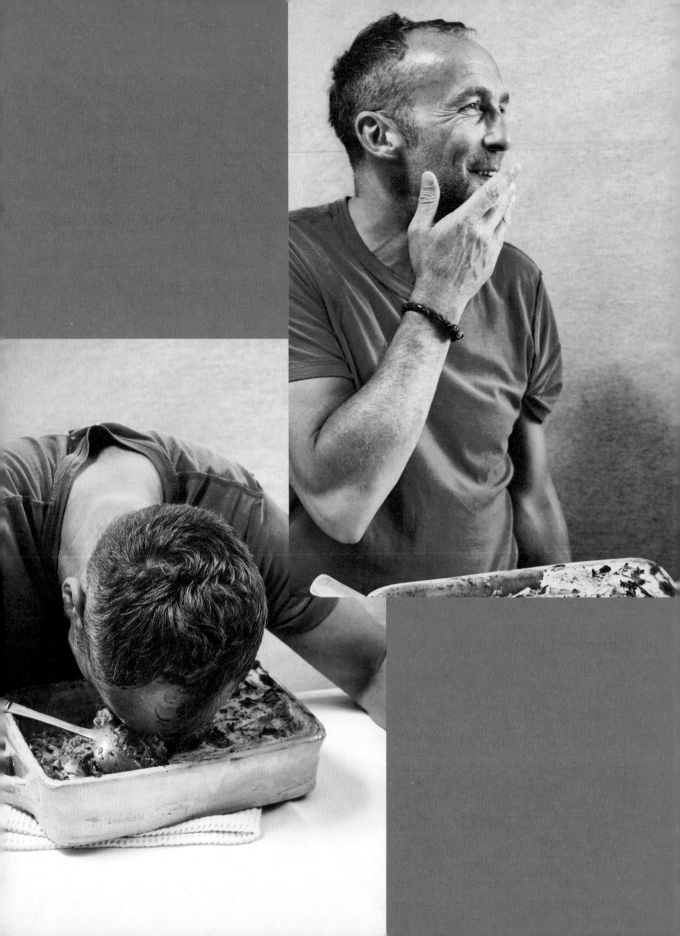

Published in 2020 by Hardie Grant Books,
an imprint of Hardie Grant Publishing

Hardie Grant Books (London)
5th & 6th Floors
52–54 Southwark Street
London SE1 1UN

Hardie Grant Books (Melbourne)
Building 1, 658 Church Street
Richmond, Victoria 3121

hardiegrantbooks.com

British Library Cataloguing-in-Publication Data. A catalogue
record for this book is available from the British Library.

The Whole Chicken by Carl Clarke
ISBN: 978-1-78488-363-8

10 9 8 7 6 5 4 3 2 1

Publishing Director: Kate Pollard
Senior Editor: Eve Marleau
Design: Evi-O.Studio | Evi O. & Nicole Ho
Photographer: Robert Billington
Food Stylist: Nicole Herft
Prop Stylist: Alexander Breeze
Editor: Kathy Steer
Proofreader: Emily Preece-Morrison
Indexer: Vanessa Bird

Colour reproduction by p2d
Printed and bound in China by Leo Paper Products Ltd.